Tutorial Guide to
AutoCAD® 2012

Shawna Lockhart

ISBN: 978-1-58503-643-1

PUBLICATIONS

Schroff Development Corporation

www.SDCpublications.com

Schroff Development Corporation
P.O. Box 1334
Mission KS 66222
(913) 262-2664
www.SDCpublications.com

Publisher: Stephen Schroff

Trademarks

Autodesk and AutoCAD are registered trademarks of Autodesk, Inc., in the U.S.A. and certain other countries.

Disclaimer:

The publication is designed to provide tutorial information about AutoCAD® and/or other Autodesk computer programs. Every effort has been made to make this publication complete and as accurate as possible. The reader is expressly cautioned to use any and all precautions necessary, and to take appropriate steps to avoid hazards, when engaging in the activities described herein.

Neither the author nor the publisher makes any representations or warranties of any kind, with respect to the materials set forth in this publication, express or implied, including without limitation any warranties of fitness for a particular purpose or merchantability. Nor shall the author or the publisher be liable for any special, consequential, or exemplary damages resulting, in whole or in part, directly or indirectly, from the reader's use of, or reliance upon, this material or subsequent revisions of this material.

Examination Copies:

Books received as examination copies are for review purposes only and may not be made available for student use. Resale of examination copies is prohibited.

Electronic Files:

Any electronic files associated with this book are licensed to the original user only. These files may not be transferred to any other party.

PREFACE

The AutoCAD® program is the most widely used design and drafting software in the world. Its position as the industry standard makes it an essential tool for anyone preparing for a career in engineering, design, or technology.

Key Features

This tutorial guide includes:

- Step-by-step tutorials written for the novice user

- Getting Started chapters for configuring the AutoCAD software for use with the tutorials

- Organization that parallels an introductory engineering graphics course

- Tips offering suggestions and warnings as you progress through the tutorials

- Exercises at the end of each tutorial providing challenges to a range of abilities in mechanical, electrical, and civil engineering, as well as architecture

- Key Terms and Key Commands listed to recap important topics and commands learned in each tutorial

- Glossary of terms and Command Summary lists the key commands used in the tutorials.

- An Index to help you locate topics throughout the manual.

Acknowledgments

I wish to thank the individuals who contributed to the conceptualization and implementation of these tutorials. Thanks to my many teaching colleagues who responded to inquiries and helped to shape the tutorials in this book. I cannot list all of the individuals who have contributed their encouragement, assistance, and ideas for this text, but I am grateful to the people listed below for their help in this and previous editions.

Special thanks go to Cindy Johnson, Christopher R. Bowman, Marc Finseth, Amy E. Monte, Michigan Technological State University, Mary Tolle, South Dakota State University, Joseph A. Gosselin, Central Connecticut State University, S. Kant Vajpayee, University of Southern Mississippi, James G. Raschka, Reuben Aronovitz, John Matson, Craig L. Miller, Michael H. Gregg, Steve Bachman, Tom Bryson, Karen Coen-Brown, Mary Ann Koen, D. Krall, Kim Manner, John Walker, Danny Hubbard, Edward C. Livingston, Mitchell Stockdale, and Levi Buckingham; Denis Cadu and the many fine people at Autodesk; to Shannon Kyles and James Bethune, authors of previous editions of tutorial guides from which some material was adapted for this manual. I would like particularly to thank the following individuals for providing exercises used in the text: James Earle, Spocad Centers of Gonzaga University School of Engineering, Karen L. Coen-Brown, D. Krall, Tom Bryson, Kyle Tage, Amy E. Monte, Mary Ann Koen, Kevin Berisso, and Mary Tolle.

A special thanks to Don Daniels and Gordon Nelson for testing the 2012 tutorials and providing valuable feedback.

Finally, I would like to once again thank all of the great students I had the pleasure to teach at Montana State University and from whom I am still learning.

I am happy to once again be able to provide frequent revision to this text, as each new software release is available. My sincere thanks to SDC Publishing for giving me this opportunity. I would like to specially thank Stephen Schroff and Mary Schmidt.

SHAWNA LOCKHART

SLockhartBooks@gmail.com

BRIEF TABLE OF CONTENTS

TABLE OF CONTENTS

PREPARING FOR THE TUTORIALS

Introduction to the Tutorials

The tutorials in this guide will teach you to use the AutoCAD® 2012 software through a series of step-by-step exercises. You will learn its fundamental operating procedures and how to use drawing tools.

The tutorials in this guide assume that you are using the software's default settings. If your system has been customized for other uses, some of the settings may not match those used in the step-by-step instruction in the tutorials. Please check your system against the configuration in this chapter so that the tutorial instructions will work for you.

If you are using the AutoCAD software on a network ask your instructor or system administrator about how the software is configured. You should not try to reconfigure the software unless instructed to do so by network personnel. Read about mouse techniques, typographical conventions, and end-of-tutorial exercises in this chapter, and then go on to GS-2, Getting Started with AutoCAD Basics.

To complete these tutorials, your system must be running Microsoft Windows XP, Windows Vista, or Windows 7. The screens shown in this manual show AutoCAD running on the Windows 7 operating system.

Basic Mouse Techniques

The tutorials in this guide are based on the assumption that you will be using a mouse or pointing device. The following terms will be used to streamline the instructions for use of the mouse.

Term	Meaning
Pick or Click	Quickly press and then release the left mouse button
Right-click	Quickly press and release the right mouse button
Double-click	Rapidly click the left mouse button twice
Drag	Press and hold down the left mouse button while you move the mouse
Point	Move the mouse until the mouse pointer (cursor) on the screen is positioned over the item you want
Select	Position the mouse pointer/drawing cursor over and item and click the left mouse button.

Recognizing Typographical Conventions

When you work with the AutoCAD software during these tutorials, you'll use your keyboard and mouse to input information. As you read this book, you'll see special type styles to help you determine the information to input.

Special symbols illustrate certain computer keys. For example, the

Objectives

This chapter describes how to prepare your computer system and the AutoCAD 2012 software for use with the tutorials in this manual. As you read this chapter, you will

1. Understand how to use a mouse during the completion of these tutorials.

2. Recognize the typographical conventions used in this book.

3. Create and prepare data file and working directories.

4. Configure your copy of the AutoCAD software for use with these tutorials.

Tip: *To click (or pick) in Windows and AutoCAD, use the left mouse button. This button is also referred to as the pick button. To show short-cut menus, enter or return, click the right mouse button. The middle or scroll button on your mouse is typically set to pan or zoom.*

Tip: *You can use the Mouse Properties selection in the Windows control panel to switch your mouse to a left-handed configuration. This will switch your pick button to the right button on the mouse. The left mouse button will then act as the enter or return button.*

Tip: *The right button on your mouse and the spacebar often perform the same function as the [Enter] key. Pressing the right mouse button can also pop up a context menu from which you can pick Enter.*

Enter or Return key is represented by the symbol [Enter].

The guide also employs special typefaces when it presents instructions for performing computer operations. Instructions are set off from the main text to indicate a series of actions or the AutoCAD command prompts. **Bold type** (often in all capital letters) is used for the letters and numbers to be input by you. ***Bold italic*** type indicates actions you are to take. Text you see on your computer screen, for example, messages and command prompts show in a Sans Serif Font.

For example,

Command: ***LINE [Enter]***

instructs you to type "Line" to start the Line command and then to press [Enter].

From point: ***click point A***

instructs you to select point A on your screen by clicking it with the mouse. The words "Command" and "From point" represent the AutoCAD command prompts that you would see on your screen. The command prompt line is always in sans serif type followed by a colon (:).

Instruction words, such as "click," "type," "select," and "press," also appear in sans serif font also and are italicized. For example, "type" instructs you to strike or press several keys in sequence. For the following instruction,

Type: ***4,4***

you would type 4,4 in that order on your keyboard. Remember to type exactly what you see, including spaces, if any. (Coordinate pairs do not have spaces between them in AutoCAD.)

"Click" tells you to click an object or an icon or to choose commands from the menu. For example,

Click: ***Line button***

instructs you to use your pointing device to select the Line icon from the toolbar on your screen. To select an icon, move the pointer until the cursor is over the icon and click the left mouse button.

Instructions shown like this:

Press: ***[Enter]***

means you should press the Enter or Return on your keyboard once. Sometimes "press" is followed by two keys, such as

Press: ***[Ctrl]+[F1]***

In this case, press and hold down the first key, press the second key once and release it, and then release the first key.

Default values that are displayed as part of a command or prompt are represented in angle brackets: < >. For example,

Specify inside diameter of donut <0.5000>:

is the command prompt when the Donut command has a default value of 0.5 for the inside diameter.

You will sometimes be instructed to perform some steps on your own. These instructions will be listed in a different font like this:

On your own, use the line command to draw a triangle.

Glossary

New terms are in italics in the text when they are introduced and are defined in the Glossary at the end of the book.

End-of-Tutorial Exercises

Exercises at the end of the tutorials provide practice for you to apply what you have learned during the tutorial. To become proficient at using the AutoCAD software, it is important to gain independent practice creating drawings such as those in the exercises.

Configuring Windows for the Tutorials

The AutoCAD 2012 software takes advantage of common Windows file operations and allows you to run the AutoCAD software while running other applications.

Windows XP/VISTA/7

The AutoCAD 2012 software can be installed with Windows XP, VISTA or Windows 7. The figures in this guide were captured in Windows 7. The screens in other Windows versions are similar to the screens that you will see in this guide. The steps are described in sufficient detail that you should be able to follow them on your own regardless of your operating system.

To run AutoCAD you need: 2 GB RAM, display resolution of at least 1024 x 768 with True Color and 1.8 GB of free space on your hard drive for the software installation. (Of course you will need additional space for creating files.) 3D modeling may require additional free space on the hard drive and higher resolution capabilities for the display.

Screen Resolution

You can change your screen resolution from the Windows Control Panel. You can skip this step if you have already set up your system and do not need to make any changes.

Launch the **Control Panel**

Double-click: **Display** (from the Control Panel)

Use the **Settings** options to select the resolution and color options.

Set your display to 16-bit color or higher (You will very likely be able to select a higher color depth such 32-bit color.)

Select a resolution of at least 1024 X 768 pixels.

Be sure to test the setting to make sure it works. Not all monitors and video cards are capable of every resolution setting displayed in the

Settings tab of the Display Properties dialog box. (Refer to your system documentation if you have trouble with your screen resolution settings.) If you use a different resolution, your screens will look slightly different from the ones captured for this book, but it should not affect the overall operation of the commands as described in the tutorials.

> *Close the dialog box and control panel on your own. If you are prompted to restart Windows do so now.*

Creating a Working Directory

To make saving and opening files easier as you complete the tutorials, you will create and specify a new working directory for the AutoCAD software. The working directory is the default directory used to open and save files. By setting a working directory, you will not have to search through the computer's directories every time you are asked to save a file.

This is a good practice in general for organizing your files. You should not save your drawing files and other work files in the same directory as the AutoCAD software because doing so makes it likely that they will be overwritten or lost when you install software upgrades. It is also easier to organize and back up your project files and drawings if they are in a separate directory. Making subdirectories within this directory for different projects will organize your drawings even further.

You will create a new shortcut for launching the AutoCAD 2012 software that will use *c:\work* as the starting directory. If you are used to keeping your files in the My Documents folder on your computer, then make a new directory named *work* inside your My Documents folder.

> On your own, use your Windows Explorer to create a new directory, **c:\work** at this time.

When you are finished, return to the Windows desktop.

Installing Data Files for the Tutorials

The next step is to create a directory for the data files used in the tutorials and install them. Throughout the tutorials, you will be instructed to work with files already prepared for you. You will not be able to complete the tutorials without these files. You can download these files with a Web browser such as Mozilla Firefox or Internet Explorer. Simply go to *http://www.schroff.com/resources*, choose the section of the site dedicated to this book, and then follow instructions to download the data files.

After you have retrieved the files, use Windows to create a new directory and name it *datafile2012*. Copy *datafile2012.zip* into the directory and use a utility such as WinZip to uncompress it. When the file is uncompressed, you will see an assortment of files in the directory, most of which have the *.dwg* extension. These tutorials assume you will make this datafile2012 directory on the root of drive c:. If you create it somewhere else, browse to your location during steps that list *c:\datafile2012*.

Configuring AutoCAD Software for the Tutorials

The tutorials in this guide are based on the assumption that you are using the AutoCAD software's default settings. If your system has been customized for other uses, some of the settings may not match those in the step-by-step instructions in the tutorials. You will now set up your system so that you can work through the tutorials as instructed.

To start the AutoCAD software,

Click: **AutoCAD 2012 shortcut from the Windows desktop** *or click Start, All Programs, Autodesk, AutoCAD 2012 - English, AutoCAD 2012 - English*

The AutoCAD graphics window appears with the Autodesk Exchange for AutoCAD open as well (Figure GS1.1).

Figure GS1.1

Use the [X] in the upper right corner to close the Autodesk Exchange window for now.

Software written for Windows operating system often have a large icon used to access commands related to opening and saving files, and other more general application wide functions. It is called the Application icon or button.

Click: **Application icon** *from the upper left of the AutoCAD software window*

Click: **Options** *from the bottom right of the list that expands*

The Options dialog box appears on your screen, as shown in Figure GS1.2.

The Options dialog box uses the Windows interface to set up the Auto-CAD software's search paths, performance, display, pointer, and printer

Options button

configurations, and various general items. When you make changes to the Options dialog box and click Apply, the AutoCAD software will update the system registry if necessary.

To change from one card to the next, you click on the named tab at the top of the dialog box. That tab will then appear on top of the stack.

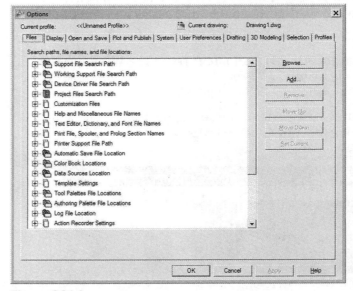

Figure GS1.2

The Options Dialog Tabs

These tutorials general expect you have AutoCAD installed using the defaults. If you have customized your software, it may behave differently than described in these tutorials. Refer to AutoCAD's Help if you need to reset your system to the default settings. The general use for the options dialog box tabs are:

The Files tab shows the search paths used during many software operations. They are how the software finds the configuration, menu, and toolbar files.

The Display tab allows for changes to the display, including fonts and colors. You can use the Crosshair size slider to adjust the size of the cursor relative to the screen.

The Open and Save tab allows you to change the default type of file created when you save, to set an automatic save time, and to control how externally referenced files are handled.

The Plot and Publish tab allows you to change the current printer and modify its settings. If you did not select a printer when you installed the AutoCAD software, the simplest way to print your drawings is to click Add or Configure Plotters and then use the Add a Plotter Wizard to select the System Printer. Doing so allows you to use any printer that you have already set up to work with Windows. If you want to choose one of the other plotter options, refer to your documentation.

The System tab allows you to select which video display driver is used and to select the pointing device, as well as other settings. Double check this card to see that you are using an appropriate pointing device. The default digitizer is the Current System Pointing Device (your mouse). The AutoCAD software can also support a tablet. To configure for a tablet, refer to your tablet documentation.

The User Preferences tab lets you customize how objects are sorted and how selections are prioritized by the software, as well as how undefined units are handled.

The Drafting tab lets you set snap and tracking features, and size the apertures and markers for these.

The 3D Modeling tab lets you control aspects of the 3D coordinate system use and appearance, navigation in 3D, and 3D object creation.

The Selection tab controls how objects are selected to be acted on by software commands.

The Profiles tab changes the AutoCAD environment to user-specified customizations. You will use this card to create your own Profile with to use during these tutorials, if desired.

User Profiles

The AutoCAD 2012 software allows you to save multiple configuration profiles, making it possible to configure the software for different uses and peripherals. If you are working on a shared machine, you can create a special profile to use for these tutorials so that another user doesn't change your settings and defaults between sessions.

If you're working on a networked computer, your professor or system administrator has probably configured the system already. Ask which profile you should use, if any.

To create a user-defined profile or configuration, first

Click: **Profiles tab**

The Profiles tab appears on top of the stack, similar to Figure GS1.3.

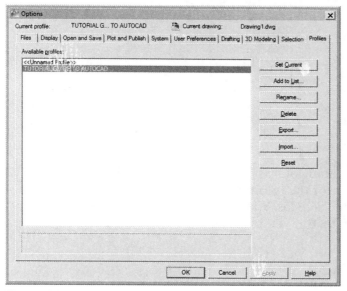

Figure GS1.3

The default profile is <Unnamed Profile>. Any changes made to the other cards will be stored in this Profile because it is selected as current. You will make a new profile for the tutorials, set it as current, and then make changes to the other cards.

> Click: **Add to List**

The Add Profile dialog box appears where you will type the name of your new Profile. A description is optional, but not necessary.

> Type: **TUTORIAL GUIDE TO AUTOCAD** *see Figure GS1.33*

> Click: **Apply & Close**

You will see "Tutorial Guide to AutoCAD" appear in the list of profiles.

> Click: **to highlight the new Tutorial Guide to AutoCAD profile**

> Click: **Set Current**

The software in the background should not change because the configuration settings for this Profile are the same as for the Unnamed Profile.

Changing the Configuration Options

Now you will make changes to the other tabs, as necessary, to follow the tutorials in this guide.

> Click: **Display tab**

The Display tab appears as shown in Figure GS1.4.

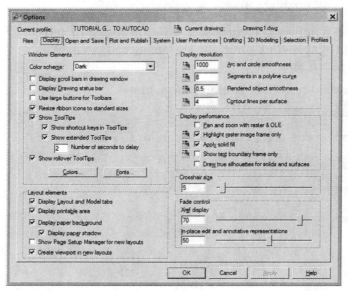

Figure GS1.4

The default background color for AutoCAD 2012 is black. The background screen color for the tutorials is set to white to make the details clearer in the printed screens. You do not have to change your background color to white. But you may using the Colors option,

> Click: **Colors...**

Warning: Changes to the AutoCAD software's configuration can affect its performance greatly. If you are working on a networked system, you must check with the network administrator before creating your own profile. Whatever changes you make must be made only to your user Profile setting.

Figure GS1.5

Click: **2D model space, Uniform background**

Click: **White** *from the color list at the right*

Click: **3D parallel projection, Uniform background**

Click: **White** *from the color list at the right*

Click: **3D parallel projection, Viewport control**

Click: **Color 8** *(a dark gray) from the color list at the right*

To accept the changes that you have just made (if any),

Click: **Apply and Close**

Backing Up AutoCAD Defaults

If you want to back up your configuration and menu files, you can do this by copying the customizable files listed below to a USB drive, separate location on your hard disk, or a remote network drive where they will not be overwritten.

To locate these files, you must determine where they are stored on your computer.

Click: **the Files tab**

Expand the list by clicking on the plus signs to see paths, settings, and file locations.

You are finished with the Options dialog box. To exit the dialog box,

Click: **OK**

The software screen appears again, with no significant changes, except the background color, if you decided to change it. Now whenever you launch the AutoCAD software, you can go to the Options dialog box and select the Tutorial Guide to AutoCAD profile to use with this guide.

Tip: *You can also export your profile and save it in a separate directory where it will not be changed by other users. To do this, pick Export from the Profiles tab and use the dialog box to save the file ending in .arg to a secure folder. When you need to restore it, pick Import from the Profiles tab and select your file ending in .arg to import.*

After you have located the files, close the AutoCAD software.

Click: [X] Windows close button (which appears like an X in the upper right corner of the software screen)

At the prompt as to whether you wish to save the drawing file.

Click: No

You return to the Windows desktop.

If you want to back up the configurable files, use Windows to copy them to a separate location as you would any file.

When you want to restore the AutoCAD software defaults, you can copy these files back to the directories where you found them or your working directory and overwrite the files there. If you are on a networked system, contact your network administrator about backing up these files.

Customizable Support Files

File	Description
.chm	AutoCAD Help files.
.cif	An *.xml* file that defines most user interface elements. The file *acad.cui* is automatically loaded when you start the AutoCAD program. This file type replaces the *.mnu*, *.mns*, and *.mnc* menu file types used in previous versions.
acad2012.cfg	AutoCAD device configuration file.
.cus	Custom dictionary files.
.dcl	AutoCAD Dialog Control Language (DCL) descriptions of dialog boxes.
acad.dcl	Describes the AutoCAD software standard dialog boxes.
.lin	AutoCAD linetype definition files.
acad.lin	The standard AutoCAD linetype library file.
.lsp	AutoLISP® program files.
acad.lsp	A user-defined AutoLISP routine that loads each time you start a drawing.
.mln	A multiline library file.
.mnl	AutoLISP routines used by AutoCAD menus. A *.mnl* file must have the same filename as the *.mnu* file it supports.
acad.mnl	AutoLISP routines used by the standard AutoCAD menu.
.mnr	AutoCAD menu resource files. Contain the bit maps used by AutoCAD menus.
.pat	AutoCAD hatch pattern definition files.

acad.pat	The standard AutoCAD hatch pattern library file.
*.pc3	AutoCAD plot configuration parameters files. Each *.pc3* file stores configuration information for a specific plotter.
acad.pgp	The AutoCAD program parameters file. Contains definitions for external commands and command aliases.
acad.fmp	The AutoCAD Font Map file.
acad.psf	AutoCAD PostScript Support file; the master support file for the PSOUT and PSFILL commands.
acad.rx	Lists ARX applications that load when you start the AutoCAD software.
*.scr	AutoCAD script files. A script file contains a set of AutoCAD commands processed as a batch.
*.shp	AutoCAD shape/font definition files. Compiled shape/font files have the extension *.shx*.
acad.unt	AutoCAD unit definition file. Contains data that lets you convert from one set of units to another.

You have completed the setup steps.

AUTOCAD® BASICS

Introduction

In this chapter, you will learn the basics of the AutoCAD software's screen display, menus, and on-line help. The chapter also describes the type of instructions you'll encounter in the tutorials.

The tutorials in this manual are based on the assumption that you are using the standard configuration.

Starting the AutoCAD 2012 Software

To start the AutoCAD software,

Click: **AutoCAD 2012** shortcut from the Windows desktop

The application window shows on your screen, similar to Figure GS2.1.

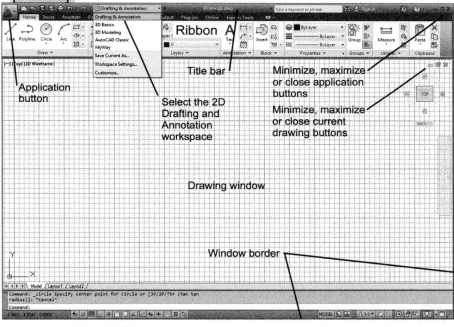

Figure GS2.1

Microsoft Windows Conventions

The AutoCAD 2012 software uses many of the same conventions as other applications that run in Windows. This section will identify some of the techniques that you will use to complete these tutorials.

You will use a mouse to work with the AutoCAD 2012 software. If you are unfamiliar with mouse operations, review your on-line Microsoft Windows tutorial for basic mouse techniques.

Objectives

In this chapter you will:

1. Minimize your drawing session and switch between other Windows applications.

2. Start a new drawing.

3. Recognize buttons, palettes, and commands.

4. Use the mouse to select commands, options, and expand palettes.

5. Work with a dialog box.

6. Access on-line help.

7. Exit from the AutoCAD software and return to the Windows operating system.

Warning: *If you are working on a network, ask your technical support person about the software configuration. Changes from the standard configuration might have been made; for example, the program might be under a different directory name or require a special command or password to launch.*

Navigating in Windows

Using a mouse is easier for many people than using the keyboard, although a combination of using the mouse and keyboard shortcuts is the most efficient way to navigate. Many standard Window keyboard shortcuts also work with AutoCAD. For information on keyboard shortcuts in Windows, see your on-line Microsoft Windows tutorial.

Basic Elements of the AutoCAD Graphics Window

The AutoCAD graphics window is the main workspace. It has elements that are common to all applications written for the Windows environment. These elements are labeled in Figure GS2.1 and described as follows.

- The close button is in the upper right corner of each window. Clicking this button closes the window.

- The title bar shows the name of the application (in this case, AutoCAD 2012) followed by the document name (in this case, Drawing1).

- The window border is the outside edge of a window. You can change the window size by moving the cursor over the border until it becomes a double-ended arrow. Holding the mouse button down while you move the mouse (dragging) resizes the window.

- The maximize and minimize buttons are in the upper right corner of the window. Clicking the maximize button with the mouse enlarges the active window so that it fills the entire screen; this condition is the default for the AutoCAD software. You will learn to use the minimize button in the next section.

Minimizing and Restoring an Application

At times you may want to leave the AutoCAD software temporarily while you are in the middle of a work session, perhaps to access another application. Minimizing allows you to leave the program running and return to it quickly.

Clicking the minimize button reduces the AutoCAD window to a title button on the taskbar and makes the Windows desktop accessible.

*Click: **the minimize application button***

The AutoCAD software is reduced to a button at the bottom of your screen. (In a working AutoCAD session, you should usually save your work before minimizing the program.)

The AutoCAD software is still running in the background, but other applications are accessible to you. When you are ready to return, click the minimized AutoCAD 2012 button.

*Click: **the minimized AutoCAD 2012 button to restore AutoCAD***

The AutoCAD graphics window returns to your screen.

MICROSOFT WINDOWS MULTITASKING OPTIONS **GS2-3**

Microsoft Windows Multitasking Options

Microsoft Windows allows you to have several applications running and to multitask between them. To switch between active applications, you press [Alt]-[Tab]. You will minimize the AutoCAD window and open another application to see how this works.

Click: *the minimize button*

Click: *to launch a different application from the Windows Start menu*

Press: *[Alt]-[Tab]* twice

A small window appears on your screen with the name of an application in it each time you press [Alt]-[Tab]. (Your AutoCAD drawing session should be on your screen. If it is not, continue pressing [Alt]-[Tab] until it appears.)

Press: *[Alt]-[Tab]*

You should have returned to your other application. (If not, continue pressing [Alt]-[Tab] until you do.)

Quit the other application now.

You will return to your AutoCAD drawing session automatically if it was the last application you were in. (If you do not see it on your screen, press [Alt]-[Tab] until you return to your AutoCAD session.)

AutoCAD Pointing Techniques

A drawing is made up of separate elements, called objects, that consist of lines, arcs, circles, text, and other elements that you create using AutoCAD commands and menu options.

The mouse is the most common means of selecting commands and menu options, selecting objects, or locating points in AutoCAD.

Clicking Commands and Menu Options

The left mouse button is referred to as the click button. The AutoCAD menus let you enter a command simply by pointing to the command and clicking to select it. In this way you are instructed to "click" specific commands. The right mouse button often pops up a short-cut menu that allows to you pick recent commands, options, or act as the [Enter] key.

Entering Points

You can specify points in a drawing either by typing in the coordinates from the keyboard or by clicking your mouse to locate the desired points in the graphics window.

When you move the mouse around on the mouse pad or table surface, "crosshairs" (the small intersecting vertical and horizontal lines on the screen) follow the motion of the mouse. These crosshairs form the AutoCAD cursor in the graphics window. You can selecting points from the screen by positioning the crosshairs at the desired location and then clicking. The crosshairs change to arrows or boxes with target areas during the execution of certain commands. You will learn about these modes in the tutorials.

Dragging

Many AutoCAD commands permit dynamic specification, or dragging, of an image of the object on the screen. You can use your mouse to move an object, rotate it, or scale it graphically. After you have selected an object in drag mode, the AutoCAD software draws tentative images as you move your pointing device. When you are satisfied with the appearance of the object, click to confirm it.

Object Selection

Tip: You can unselect an item by holding down [Shift] and clicking on it.

Many editing commands ask you to select one or more objects for processing. This collection of objects is called the *selection set*. You can use your mouse to add objects to the selection set or remove objects from it. You often use the cursor to point to objects in response to specific prompts. The objects highlight as you select them. You will learn about the various ways to select objects in the tutorials.

AutoCAD Commands and Options

There are several ways to enter commands. You can select commands from the ribbon, from toolbars, from the menus, or type them at the command prompt. You can also use dynamic and pointer input, which you will learn about in Tutorial 1.

How you start a command may affect the order and wording of the prompts displayed on the screen. These differences offer you options for more efficient use of the software. Most AutoCAD commands can be typed at the command prompt, but clicking them from the ribbon or a toolbar may be easier for you. For the purposes of the tutorials in this manual, you should click or type commands exactly as instructed.

The command selection location you should use will be indicated. When you are supposed to type a command it will appear in all capital letters and bold (e.g., *NEW*). You must press the [Enter] key to activate the command once typed. When you are supposed to start a command by clicking its button, the button name appears in the instruction line (e.g., *Click: New button*).

You will learn about the benefits of choosing commands in different ways in different situations. For the purposes of the tutorials in this manual, you should click or type commands exactly as instructed.

Typing Commands

The command window at the bottom of your screen is very important for using AutoCAD. All commands that you select by any means are echoed there, and additional prompts inform you what to do next. The prompt "Command:" in this window is a signal that the program is ready for a command. You can use the scroll arrows at the right of the command window to review the lines that may have been passed. You can also enlarge the window by positioning the cursor at the border of the window and dragging to enlarge the window so that it shows more lines.

Position the cursor at the top border of the command window.

Your cursor will change to a double-headed arrow.

Hold down the cursor and drag the mouse up to enlarge the command window.

Your screen should look like Figure GS2.2.

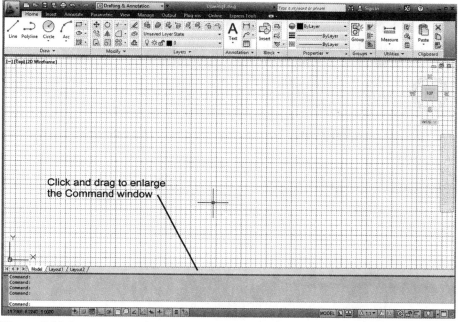

Figure GS2.2

Return your **command window** to its original three-line display on your own.

You can also show an AutoCAD text window (Figure GS2.3). Press the [F2] key to toggle to the text window. This shows the command window information in a text window. To return to your graphics window, press [F2] again or use the Windows close button in the upper right of the Text Window.

```
AutoCAD Text Window - Drawing1.dwg                    _ □ ×
Edit
Command: LINE
Specify first point:
Specify next point or [Undo]:
Specify next point or [Undo]:
Specify next point or [Close/Undo]:
Command: e ERASE
Select objects: 1 found

Select objects:
Command: c CIRCLE Specify center point for circle or [3P/2P/Ttr (tan tan
radius)]:
Specify radius of circle or [Diameter]:
Command:  CIRCLE Specify center point for circle or [3P/2P/Ttr (tan tan
radius)]: 3p Specify first point on circle:
Specify second point on circle:
Specify third point on circle:

Command: |
```

Tip: *You can also drag the command window to the top of the drawing area. This may make it easier for you to notice the command prompt.*

Figure GS2.3

When you are supposed to type a command, it will appear in all capital letters (e.g., LINE). Watch the command line in the window as you type.

Command: **LINE [Enter]**

The Line command is activated when you press [Enter], and the Line command prompt "Specify first point:" is in the command window. This prompt tells you to enter the first point from which a line will be drawn. You will learn about the Line command in Tutorial 1. For now,

Press: **[Esc]** to cancel the command

Switching the Workspace

AutoCAD 2012 can be customized to your preferences. Customization is great when you are familiar with the software. While you are starting out, it is helpful is you can locate the commands in standard positions on the ribbon. The ribbon is the main toolbar which appears by default across the top of the screen. To provide some quick customizations for different purposes, you can select from premade workspaces. To switch the workspace,

Click: **2D Drafting and Annotation** to show the pull-down list (Figure GS2.4)

Figure GS2.4

Click: **3D Basics**

Notice the ribbon changes to display a different set of palettes and tools.

Click: **2D Drafting and Annotation** from the Workspace pull-down list as shown in Figure GS2.4.

So that you can find the commands as directed, make sure to use the 2D Drafting and Annotation Workspace unless you are instructed otherwise in the tutorial.

Using the Ribbon

The ribbon contain tabs, palettes and buttons that are used to select commands and tools. You can "tear off" palettes from the ribbon and "float" them on your screen.

Click and Drag: **on the title bar of the Draw palette** and move it off of the ribbon as shown in Figure GS2.5

Click: the **expand button** to show the additional tools on the Draw palette

Figure GS2.5

Figure GS2.6

The floating palette has very small buttons on it. You can use them to return the panel to the ribbon, or you can drag the panel back onto the ribbon.

Move your cursor over the Draw palette

Additional buttons show along its edges.

Click: **Return panels to ribbon button**

Figure GS2.7

When pointing to a button, the cursor changes to an arrow that points up and to the left. You use this arrow to select command buttons. When you move the pointing device over an button, the name of the button appears below the cursor. This feature is called a *tool tip* and is an easy way to identify buttons.

Warning: *The term "button" used in conjunction with a dialog box refers to these selection options and should not be confused with the buttons on your mouse.*

Buttons with a small black triangle expand or *flyout* to show associated commands or subcommands.

> *Click the mouse near the triangle in the lower portion of the Circle item on the Draw panel to show the additional options, as shown in Figure GS2.8.*

Figure GS2.8

Next you will try the Circle Center Radius button from the Draw toolbar to see the options that appear. The button looks like a circle with a radius drawn in it. As you move your mouse over the buttons (you may need to pause), the command names are confirmed by the tool tips that appear below your cursor. (Sometimes the tool tip command name is slightly different from the name echoed at the command prompt or the command that you would type at the command prompt. If you are confused about a specific command name, check the AutoCAD Help.)

As new commands are introduced in the tutorials in this manual, their toolbar buttons will appear as the Circle button does here.

 Click: **Circle button**

The following options appear at the command line.

Specify center point for circle or [3P/2P/Ttr (tan tan radius)]: ***press [Esc] to cancel the command***

The letters that appear at the command prompt, 3P/2P/Ttr, are command options for the Circle command. Subcommands and command options function only when entered in response to the appropriate prompts on the command line. When a subcommand or option includes one or more uppercase letters in its name, it is a signal that you can type those letters at the prompt as a shortcut for the option name; for example, X for eXit. If a number appears in the option name—for example, 2P for Circle 2 Points—which creates a circle using two endpoints of the diameter—you need to type both the number and the capital letter(s).

Many buttons on the panels, select the suboptions for you automatically. For example, clicking on 2-Point from the Circle flyout will select that command suboption.

Backing Up and Backing Out of Commands

When you type a command name or any data in response to a prompt on the command line, the typed characters "wait" until you press the spacebar or [Enter] to act on the entered data.

If you have not already pressed [Enter] or the spacebar, you can use the [backspace] key (generally located above and to the right of the [Enter] key on standard PC keyboards and represented by a long back arrow) to delete one character at a time from the command line. Pressing [Ctrl]-H has the same effect as pressing [backspace].

Pressing [Esc] terminates the currently active command (if any) and reissues the Command: prompt. You can cancel a command at any time: while typing the command name, during command execution, or during any time-consuming process. A short delay may occur before the cancellation takes effect and the prompt *Cancel* confirms the cancellation.

Pressing [Esc] is also useful if you want to cancel a selection process. If you are in the middle of selecting an object, press [Esc] to cancel the selection process and discard the selection set. Any item that was highlighted because you selected it will return to normal.

If you complete a command and the result is not what you had expected or wanted, click the Undo button or type U to reverse the effect.

Repeating Commands

You can press the spacebar or [Enter] at the command prompt to repeat the previous command, regardless of the method you used to enter that command. You can also right-click and use the short-cut menu to repeat the command. You will try this now by starting a command and then press [Esc] to cancel it. Then you will repeat the command.

Type: **LINE [Enter]**

Specify first point: **[Esc]**

*Right-click: **to show the short-cut menu***

A menu will appear as shown in Figure GS2.9. It can be used to repeat the command.

To remove the menu from your screen,

Press: [Esc]

Figure GS2.9

Working with the Ribbon

Clicking on a tab changes the list of palettes shown on the ribbon to those associated with tab.

Click: **Annotate tab** *from the ribbon*

The ribbon appearance changes to show a new set of palettes and tools as shown in Figure GS2.10. Some tabs, have some commands duplicated on that tab to minimize the time spent switching between tabs.

Tabs that have a down pointing arrow next to their title will expand to show more tools.

Click: **the small downward right-pointing arrow in the right of the Dimension panel title bar, but don't click the mouse button**

At first the tool tip shows, the as the cursor sits there longer, the expanded contextual help shown in Figure GS2.10 appears.

Pick small downward arrow to show the Dimension Style Manager

Figure GS2.10

Working with Dialog Boxes

Clicking the small downward right-pointing arrow next to a palette title bar opens the associated manager dialog box. An ellipsis (...) after a menu item also indicates that it will open a dialog box. Several commands let you set AutoCAD modes or perform operations by checking boxes or filling in fields in a dialog box.

Click: **to show the Dimension Style Manager** *using the small downward right-pointing arrow at the right of the Dimension palette title bar*

The dialog box shown in Figure GS2.11 appears on your screen.

Figure GS2.11

When a dialog box is displayed, the cursor changes to an arrow. You use this arrow to select items from the dialog box. Some dialog boxes have subboxes that pop up in front of them. When this occurs, you must respond to the "top" dialog box and close it before the underlying one can continue. The New, Modify, Override, and Compare buttons at the right of the dialog box bring up such subboxes.

*Click: **Modify***

The Modify Dimension Style dialog box shown in Figure GS2.12 appears on your screen.

Figure GS2.12

The Modify Dimension Style Manager is a typical dialog box. Most dialog boxes have an OK (or Close) button that confirms the settings or

Tip: *A feature of many Windows dialog boxes allows you to double-click on the desired selection to select it and exit the dialog box in one action.*

options that you have selected in the dialog box. Clicking it is like pressing [Enter] to finalize a typed command. Clicking the Cancel button disregards all changes made in the dialog box and closes the dialog box; it has the same effect as pressing [Esc]. You can use the Help button to get more information about a particular command.

Any item in a dialog box that is "grayed" cannot be selected, such as the Extend beyond ticks option in the Dimension Lines section.

Most dialog boxes have several types of buttons that control values or commands.

Check buttons: A check button is a small rectangle that is either blank or shows a check mark. Check buttons control an on/off switch—for example, turning Suppress Dim Line 1 on or off—or control a choice from a set of alternatives—for example, determining which modes are on. A blank check button is off.

Radio buttons: A radio button looks like a circle with a dot at the center. It also turns an option on or off. A filled-in radio button is on. You can select only one radio button at a time; clicking one button automatically turns any other button off. Click on the Fit tab of the Modify Dimension Style dialog box to see radio buttons.

Action buttons: An action button doesn't control a value but causes an action. The OK action button causes the dialog box to close and all the selected options to go into effect. When an action button is highlighted (outlined with a heavy rule), you can press [Enter] to activate it.

Text boxes: A text box allows you to specify a value, such as Baseline Spacing in Figure GS2.12. Clicking a text box puts the cursor in it and lets you type values in it or alter values already there. If you enter an invalid value, the OK button has no effect; you must highlight the value, correct it, and select OK again.

Input buttons: An input button chooses among preset options, such as the Color button in Figure GS2.12. Input buttons have a small arrow at the right end. Clicking the arrow causes the value area to expand into a menu of options that you can use to select the value for the button.

You can also use the keyboard to move around in dialog boxes.

Tab key - Pressing [Tab] moves among the options in the dialog box.

Try this by pressing **[Tab]** several times now.

Arrow keys - Once you have highlighted a text box or input button, you can use the arrow keys to move the cursor in text boxes or to cycle among input options.

Spacebar - The [spacebar] toggles options on and off. (When you are not in a dialog box, it acts like pressing the [Enter] key.

Scroll bar - Another common feature of dialog boxes is the scroll bar. A dialog box may contain more entries than can be displayed at one time. You use the scroll bars to move (scroll) the items up or down.

Most dialog boxes save changes to the current drawing only. Two exceptions to this rule are the Options dialog box and the Plot dialog box; these dialog boxes change the way AutoCAD operates, not just the current drawing itself.

The Cancel button ignores all the selections that you made while this dialog box was open and returns you to the most recent settings. To return to the graphics window without making any changes,

Click: **Cancel**

Click: **Close**

You return to the graphics window.

Accessing On-Line Help

AutoCAD has context-sensitive on-line help.

You can get help in a number of ways. You can click the Help button, type HELP or ? at the command prompt, or press [F1] to bring up the Help window.

You will use the Help button, which looks like a question mark, from the Quick Access toolbar at the top right of the application window to open AutoCAD on-line help.

? *Click:* **Help button**

The AutoCAD 2012 Help window is shown in Figure GS2.13.

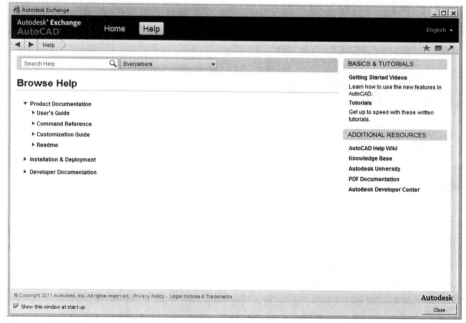

Figure GS2.13

Tip: *For information on what's new in the AutoCAD 2012 software, you can select Learn how to use the new features in AutoCAD from the Help menu.*

The left panel of the window shows a list of general topics set up for you. You can also type a search term in the input box at the upper right to locate help for your term or phrase.

Click: **Command Reference** *from the topics list*

The Command reference portion of the dialog box appears on your screen.

Click: **Commands**

An alphabetical list of help topics appears in the Help window.

You will now type in an AutoCAD command instructing it to locate a particular topic in the Index.

Type: **ERASE [Enter]** *into the input box at the top right*

The help screen for the Erase command appears on your screen.

To return to the previous screen (if there was a previous screen), you can select Back from the menu bar.

You will use the Windows close button to close the Help window and return to the AutoCAD graphics window.

Click: **the Windows close button** *in the top right of the Help window*

On-line help is a great resource for learning how to use the powerful AutoCAD software. You should use help whenever you want more information about commands and options as you work through the tutorials.

Using Classic Pull-Down Menus

You can change the workspace to select the classic pull-down style menus used in earlier AutoCAD versions.

Click: **2D Drafting and Annotation** *to show the pull-down list (Figure GS2.14)*

Click: **AutoCAD Classic**

Figure GS2.14

The ribbon is removed and replaced with the pull-down menus similar to that used in previous versions.

Figure GS2.15

The menu bar and its associated pull-down menus provide another way to select commands. The menu bar operates the same as in other Windows software. When in the menu area, the cursor changes to a selection arrow. To practice,

Click: **Draw** *from the menu bar*

Clicking a menu item executes the commands associated with it, opens a submenu of options, or opens a dialog box of options to be used to control the command. A triangle to the right of a menu item indicates that a submenu is associated with it. You will click Inquiry to see its submenu.

Click: **Circle** *from the Draw menu*

The Circle submenu shown in Figure GS2.15 appears next to the Draw menu.

A pulled-down menu remains displayed until you

- click an item from it,
- click on the menu name again,
- pull down another menu by clicking it from the menu bar,
- remove the menu by clicking an unused area of the menu bar,
- click a point in the graphics window,
- type a character on the keyboard, or
- click an item from a tablet or button menu.

To remove the Draw menu from the screen,

Click: *a point in the graphics window*

On your own, click **2D Drawing and Annotation** from the Workspace list to restore the ribbon menu

GS2-16 Getting Started 2 AUTOCAD® BASICS

Working with Documents

All the documents that you will be instructed to use are held in the directories *c:\datafile2012* and *c:\work*, which you should have already created in Getting Started-1. The best procedure is to save all files on your hard drive because it has more storage space and is faster than accessing a removable drive. Saving directly from the AutoCAD program to a removable drive can result in unrecoverable, corrupted drawing files if you remove the drive before the software is fully closed.

Exiting an AutoCAD Session

When you have finished an AutoCAD session, you will exit the program by choosing the Application icon and then clicking Exit or by using the Window close box for the application..

Click: **Application icon, Exit AutoCAD 2012**

Because quitting unintentionally could cause the loss of a lengthy editing session, the AutoCAD software prompts you to save the changes if you want to. An AutoCAD dialog box appears that contains the message, Save Changes to *DRAWING1.dwg*? It gives you three options: Yes, No, and Cancel.

Click: **No**

You are returned to Windows.

You are now ready to complete the tutorials in this manual.

Tip: *If you have made some irreversible error and want to discard all changes made in an AutoCAD session, you can choose Exit from the File menu (or type QUIT at the command prompt) and select No so that the changes are not saved to your file.*

STUDYING FOR THE AUTOCAD® CERTIFICATION EXAM

General Study Tips

Good exam taking strategies are helpful to keep in mind.

Prepare — The exam includes performance based testing for which you will need hands-on experience. Use the software, as well as studying written material. Practice your skills by making drawings. During the test you may not use calculators, books, or other electronic equipment, so don't plan to rely on them. But keep in mind the useful functions built into the software: the *Help* command is key, but don't forget the *Quick Calculator* and reading the *command prompts*.

Review the information available at:
http://autodesk.starttest.com
This is the official web site and provides information about the exam. You can also purchase practice exams here.

Look for free practice exams on the web at locations like
http://www.docnmail.com/tests/computers/autocad.htm.
Practice exams that are not official Autodesk exams may not be very similar to the actual certification exam, but still give you a chance to practice your exam taking skills and test your knowledge of the Auto-CAD software.

Be well rested, comfortable, and ready at exam time.

Manage your time during the exam — Specific objectives are being test, so read the questions carefully and make sure you know what is asked for. Pay attention to the introductory tutorial giving information on using the Autodesk Online testing system, **location of files**, instructions for answering questions, and general test information.

Make a quick judgement about how long it will take to answer the question. During the exam, you are able to save datafiles and mark questions to return to later. Do the questions that are quick and easy for you first and mark the more difficult questions to work later if time permits. You do not have to earn 100% to pass.

Review your answers — Check the review screen before submitting your exam to make sure you have answered all of the items. If you don't know and have time, make educated guesses. Use the strategies of ruling out answers you know to be incorrect, or off target and selecting from the remaining ones. Sometimes you may have to select the answer that is the least incorrect from a number of poor answer options.

Have a good attitude — Regardless of your performance on the exam, you will get valuable feedback about which areas you have mastered and which you still need to work on. Look at the exam as another learning opportunity, as well as a chance to show your abilities.

Objectives

This chapter describes how to use this text to study for the AutoCAD Certication Exam. As you read this section you will:

1. Get general study tips for the exam.

2. Find web resources for studying for and taking the certification exam.

3. Learn how to identify which topics in this text may appear on the certification exam.

Exam Objectives

Check your proficiency on the exam sections. Likely examples are listed below. You can purchase the official guide for the exam at *store.autodesk.com* or for schoools at *autodesk.com/education* by selecting "locate a reseller".

Certified Associate Exam

Tutorial 1	### The AutoCAD Tour

Example   Describe and set the workspace.

Tutorial 1 & 2   ### Creating Drawings

Examples: Use running object snaps and object snap overrides to select snap points in the drawing.

Use Polar Tracking and PolarSnap

Use object snap tracking to position geometry.

Use the Units command to set drawing units.

Select objects for grip editing.

Identify the type of editing that can be done using grips.

Tutorial 4   ### Manipulating Objects

Examples: Use several different selection methods to select objects.

Move objects in the drawing using object snaps, object tracking, and coordinate entry, for precise placement.

Use the Copy command to copy objects in the drawing.

Use the Rotate command to rotate objects in the drawing.

Use the Mirror command to mirror objects in the drawing.

Use the Array command to pattern objects in the drawing.

Tutorial 2, 3 & 5   ### Drawing Organization and Inquiry Commands

Examples: Use Layer tools.

Use the Match Properties command to apply the properties from a source object to destination objects.

Use the Inquiry commands (Distance, Radius, Angle, Area, List, and ID) to obtain geometric information from the drawing.

Tutorial 3   ### Altering Objects

Examples: Use the Join command to combine multiple objects into a single object.

Use the Fillet Command to create radius geometry connecting two objects.

Tutorial 5	## Working with Layouts
	Example Create a new layout.
	Create and manipulate viewports.
Tutorial 1 & 7	## Annotating the Drawing
	Example Use the Multiline Text command to create and format paragraphs of text.
	Create and use text styles.
Tutorial 7	## Dimensioning
	Example Create different types of dimensions on linear objects.
	Create and modify dimension styles to control the appearance of dimensions.
	Create and edit multileaders.
Tutorial 9	## Hatching Objects
	Example: Create hatch patterns and fills.
Tutorial 10	## Working with Reusable Content
	Example: Use the Block command to create a block definition.
	Use the Insert command to insert a block reference in a drawing.
Tutorial 3	## Creating Additional Drawing Objects
	Example: Work with polylines.
	Edit polylines.

INTRODUCTION TO THE AUTOCAD® SOFTWARE

Introduction

This tutorial introduces the fundamental operating procedures and drawing tools of the AutoCAD 2012 software. It explains how to create a new drawing; draw lines, circles, and rectangles; and save a drawing to a new name. You will learn how to erase items and select groups of objects. This tutorial also explains how to add text to a drawing.

Starting

Launch the AutoCAD 2012 software from your Windows Desktop.

If you need assistance with this, refer to Getting Started 1 and 2.

A blank drawing area appears on your screen. By default, it is named *Drawing1.dwg*, as shown in its title bar.

The AutoCAD Screen

Your computer display screen should look like Figure 1.1, which shows the AutoCAD application window. If you are not showing the 2D Drafting and Annotation workspace at the top of the screen, select it now.

Next, familiarize yourself with the areas of the AutoCAD screen.

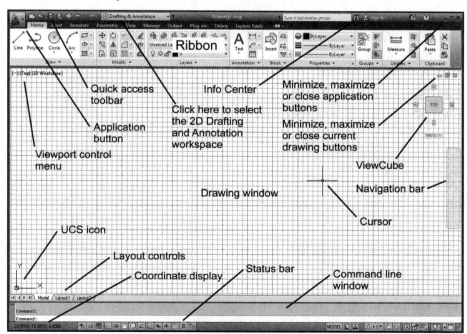

Figure 1.1   The AutoCAD Application Window

Objectives

When you have completed this tutorial, you will be able to

1. Use the Ribbon to select commands.

2. Create new drawing files.

3. Work with multiple drawings.

4. Use the Help command.

5. Enter coordinates.

6. Draw lines, circles, and rectangles.

7. Erase objects.

8. Select objects, using Window and Crossing.

9. Add and edit drawing text.

10. Save a drawing and transfer it from one drive to another.

Warning
If your screen does not look generally like Figure 1.1, verify that you configured the AutoCAD software properly. Refer to Getting Sarted 1 and 2 of this manual.

*Check that the **2D Drafting and Annotation** workspace is selected.*

Screens in this book are shown with a white background for the best visibility. You may prefer to use other colors on your system.

The Drawing Window is the central part of the screen, which you use to create and display drawings. The drawing's title bar appears above the blank area of the screen listing the drawing's name. *Windows control buttons* are located at the right of the title bar allowing you to minimize, maximize/tile, or close the drawing window.

The Graphics Cursor, or Crosshairs shows the location of your pointing device in the graphics window. You use the graphics cursor to draw, select, or pick command items. The cursor's appearance depends on the command or option you select.

The Command Line Window (Figure 1.2) is usually located at the bottom of the screen. It is a *floating window* so you can move it anywhere on your screen. You can also resize it to show more or fewer command lines. You can scroll using the Up arrow on your keyboard to see past commands that are not visible in the active area. Pay close attention to the command window because that is where you are prompted to enter information or make selections.

The User Coordinate System (UCS) Icon helps you keep track of the current X-, Y-, Z-coordinate system that you are using and the direction from which the coordinates are being viewed in 3D drawings.

The Status Bar (Figure 1.2) at the bottom of the application window shows important settings and modes that may be in effect. The *coordinate display* shows the crosshairs' location at the left of the status bar as three numbers with the general form X.XXXX, Y.YYYY, and Z.ZZZZ. The specific numbers displayed on your screen tell you the location of your crosshairs. Tools for Infer Constraints, Snap, Grid, Ortho, Polar, Osnap, 3D Object Snap, Object Snap Tracking, Allow/Disallow Dynamic Ucs, Dynamic Input, Show/Hide Lineweight, Show/Hide Transparency, Quick Properties and Selection Cycling appear to the right of the coordinates on the status bar. These buttons turn these special modes on and off. When these modes are in effect, their buttons are highlighted. Additional buttons at the left of the status bar let you manage the workspace.

The Layout Controls let you quickly switch from the model space to the paper layout space, where you manage your drawings for printing on sheets. You will learn to use layouts in Tutorial 5. For now, leave the Model tab selected.

The Viewport Controls, View Controls, and Visual Styles Controls located at the upper left of the drawing window let you quickly manipulate the *viewport* or drawing window. These tools are particularly useful when working in 3D. Don't change these settings for now.

The Application Button is used to select menu items for opening, saving, exporting, drawing utilities, printing, and other typical software functions.

The Quick Access Toolbar provides buttons for opening, saving, and plotting (printing) files. It also has an Undo and Redo button.

The Info Center is used to access and search help files, save favorite search results, and access product information.

Tip: *Switching on or off modes from the status bar changes the display and function of some commands. If you have trouble following the steps in these tutorials, make sure your status bar modes are set the same as those shown in the tutorial.*

Minimize, maximize or close application buttons for the **AutoCAD software** are located in the upper right of the application window. Use these buttons to minimize, maximize or close the AutoCAD software.

Minimize, maximize or close buttons for the **drawing window** are located in the upper right of the drawing window. Use these buttons to minimize, maximize or close the drawing currently open.

Figure 1.2   The Status Bar and Command Line Window

The Ribbon

The Ribbon (Figure 1.3) is used to select commands and tools. It is grouped into *tabs* and *panels*, which include buttons for frequently used commands. Right-clicking on the ribbon allows you to select which tabs and panels are shown there.

Figure 1.3   The Ribbon

Move the graphics cursor up into the Ribbon area.

Note that the cursor changes from the crosshairs to an arrow when it moves out of the graphics window.

Click on the View tab.

The ribbon changes to display a new set of panels used to select commands and tools for viewing your drawing as shown in Figure 1.4.

Figure 1.4   The View Tab

Tip: *When you are closing a drawing, double check to make sure you are using the drawing window close box. Accidentally choosing to close the AutoCAD application may cause you to lose unsaved work and takes time to restart the software.*

Tip: *Panels at the right of the ribbon automatically minimize as you resize your software window smaller. You may see minimized panels, which expand automatically when you move your cursor over them.*

Minimized panels

Click on the Home tab to show it on the ribbon.

Position the arrow cursor over the Line button on the Draw panel, but do not click the mouse button.

After the arrow cursor remains over a button for a few seconds, the button's tool tip appears below it as shown in Figure 1.5.

Leaving the cursor over the item even longer displays more detailed help for the command as shown in Figure 1.6.

Figure 1.5   **The Line Command Tool Tip**

Figure 1.6

If you are unsure about which command an icon represents, use the tool tip to help identify it.

Move the arrow cursor over each button in turn to familiarize yourself with the buttons on the Draw panel.

The Ribbon can quickly be minimized to tabs, titles, buttons or cycled through these appearances using the tool shown in Figure 1.7. This tool is a toggle. Clicking it once changes the appearance of the Ribbon. Click it a second time to change the appearance of the Ribbon again.

Click the small downward arrow at the right of the Ribbon tabs to expand the menu choices.
Click: Minimize to Panel Buttons

The Ribbon minimizes to a button for each of the tabs as shown in Figure 1.8.

Figure 1.7   **Expanding the Menu Choices for the Ribbon Appearance**

Figure 1.8   **The Ribbon Minimized to Panel Buttons**

Tip: *If you select a command by accident, press the [Esc] key on your keyboard to cancel the command.*

Click the small downward arrow at the right of the Ribbon tabs to expand the menu choices as shown in Figure 1.7.
Click: **Cycle through All**

Click the left small arrow at the right of the Ribbon tabs to toggle the appearance of the Ribbon.

Figure 1.9   Toggle the Appearance of the Ribbon

Continue to click until you show the full Ribbon again.

Figure 1.10   The Full Ribbon

The Draw Panel

The Draw panel is shown on the Home tab of the Ribbon by default (Figure 1.11). The Draw panel provides commands to create new objects in your drawing, such as lines, circles and other drawing geometry. You also use it to create helices, insert hatch patterns, revision clouds and other objects.

Figure 1.11   The Draw Tab

Click the Line tool

The command window displays, "_line Specify first point:" indicating that the software is ready for you to select an endpoint to start your line. The Dynamic Input box appears near the cursor on the screen as shown in Figure 1.12.

Clean Screen button

Clean Screen (Ctrl+0)

Tip: *To quickly erase everything and start with a fresh blank screen, you can press [Ctrl]+0 or pick the Clean Screen button from the lower right of the status bar.*

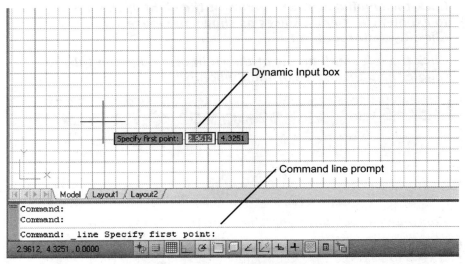

Figure 1.12   The Dynamic Input Box Appears Near the Cursor

Canceling Commands

You can easily cancel commands by pressing [Esc]. If you make a selection by mistake, press [Esc] to cancel it. Sometimes you may have to press [Esc] twice to cancel a command, depending on where you are in the command sequence.

*Press: **[Esc]** to cancel the line command*

Typing Commands

You can type commands directly at the *command prompt* in the command window. To do so, you must type the exact command name or *alias*. Remember that many of the words on the tool tips are tool names, not command names. Only the actual command name, not tool names, when typed, activate a command. You will type the command, Line, in the command prompt area. You may type all capitals, capitals and lowercase, or all lowercase letters; AutoCAD commands are not *case-sensitive*.

Command: **LINE [Enter]**

Specify first point: **[Esc]**

Pressing [Esc] cancels the command. You will learn more about the Line command later in this tutorial.

Command Aliasing

You can type commands quickly through *command aliasing*. Many AutoCAD users feel that this is the fastest method of selecting commands. You can give any command a shorter name, called an *alias*. Many commands already have aliases assigned to them to help you get started. They are stored in the file *acad.pgp*, which is part of the AutoCAD

Tip: *When you see the [Enter] key in an instruction in this manual, you must press [Enter], (sometimes labeled Return) on your keyboard, to finalize the command or response. A quick shortcut is to press the space bar on your keyboard or click the right mouse button and select Enter from the menu that pops up. When you are entering text during a text command you must press the actual [Enter] key.*

Tip: *If you drew some lines before cancelling the command, they will not be erased. You can delete the lines by clicking them so they are selected and then pressing the Delete key on your keyboard.*

software and is found in the directory that you have set in your support files search path. To edit the *acad.pgp* file, click the Manage tab, then select Edit Aliases from the Customization panel.

You can edit the file *acad.pgp* with a text editor and add lines with your own command aliases. (These lines take the form ALIAS, *COMMAND in the *acad.pgp* file.) After doing so, you can use the shortened name at the AutoCAD command prompt. The commands in the margin are some for which aliases have already been created. When you need one of these commands, you can type its alias at the command prompt instead of the entire command name.

Remember these are only a few of the aliases available. For a more complete list, use the software Help or reference the Command Summary at the end of this book. The Command Summary indicates where to find a command, its button, the actual command name (which you can type to start the command) and its alias, if there is one. Try typing the alias for the Line command.

Command: **L [Enter]**

Specify first point: **[Esc]**

There are many different ways to select each command. After you have worked through the tutorials in this book, decide which methods work best for you. While you are working through the tutorials, however, be sure to select the commands from the locations specified. The subsequent command prompts and options may differ, depending on how you selected the command.

Dynamic Entry

Another way to give input and select command options is to enter values and options using the dynamic input boxes that appear near the cursor location. Dynamic input allows you to type input at your pointer location, specify dimensions during many draw commands and to select from command option prompts.

Right-click: **Dynamic Input** *button on the status bar (see Figure 1.13)*

Click: **Settings**

Figure 1.13   Dynamic Input Button and Menu

Command	Alias
A	ARC
AA	AREA
AL	ALIGN
AR	ARRAY
B	BLOCK
C	CIRCLE
CH	PROPERTIES
CP	COPY
D	DIMSTYLE
DI	DIST
DIV	DIVIDE
E	ERASE
F	FILLET
G	GROUP
H	HATCH
I	NSERT
L	LINE
LA	LAYER
L	LIST
M	MOVE
MI	MIRROR
O	OFFSET
P	PAN
PE	PEDIT
PL	PLINE
PO	POINT
PR	PROPERTIES
R	REDRAW
RA	REDRAWALL
RE	REGEN
RO	ROTATE
SN	SNAP
SP	SPELL
SPL	SPLINE
T	MTEXT
TR	TRIM
UC	UCSMAN
UN	UNITS
W	WBLOCK
X	EXPLODE

Tip: *The status bar buttons appear gray when they are off. When they are turned on they appear in the highlighting color (the defult is blue).*

Figure 1.14   Drafting Settings Dynamic Input Tab

The Drafting Settings dialog box appears on your screen with the Dynamic Input tab uppermost as shown in Figure 1.14. You can use this dialog box to customize which dynamic input options are shown at the cursor location. Do not change any settings now.

*Click: **Cancel** to close the dialog box*

Check to see that the Dynamic Input button on your status bar is on.

Command: ***C [Enter]***

You should see the Circle command prompts appear on your screen along with the dynamic input boxes at the cursor location as shown in Figure 1.15.

Figure 1.15   Circle Command Prompts and Dynamic Input Box

Tip: *Notice that as you type a command, the autocomplete feature pops up a list with the command names that use those letters. When the command you want to use appears, you can click on it from the list to start the command. The command named AUTOCOMPLETE lets you control how this features appears.*

During these tutorials take care to select the commands as directed, otherwise you may see different prompts than those in the directions.

Once you have selected a command, a number of options may appear at the command prompt. To see them in the dynamic input menu,

> *Press: **down arrow** on your keyboard*

The options for the circle command appears near the cursor location as shown in Figure 1.16.

Figure 1.16   **Use Down Arrow to Show Command Options**

> *Click: **2P** from the options that appear dynamically*
>
> *Type: **10** into the first input box to specify the x-coordinate*
>
> *Press: **[Tab]***
>
> *Type: **10** into the second input box to specify the y-coordinate*
>
> *Press: **[Enter]***
>
> *Type: **8** into the input box that appears to specify the second end-point of the circle's diameter*
>
> *Press: **[Enter]***

The completed Circle appears on your screen.

Typing a Command Option Letter

The prompt shown in the command line gives the options for the selected command. You can type the option letter or letters that are capitalized and then press [Enter] to select the option you want. Next, use the Circle command and specify three points on the circumference of the circle to define it.

> *Click: **to turn off the Dynamic Input button on your status bar.***
>
> Command: *C [Enter]*
>
> Specify center point for circle or [3P/2P/Ttr (tan tan radius)]: *3P [Enter]*
>
> Specify first point on circle: *pick a point from the screen*
>
> Specify second point on circle: *pick a second point from the screen*
>
> Specify third point on circle: *pick a third point from the screen*

A second circle appears on your screen.

You will practice with multiple drawings next by creating a second drawing. Do not close this circle drawing.

Starting a New Drawing

To start a new drawing,

Click: **Application button, New**

The Select template dialog box (shown in Figure 1.17) allows you to select a pre-existing template file as a starting point for the new drawing. A *template* can contain useful settings, borders, and other items that then become a part of the new drawing. A number of standard templates are available and you can create your own from any Auto-CAD drawing. You will learn more about creating and using templates in Tutorial 5. The default option, *acad.dwt*, is a template with minimal settings for starting an essentially blank drawing.

Figure 1.17   **Select Template Dialog Box**

Click: **acad.dwt** *(if it is not already highlighted)*, then click **Open**

Naming Drawing Files

After the Select template dialog box closes, you should see the name of the new drawing, *Drawing2.dwg*, in the title bar at the top of the application window. Next, you will save the drawing and name it *shapes.dwg*.

Click: **Application button, Save**

The Save Drawing As dialog box shown in Figure 1.18 appears, which you can use to name your file and select the drive and directory.

Type: **SHAPES**

Tip: *Clicking New directly opens the Select template dialog box. Notice there is also a flyout triangle indicating more selections. Hovering your mouse on New will expand the menu choices to show options for Drawing or Sheet Set. You may also start the Select Template dialog box by selecting Drawing from this expanded menu.*

Tip: *Windows operating system settings control how you view file extensions (like the .dwt for template files.) Use the Windows Explorer Tools menu to pick Folder options and then View to see where you can change the settings.*

Tip: *Double-clicking on a file name or template name opens it in one step.*

Tip: *It is not generally good practice to include periods (.) or spaces in your AutoCAD drawing names. Periods are generally used to divide the file name from the file extension (for example, shapes.dwg). Using a period within the name of the file may cause confusion with the extension and can make it difficult to use the file with other operating system versions, or inside other AutoCAD drawings.*

Tip: *When a drawing has not been saved previously, the Save command allows you to specify the filename, similar to using SaveAs.*

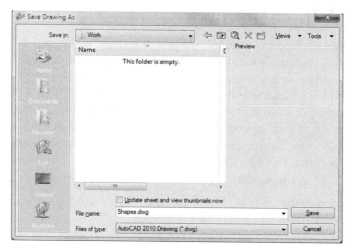

Figure 1.18   Save Drawing As Dialog

The AutoCAD software follows the Windows rules for naming a file. Names may include as many characters and/or numbers as you choose, along with other characters: underscores (_), dashes (-), commas (,), and periods (.). However, forward slashes (/) and backward slashes (\) aren't allowed in the drawing name.

All AutoCAD drawing files are automatically assigned the *file extension* *.dwg*, so typing the extension is unnecessary. Use drawing names that are descriptive of the drawing being created. Descriptive names make recognizing completed drawings easier. Drawing names can include a drive and directory specification. If you don't specify a drive, the drawing is saved in the *default directory*. In Getting Started 1 of this manual, you should have already created a default working directory, called *c:\work*, where you will save your drawing files..

On the left side of the dialog box are icons for History, My Documents, Favorites, FTP, Desktop, and Buzzsaw that allow you to maneuver through your files and connect to Web resources. If you cannot see the full set of icons, use the scroll bars to enlarge the Save Drawing As window. If necessary, click the Desktop icon and use the resources there to help you browse to the directory where you want to store your files. Keeping your files organized so that you can retrieve them later is an important aspect of using CAD.

Click: **Save**

This action returns you to the drawing editor, where you can begin work on your drawing, called *shapes.dwg*. Unless you are using a different drive or working directory on your system, the entire default name of your drawing is *c:\work\shapes.dwg*. Note that the name *shapes.dwg* now appears in the title bar as the current file name. Depending on your system, the *.dwg* extension may not show up in the title bar; however, the AutoCAD software recognizes it as such.

Tip: *If you cannot open your drawing for use with the AutoCAD program because it is corrupted, you may be able to recover it with the selection Application icon, Drawing Utilities, Recover from the menu bar.*

Warning *Saving a drawing directly to a floppy disk or removable USB drive can lead to problems. If you named your drawing so that it is stored on a removable disk, be sure to exit the AutoCAD program before you remove your disk from the drive. Always leave the same disk in the drive for the entire AutoCAD session. Otherwise, you can end up with part of your drawing not saved, which will result in an unrecoverable, corrupted drawing file.*

As you create a drawing, more and more data are stored in the drawing file. If the file size exceeds the remaining capacity of a disk, a FATAL ERROR may occur, resulting in the loss of the drawing file. To prevent problems with files that may become too large for your removeable storage media, create all drawings on the hard drive or a network drive and then use your operating system to transfer them to another disk for storage after you exit the AutoCAD program. File loss from improperly using removable media can occur in many programs and even some operating system operations.

Working with Multiple Drawings

You should now have two open drawings: *Shapes,* the drawing you just created, and Drawing1, the previous drawing, where you experimented with selecting commands and drew circles using the 2P and 3P options of the Circle command. You can use the Window panel from the Ribbon's View tab to tile the drawings *horizontally* or *vertically,* cascade the drawings so that they appear in a neat stack, or switch between drawings that are currently open. The open drawings are listed at the bottom of the Switch Window button as you see in Figure 1.19. You can click on a drawing name to make it the active drawing.

Click: **Switch Window button** *from the View tab Window panel, then select* **Drawing1.dwg** *from the list*

Figure 1.19   Switch Window button on View tab Window Panel of Ribbon

Drawing1.dwg becomes the active drawing window. Notice its name is now in the AutoCAD title bar. You can show both your new drawing, Shapes.dwg, and Drawing1.dwg at the same time. To do this,

Click: **Tile Vertically button** *from the View tab Window Panel*

Both drawings should now appear on your screen arranged side by side vertically as shown in Figure 1.20. Next you will click on the title bar for *shapes.dwg* so that it becomes the active drawing. The border and title bar of the active drawing appear darker.

Click: **on the title bar for shapes.dwg**

Tip: *You can cut and paste objects from one drawing window to another.*

Tip: *You can turn on AutoCAD Classic from the Workspace drop down as a quick way to return to the menus used in previous AutoCAD versions.*

Figure 1.20   Two Drawings Tiled Vertically

Click: *Cascade button from the View tab Window panel*

The drawings now appear as shown in Figure 1.21, arranged so that they appear stacked and so you can see the window controls for each drawing.

Figure 1.21   Cascaded Drawings

Next you will close Drawing1 by clicking its Windows Close button. Make sure not to close the application window.

Click: *Drawing1 so that it becomes active*

 Click: *Close button for Drawing1.dwg*

At the prompt, "Save changes to *Drawing1.dwg*?",

Click: *No*

Drawing1.dwg is removed from your screen leaving only *shapes.dwg*. Next you will maximize this drawing to fills the graphics area.

 Click: *Maximize button in the title bar of shapes.dwg*

Drawing Shapes should fill the graphics area as shown in Figure 1.22. Typically, you will work with the drawing maximized as you see now. Notice that the drawing no longer has a separate title bar and its window controls are below the controls to close, minimize, and maximize the AutoCAD program window.

Tip: *Drawings may also be minimized or maximized. Minimized drawings appear at the bottom of the drawing window. Use the buttons on the title bar of the minimized drawing to maximize it if needed.*

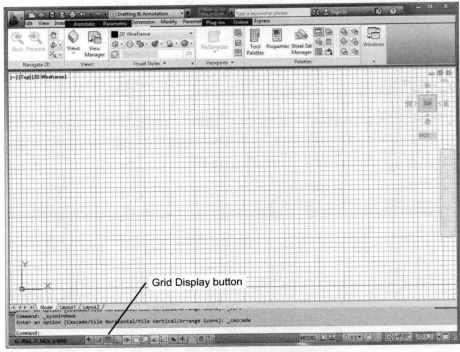

Figure 1.22   Shapes Drawing Maximized to Fill Screen

Tip: *The default setting displays an "adaptive" grid. If you set a grid size that is smaller than could be seen on the display, the grid is adapted to show larger subdivisions. To turn on or off the adaptive grid feature, type the Grid command at the prompt.*
Command: grid [Enter]
Specify grid spacing(X) or [ON/OFF/Snap/Major/aDaptive/Limits/Follow/Aspect] <0.0010>: **D [Enter]**
Turn adaptive behavior on [Yes/No] <Yes>: N [Enter] *turns off the adaptive grid.*

Tip: *If you set the GRID spacing to 0.0000, and then set the SNAP, the grid spacing will automatically follow the same spacing as Snap Mode.*

Tip: *Pressing [Ctrl]-G or [F7] also toggles the grid on and off; [Ctrl]-B or [F9] toggles the snap function.*

Using Grid

Adding a grid to the graphics window gives you a helpful reference for your drawing. A *grid* is a background of regularly spaced lines or dots. The grid does not show up in your drawing when you print. If it is not already on, turn on the background grid. The grid is a toggle button, so clicking it when it is on will turn it off, and vice-versa.

Click: **Grid Display button** *(from the status bar)*

The grid appears on your screen (or disappears if it was already on-if so press the button again to turn it on). The Grid Display button should now be highlighted on to let you know that the grid is turned on. (At times the grid can be too large or small to be visible.)

You can also type the Grid command which turns it on and shows you options for setting the grid spacing.

Command: **GRID [Enter]**

The grid spacing prompt displays the options available for the command. The default option, in this case <0.5000>, appears within angle brackets. Pressing [Enter] accepts the default selection shown in the angled brackets. To set the size of a grid, you type in the numerical value of the spacing and then press [Enter]. You will change the grid spacing to 1 unit.

Specify grid spacing(X) or [ON/OFF/Snap/Major/aDaptive/Limits/Follow/Aspect] <0.5000>: *1 [Enter]*

Notice that the grid in the drawing window changes to a spacing with grid lines 1 unit apart.

Using Zoom

The Zoom command enlarges or reduces areas of the drawing on your screen. It is different from the Scale command, which actually makes the selected items larger or smaller in your drawing database. Use the Zoom command when you want to enlarge something on the screen so that you see the details clearly. You can also zoom out so objects appear smaller to fit on your display. The Zoom command options are located on the ribbon View tab Navigate panel.

Using Zoom All

The *Zoom All* option displays the *drawing limits* or shows all of the drawing objects on the screen, whichever is larger. Zoom All is located on the Zoom flyout on the View tab Navigate 2D panel. You will learn more about Zoom in Tutorial 2.

> Click: **Zoom, All** *from the Navigate 2D panel on the View tab*

Your screen should look like Figure 1.23, which shows a background grid drawn with 1-unit spacing.

Figure 1.23

Zoom Flyout

Using Snap Mode

When *Snap Mode* is on, your cursor jumps to the specified intervals. This is helpful for locating objects or distances in a drawing. If each jump on the snap interval were 0.5 unit (horizontally or vertically only, not diagonally), you could draw a line 2.00 units long by moving the cursor four snap intervals. To be useful, align the snap spacing with the grid size so it is the same as the grid spacing, at half the grid spacing, or some other even fraction of the grid spacing. Since the grid spacing

Tip: *The flyouts show the last button you selected as the upper button. This is done to make it quick to reselect commands you use frequently. It can be confusing at first.*

is now set to 1; accept the snap default value of <0.5000>, so the snap increment will be one-half of the grid spacing.

Command: **SNAP [Enter]**

Snap spacing or [ON/OFF/Aspect/Style/Type] <0.5000> : **[Enter]**

Note that Snap Mode is highlighted on the status bar to let you know that Snap is in effect. Once you start a command, instead of the smooth movement that you saw previously, the crosshairs jump or "snap" from point to point on the snap spacing.

Click: **L [Enter]** (the alias for the Line command)

Specify first point: **move the cursor around on the screen**

Notice the cursor now jumps to stay on the snap interval.

Grid and Snap Toggles

You can quickly turn Grid Display and Snap on and off by clicking their buttons on the status bar. If their buttons on the status bar appear *highlighted* they are on; buttons that are darker are off. Each button on the status bar acts as a *toggle*: that is, clicking it once turns the function on; clicking it a second time turns the function off. You can toggle Grid and Snap on and off during the execution of other commands.

Click: **Snap Mode** button

Now the curove the crosshairs around on the screen. Note that they have been released from the snap constraint. To turn Snap on again,

Click: **Snap Mode** button

The crosshairs jump from snap location to snap location again.

Click: **Grid Display** button

The grid disappears from your screen, but the snap constraint remains. To show the grid again,

Click: **Grid Display** button

Notice how the command window keeps a record of all past commands. You should still see the prompt for the line command.

Specify first point: **press [Esc] to cancel the command.**

Drafting Settings

You can also adjust Snap and Grid using the Drafting Settings dialog box. This dialog box appears when you right-click on the Snap or Grid button on the status bar and then click Settings as shown in Figure 1.24

Right-click: **Snap button** to show the context menu

Click: **Settings**

The Drafting Settings dialog box appears on your screen as shown in Figure 1.24. The Snap and Grid tab should appear on top. You will learn about Polar Tracking and Object Snap in later tutorials.

Type: **.25 into the Snap X spacing input box**

The Y Spacing box automatically changes to match the X Spacing box when you click in the Snap Y Spacing input box. If you want unequal spacing for X and Y, you can change the Y spacing separately.

*Click: **OK** (to exit from the dialog box)*

Figure 1.24   Drafting Settings Dialog Box

Tip: *Pressing [Enter] automatically closes the Drafting Settings dialog box. To quickly set a new snap or grid increment, type the value in the appropriate input box and then press [Enter] to close the dialog box.*

Using Line

The Line command draws straight lines between endpoints that you specify. For the next sequence of commands, you will use the ribbon Home tab Draw panel to select the Line command. (The toolbars, panels and menus are similar to spoken English. This is helpful when you are trying to remember where commands are located. For example, you might say, "I want to draw a line.") When selecting the Line command, be sure to click the button that shows dots at both endpoints. This icon indicates that the command draws a line between the two points selected. You can continue drawing lines from point to point until you press [Enter] to end the command.

Check that the status bar Dynamic Input button is turned off, for now.

 *Click: **Line button***

You are prompted for the starting point of the line. You can answer prompts requesting the input of a point:

· By moving the cursor into the graphics window and clicking the left mouse button to choose a screen location (Grid and Snap help to locate a specific point)

· By entering X-, Y-, and Z-coordinate values for the point

Figure 1.25

Coordinates display at the left of the status bar. Pick on them to toggle the coordinates on and off and between modes during commands.

Tip: *Remember that the spacebar acts the same way as the [Enter] key, to end a command. When typing in coordinates, enter only commas between them. Do not enter a space between the comma and the following coordinate of a coordinate pair because a space has the same effect as [Enter]. Recall that you can press the spacebar to enter commands quickly.*

Tip: *If you enter a wrong point while still in the Line command, you can back up one endpoint at a time with the Undo option by typing the letter U and pressing [Enter].*

Warning: *Undo functions differently if you pick it as a command. If you select Undo at the command prompt, you may undo entire command sequences. If necessary, you can use Redo to return something that has been undone.*

Entering Coordinates

Your drawing geometry is stored using *World Coordinates*, which is the AutoCAD default *Cartesian coordinate system*, where X-, Y-, and Z-*coordinate values* specify locations in your drawing. The UCS icon near the bottom left corner of your screen shows the positive X- and positive Y-directions on the screen. The default orientation of the Z-axis is as though in front of the monitor are positive values and inside the monitor are negative values. The AutoCAD software uses the right-hand rule for coordinate systems. If you orient your right hand palm up and point your thumb in the positive X-direction and index finger in the positive Y-direction, the direction your other fingers curl will be the positive Z-direction (Figure 1.25). Use the right-hand rule and the UCS icon to figure out the directions of the coordinate system. You can specify a point explicitly by entering the X-, Y-, and Z-coordinates, separated by a comma. You can leave the Z-coordinate off when you are drawing in 2D, as you will be in this tutorial. If you do not specify the Z-coordinate, it is assumed to be the current elevation in the drawing, for which the default value is 0. For now, type only the X- and Y-values, and the default value of 0 for Z will be used.

Using Absolute Coordinates

You often need to type the exact location of specific points to represent the geometry of the object you are creating. To do so, type the X-, Y-, and Z-coordinates to locate the point on the current coordinate system. Called *absolute coordinates*, they specify a distance along the X-, Y-, Z-axes from the *origin* (or point $(0, 0, 0)$ of the coordinate system).

Resume use of the Line command and use absolute coordinates to specify endpoints for the line you will draw. (Restart the Line command if you do not see the Specify first point: prompt.)

Specify first point: *5.26,5.37 [Enter]*

As you move your cursor, you will see a line rubberbanding from the point you typed to the current location of your cursor. The next prompt asks for the endpoint of the line.

Specify next point or [Undo]: *8.94,5.37 [Enter]*

After you enter the second point, the line appears on the screen. The rubberband line continues to stretch from the last endpoint to the current location of the cursor, and you are prompted for another point. This feature allows lines to be drawn end to end. Continue as follows:

Specify next point or [Undo]: *8.94,8.62 [Enter]*

Specify next point or [Close/Undo]: *5.26,8.62 [Enter]*

The Close option of the Line command joins the last point drawn to the first point drawn during that instance of the Line command. To close the figure, you will type C in response to the prompt.

Specify next point or [Close/Undo]: *C [Enter]*

Drawing Using Grid and Snap

Use the grid and snap settings to draw another rectangle to the right of the one you just drew, as shown in Figure 1.26.

Figure 1.26

Click: **Line button**

On your own, choose the starting point on the grid by moving the cursor to point A, as shown in Figure 1.26 and clicking the left button on the mouse. Remember to use the coordinate display on the status bar to help you select the points.

Create the 2.5-unit long horizontal line by moving the cursor 10 snap increments to the right and clicking to select point B.

Complete the rectangle by drawing a vertical line 8 snap increments (2.00 units) long to point C and another horizontal line 10 snap increments (2.5 units) long to point D.

Use the Close command option to complete the rectangle, then press [Enter] to end the Line command.

Using Last Point

The software remembers the last point that you specified. Often you will need to specify a point that is exactly the same as the preceding point. The @ symbol on your keyboard is the AutoCAD name for the last point entered. You will use last point entry with the Line command. This time you will restart the Line command by pressing [Enter] at the blank command prompt to restart the previous command.

Command: *[Enter]*

Specify first point: *2,5 [Enter]*

Specify next point or [Undo]: *4,5 [Enter]*

Specify next point or [Undo]: *[Enter]*

Press: **[Enter]** *(or the right button on your mouse and use the menu to select Repeat Line)*

Specify first point: *@ [Enter]*

Your starting point is now the last point you entered in the previous step (4,5). Note the line rubberbanding from that point to the cursor as shown in Figure 1.27.

Tip: *Be sure that Snap is highlighted on the status bar. If it is not, pick Snap Mode on the status bar or press [F8] to turn it on.*

Tip: *When drawing, moving the cursor away from the point you have selected can help you see the effect of the selection. You will not notice rubberband lines if you leave the cursor over the previously selected point.*

Tip: *Because Line was the last command used, you could restart the command by pressing the [Enter] key, the spacebar, or right-clicking and selecting Repeat Line from the pop-up menu.*
Using these shortcuts will help you produce drawings in less time. Keep in mind, that restarting a command has the same effect as typing the command name at the prompt. Some toolbar and menu selections contain special programming to select certain options for you automatically, so they may not function exactly the same when restarted by pressing [Enter].

Tip *Once in the Line command, you can also press the spacebar or [Enter] at the Specify first point: prompt to start your new line from the last point. Or you can press the right mouse button to return to the last point.*

Tip: *You can press and drag with the middle mouse button to position your view (Pan). Scrolling with the middle mouse enlarges and reduces your view scale (Zoom).*

Tip: *You can get help during any command by using the transparent Help command. A transparent command is one that you can use during execution of another command. When transparent commands are entered at the command line, they are preceded by an apostrophe ('). You can type '? or 'Help, press [F1], or select the Help button during a command to show the Help dialog box. The Help button is in the upper right of the application window and looks like a question mark (?).*

Tip: *Clicking on the coordinates displayed on the status bar toggles their display off or on. When you toggle the coordinate display off, the coordinates do not change when you move the crosshairs and they appear grayed out on the status bar. When you toggle the coordinates back on, they once again display the X-, Y-, and Z-location of the crosshairs. During execution of the commands a third toggle is available for the coordinate display: In a command such as Line, you can click the coordinate display to display the length and angle from the last point picked. This display can be very useful in helping you determine approximate distances and angles for polar coordinate entry. You can also toggle the coordinates by pressing [F6] or [Ctrl]-D.*

Figure 1.27   **Line Rubber Bands from Last Point**

Using Relative X- and Y-Coordinates

Relative coordinates allow you to select a point at a known distance from the last point specified. To do so, use the @ symbol before your X- and Y-coordinate values. Now, continue the Line command.

    Specify next point or [Undo]: *@0,3 [Enter]*

Your line is drawn 0 units in the X-direction and 3 units in the positive Y-direction from the last point specified (4,5). Complete the shape.

    Specify next point or [Undo]: *@–2,0 [Enter]*

    Specify next point or [Close/Undo]: *@0,–3 [Enter]*

    Specify next point or [Close/Undo]: *[Enter]*

Your drawing should look like Figure 1.28. You may need to scroll your screen to see all three rectangles.

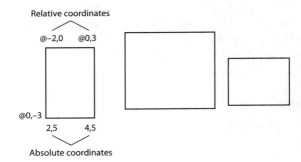

Figure 1.28

Using Polar Coordinates

Polar coordinate values use the format @DISTANCE<ANGLE. Later on, you will learn how to select different units for lengths and angles. When using the default decimal units, you don't need to specify any units when typing the angle and length. When you are using polar coordinates, each new input is calculated relative to the last point entered. The default for measuring angles defines a horizontal line to the right of the current point as 0°. As shown in Figure 1.29, angular values are positive counterclockwise. Both distance and angle values may also be negative.

Figure 1.30 shows an example of lines using relative coordinate entry. In the figure, line 1 extends 3 units from the starting point at an angle of 30°. Angle 0° is at a horizontal line to the right of the starting point. Line 2 starts at the last point of line 1 and extends 2 units at an angle of 135°, again measured from a horizontal line to the right of that line's starting point. Polar coordinates are often useful for creating drawings.

Figure 1.29   Angle Values

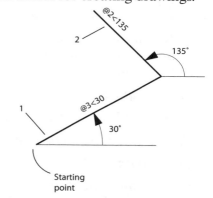

Figure 1.30   Polar Coordinates

Next, draw a rectangle using polar coordinate values. The starting point is point A in Figure 1.31 Use the toolbar to select the Line command. You will draw a horizontal line 3.5 units to the right of the starting point by responding to the prompts.

Click: **Line button**

Specify first point: **pick point A in Figure 1.31, coordinates 1.0,4.0**

Specify next point or [Undo]: **@3.5<0 [Enter]**

Specify next point or [Undo]: **[Enter]**

You will draw the next segment using dynamic input.

Click: **Dynamic Input button** *on the Status bar to toggle it on*

Check that the only status bar modes you have turned on are Snap Mode, Grid Display and Dynamic Input.

Click: **Line button**

Specify next point or [Undo]: **[Enter]** *(a quick way to return to the last endpoint)*

The dynamic entry inputs appear near the cursor location as shown in Figure 1.31

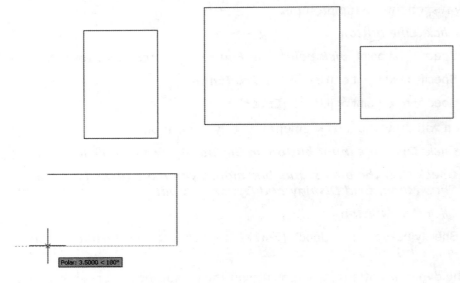

Figure 1.31   **Dynamic Input**

The dynamic input mode shows tooltips near the cursor that update as the cursor moves. You can type values in the tooltip input boxes. This mode lets you focus your attention near the cursor.

> *In the highlighted input box, type 2.00*
>
> *Press [Tab] to move to the angle input box*
>
> Type: *90 (for the angle) [Enter]*
>
> Click: *Dynamic Input button to toggle it off*
>
> Click: *Polar Tracking button to toggle it on*

With Polar Tracking turned on, as you move your cursor near preset angles, an alignment and tooltip appears near the cursor as shown in Figure 1.32. The default angle for the alignment path is 90°.

Tip: *You can turn Dynamic Input off by pressing the F12 key. You can turn it off temporarily by holding down the F12 key. This is useful when you want to see what is below the dynamic input box.*

Figure 1.32   **Polar Tracking**

On your own, complete the rectangle, using polar tracking.

Your drawing should look like that in Figure 1.33.

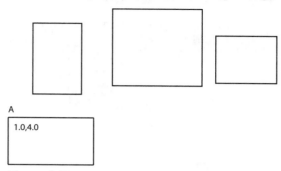

A

1.0,4.0

Figure 1.33

Using the Exchange to Get Help

AutoCAD's Help feature provides a wide variety of assistance. You can use it to find information about commands, how to use them, ways to select them, installation and customization information, and lots more.

⊘ *Click:* **Help button**

Clicking the Help button opens the Autodesk Exchange window in a standard browser (Figure 1.34). The Exchange window provides general help, training tips, advice and much more for the AutoCAD user community. The main topics are : Home and Help.

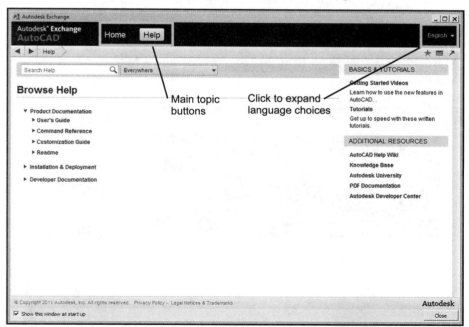

Figure 1.34 **The Autodesk Exchange Window**

Click: **Home**

The Home page of the Exchange appears on your screen as shown in Figure 1.35.

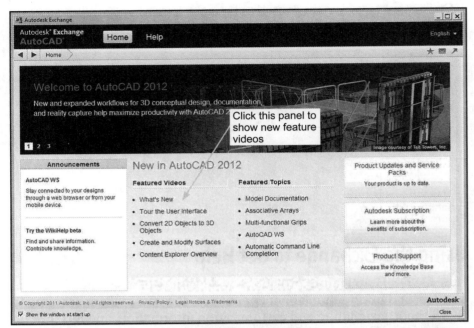

Figure 1.35   The Autodesk Exchange Home Page

The Home page provides useful links and information. If the box at the lower left is checked, this page shows when you start up the software.

*Click: **What's New** from the center of the Exchange window*

The Help page showing the Getting Started Videos appears as shown in Figure 1.36.

Figure 1.36   Help Page Showing Getting Started Videos

On your own, explore the getting started video tutorials. These provide a quick introduction to the software and new tools.

*Click: **Help button** to return to the Help list shown in Figure 1.37*

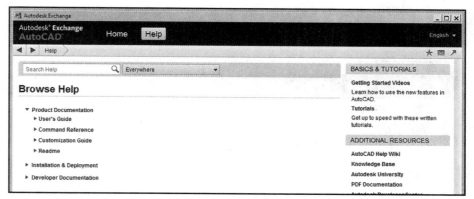

Figure 1.37

The left side of the Help page contains a list of topics: Product Documentation, User's Guide, Command Reference, Customization Guide, Readme, Installation & Deployment and Developer's Documentation.

Click: **Command Reference**

The main window shows Commands with an list of topics in that section below it: Commands, Command Modifiers, System Variables and Utilities

Click: **Commands** *to show the list as seen in Figure 1.38*

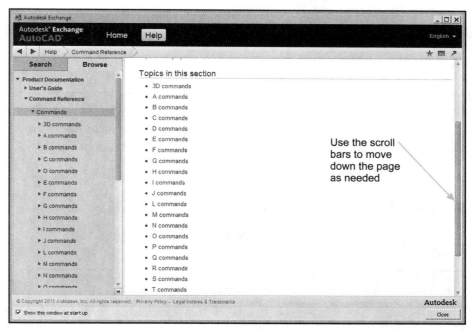

Figure 1.38

Click: **L Commands**

The window updates to show the list of commands which start with letter "L".

Click: **Line** *(you may need to scroll down to see it)*

Detailed information for the Line command appears in the main window, including all of the different ways to select the command. You can scroll to see additional information. A lot of up-to-date information is available through using help. This is the first place you should turn to when you have questions about how to use your software. As you work through this book, use Help to look for additional information.

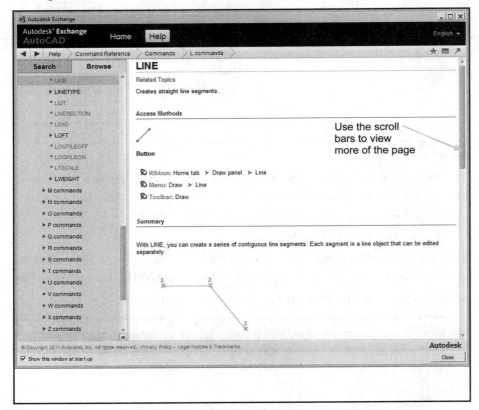

Figure 1.39   **Help for the Line Command**

As with other Windows applications, you may use the Close button in the upper right-hand corner to close the Autodesk Exchange window.

Click: ***Close button***

Finding Help Using the Infocenter

The Infocenter search box is located at the top of the application window as shown in Figure 1.40.

Figure 1.40

Type: ***GRID [Enter]***

The Autodesk Exchange window opens showing information for the Grid command as shown in Figure 1.41. Clicking on a link changes the window to show that topic in the browser.

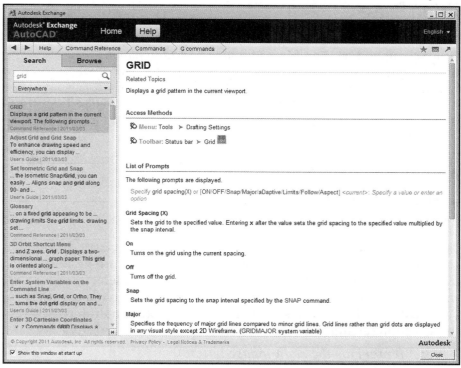

Figure 1.41 **Grid Search Results**

Click: **Browser Close button**

Using Save

The *Save* command lets you save a drawing to the file name you have previously specified, in this case *shapes.dwg.* You should save your work frequently. If the power went off or your computer crashed, you would lose all the work that you had not previously saved. This time use the Save button on the Quick Access toolbar.

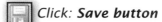 *Click:* **Save button**

Your work will be saved to *shapes.dwg.* If you had not previously named your drawing, the Save Drawing As dialog box would appear, allowing you to specify a name for the drawing. Save your work periodically as you work through these tutorials.

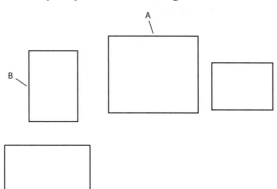

Figure 1.42

Tip: *You can use the Options dialog box to specify a time period and set up automatic saves, as well as controlling whether back-up files are created. But, it is still best to save your work periodically and not rely only on automatic saving. Why not use both? Its like wearing a belt and suspenders. To access the Options dialog box, click the Application button (which looks like a large A at the top left of the application window) then the Options button at the bottom right of the expanded list. From the Open and Save tab set a time for Automatic save and make sure the box for it is checked.*

Tip: *Typing E [Enter] (the command alias) will also start the Erase command.*

Tip: *If Snap is turned on, turning it off makes object selection easier.*

Tip: *Don't position the selection cursor at a point where two objects cross because you cannot be certain which will be selected. The entire object is selected when you point to any part of it, so select the object at a point that is not ambiguous.*

Using Erase

The *Erase* command removes objects from a drawing. You can find the Erase command on the ribbon Home tab, Modify panel.

 Click: **Erase button**

Use the status bar to turn Snap off to make selecting easier.

A small square replaces the crosshairs, prompting you to select objects. To identify an object to be erased, position the cursor over the object and click. Each line that you have drawn is a separate drawing object. Refer to Figure 1.42.

Select objects: *click on line A*

Select objects: *click on line B*

The lines you have selected are highlighted but are not erased. You can select more than one item as a *selection set*. You will learn more ways to do so later in this tutorial. When you have finished selecting, you will right-click the mouse button or press the [Enter] key to indicate that you are done selecting. Pressing [Enter] or the return button completes the selection set and erases the selected objects.

Press: **[Enter] (or the right mouse button)**

The selected lines are erased from the screen.

If you erase an object by mistake, you may use the OOPS command at the command prompt.

Type: **OOPS [Enter]**

The lines last erased are restored on your screen. OOPS restores only the most recently erased objects. However, it will work to restore erased objects even if other commands have been used in the meantime, which can be handy.

Erasing with Window or Crossing

Next you will clear your graphics window to make room for new shapes by erasing all the rectangles on your screen. Selecting multiple objects is easy using the Window or Crossing modes.

To use implied Windowing mode, click a point on the screen that is not on an object and move your pointing device from left to right. A window-type box will start to rubberband from the point you selected. In the *implied Windowing* mode (a box drawn from left to right), the window formed selects everything that is entirely enclosed in it. However, drawing the box from right to left causes the *implied Crossing* mode to be used. Everything that either crosses the box or is enclosed in the box is selected. You can use implied Windowing and implied Crossing to select objects during any command in which you are prompted to select objects.

You can turn implied Windowing on and off. Before using it, you will check to see that implied Windowing is turned on.

Click: **Application button, Options button** (lower right)

The Options dialog box appears on your screen showing a number of tabs that can be used to control the way AutoCAD functions.

Click: **the Selection tab**

Figure 1.43   The Options Dialog Selection Tab

The Selection tab pops to the top of the stack as shown in Figure 1.43. For implied Windowing to work, it must be selected (a check must appear in the box to the left of Implied windowing).

On your own, ensure that Implied Windowing is selected.

Click: **Visual Effect Settings**

Figure 1.44   Visual Effects Settings Dialog

The Visual Effect Settings dialog box allows you to set highlighting, window, and crossing box appearances. The default is that a window which selects only objects fully enclosed in the drawn box is colored blue, and a crossing selection box which selects any object the box crosses is shown with green. Leave the settings at the default colors for now as shown in Figure 1.44.

Use Cancel to exit each dialog box without making any changes if the settings were correct. If not correct them on your own.

Click: **Erase button**

Select objects: *click above and to the left of your upper three rectangles, identified as A in Figure 1.45*

Other corner: *click a point below and to the right of your upper three rectangles, identified as B*

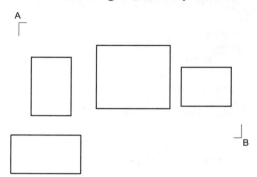

Figure 1.45

Note that a "window" box formed around the area specified by the upper left and lower right corners. Your screen should look like that in Figure 1.46.

Tip: *A helpful visual cue when you are drawing a crossing box (right to left) is that the box is drawn with a dashed line and filled in green. When drawing a window box (left to right) the box is drawn with a solid line and filled in blue. You can use the dialog box to change to colors.*

Figure 1.46   Selecting Using Window

When you chose the second corner of the window (point B), the objects that were entirely enclosed in the window became highlighted. You will end the object selection by pressing [Enter] and erasing the selected objects.

Select objects: *[Enter] or right-click and select Enter from the menu*

Only objects that were entirely within the window were erased. The fourth rectangle (represented by four separate lines) was not completely enclosed and therefore was not erased.

Next, restart the Erase command using the *context menu,* which appears when you right-click.

Right-click: **in a blank area of the screen to show the menu**

Click: **Repeat Erase (from the context menu)**

Select objects: **click below and to the right of the remaining rectangle**

Other corner: **click above and to the left of the rectangle**

Select objects: **[Enter]**

The remaining rectangle is erased from the drawing.

Using Undo

The *Undo* command removes the effect of previous commands. If you make a mistake, select the Undo command from the Quick Access toolbar, and the effect of the previous command will be undone.

 Click: **Undo button**

The last rectangle you erased reappears.

Line and some other commands also include Undo as a command option that allows you to undo the last action within the command.

Click: **Line button**

Specify first point: **click any point**

Specify next point or [Undo]: **click any point**

Specify next point or [Undo]: **click any point**

Specify next point or [Close/Undo]: **click any point**

Specify next point or [Close/Undo]: **U [Enter]**

Specify next point or [Close/Undo]: **[Enter]**

One line segment disappeared while you remained within the Line command. Now, you will undo the entire Line command with the Undo command from the Quick Access toolbar.

Click: **Undo button**

All the line segments drawn with the last instance of the command disappear.

Typing Undo at the command prompt offers more options for undoing your work. You will draw some lines to have some objects to undo.

On your own, use Erase from the toolbar and erase all remaining objects in your graphics window. Use Line on your own to draw six parallel lines anywhere on your drawing screen. Use Snap and Grid as needed.

In the next step, you will type the Undo command to remove the last three lines that you drew.

Type: **UNDO [Enter]**

Enter the number of operations to undo or [Auto/Control/BEgin/End/Mark/Back] <1>: **3 [Enter]**

Tip: *If you undo the wrong object, the Redo command lets you restore the items you have undone. It is the icon to the right of Undo on the Quick Access toolbar.*

The last three lines drawn should disappear, corresponding to the last three instances of the Line command. You could have selected any number, depending on the number of command steps you wanted to undo.

Using the Undo Flyout

The flyout symbol next to the Undo command on the Quick Access toolbar lets you view the command history of selections you have made. You can undo them one by one using this option.

Click: on the flyout triangle next to the Undo button

Click: *on the first Line command in the Undo flyout*

The line is undone from your screen.

Click: on the flyout triangle next to the Undo button to show the command history

Click: on the second Erase command listed in the history

The Erase command is undone and the boxes that you erased earlier return to the screen.

Using Redo

If the last command undid something you really did not want to undo, you can use the *Redo* command to reverse the effects. The Redo button appears on the Quick Access toolbar to the right of Undo.

Click: Redo button

The erased boxes are removed again as the Erase command is Redone.

Click: the flyout triangle next to Redo

You should see a command history of the items that you have Undone. You can choose from the list to redo them.

Using Undo Back

The Back option of the Undo command takes the drawing back to a mark that you set with the Mark option or to the beginning of the *drawing session* if you haven't set any marks. Be careful when selecting these options or you may undo too much.

Type: UNDO [Enter]

Enter the number of operations to undo or [Auto/Control/BEgin/End/Mark/Back] <1>: *B [Enter]*

This will undo everything. OK? <Y>: *[Enter]*

All operations back to the beginning of the drawing session (or mark, if you had previously set one with the Mark option of the Undo command) will be undone. (You can use Help to find out what the remaining options, Auto, Control, Begin, and End, are used for.)

Click: to flyout the command history next to Redo

The list of commands that you have selected in the drawing should appear in the command history window.

On your own, select some of the commands from the list to Redo.

Next, close drawing *Shapes.dwg*.

Click: **Application button, Close**

You will be prompted "Save changes to *c:\work\shapes.dwg*?"

Click: **No**

The drawing will close, and the graphics area will appear gray to indicate that there is no drawing open. Notice that now there are only the New, Open, Sheet Set Manager buttons available on the Quick Access toolbar.

Drawing a Plot Plan

Next, you will create a new drawing showing a plot plan. A plot plan is a plan view of a lot boundary and the location of utilities.

The *New* button on the Quick Access toolbar is a quick way to start new drawings. It is the leftmost button.

 Click: **New button**

The Select template dialog box appears on your screen. The default template *acad.dwt* should be highlighted.

Click: **acad.dwt (if it is not already highlighted)**

Click: **Open**

Click: **Application button, Save As** and save this drawing to a new name: *plotplan.dwg*

Be sure to create the new drawing in the **c:\work directory.**

Click: **Save (to exit the dialog box)**

Setting the Units

When you create a drawing, work in the type of units that are appropriate for that drawing. The *default units* are decimal. The units represent any type of real-world measurement you want to consider: decimal miles, furlongs, inches, millimeters, microns, or anything else. When the time comes to plot the drawing, you determine the final relationship between your drawing database, in which you create the object the actual size it is in the real world, and the paper plot.

You can change the type of units for lengths to *architectural units* that appear in feet and fractional inches, *engineering units* that appear in feet and decimal inches, *scientific units* that appear in exponential format, or *fractional units* that are whole numbers and fractions. When you use architectural or engineering units, one drawing unit is considered to be one inch. You specify feet by typing the feet mark after the numerical value (e.g., 50.5' or 20'2" or 35'-4").

Tip: *If the coordinate display does not show a larger size, check to see that you set the limits correctly and that you picked Zoom All. Be sure that the coordinates are turned on by clicking on the coordinates located on the status bar until you see them change as you move the mouse.*

Angular measurements can be given in decimal degrees; degrees, minutes, and seconds; gradians; radians; or *surveyor units*, such as the bearing N45°0'00"E.

Click: **Application icon, Drawing Utilities, Units** *as shown in Figure 1.47*

Figure 1.47

Figure 1.48   Unit Types

The Drawing Units dialog box appears on your screen. Use the Length area, Type pull down list to select from the available length units for the drawing. Figure 1.48 shows the types of length units expanded.

Click: **to expand the list of available unit types**

Click: **Architectural** *(from the list)*

The dialog box changes to show Architectural as the type of units. You can select only one type at a time. Note that the units displayed under the heading Precision change to architectural units. Again use the Length Type area to:

Click: **Decimal**

Note that the units in the Precision area change back to decimal units. The dimensions for the plot plan that you will create will be in decimal feet, so you will leave the units set to Decimal.

Figure 1.49   Decimal Precision

Click: ***to expand the choices displayed in the box below Precision***

Click: ***0.00*** *(as shown in Figure 1.49)*

Now the display precision is set to two decimal places. When specifying coordinates and lengths, you can still type a value from the keyboard with more precision and the AutoCAD drawing database will keep track of your drawing with this accuracy. However, because you have selected this precision, only two decimal places will be displayed. Units precision determines the *display* of the units on your screen and in the prompts, not the accuracy internal to the drawing. The AutoCAD software keeps track internally to at least fourteen decimal places, but only eight decimal places of accuracy will ever appear on the screen. You can change the type of unit and precision at any point during the drawing process.

The right side of the dialog box controls the type and precision of angular measurements. Remember that the default measurement of angles is counterclockwise, starting from a horizontal line to the right as 0°. You can change the default setting by clicking on the Direction button and making a new selection. Leave the direction set at the default of 0 degrees toward East. Use the Type setting in the Angle area to:

Click: **Surveyor's Units**

Note that the display in this Precision area changes to list the angle as a bearing. When this mode is active, you can type in a surveyor angle and the program will measure the angle from the specified direction, North or South, toward East or West, as specified. The default direction, North, is straight toward the top of the screen. If you want to view greater angle precision, click on the box containing the precision, N 0d E. The list of the available precisions pops down, as shown in Figure 1.50, allowing you to choose to display degrees, minutes, and seconds.

To display degrees, minutes, and seconds:

    Click: **N0d00'00"E**

Figure 1.50   **Surveyor's Unit Precisions**

The Insertion scale area of the dialog box controls the scaling factor for blocks that are dragged into the current drawing from Tool palettes. You will learn more about the Tool palettes in Tutorial 10. Since this drawing will be created in decimal feet,

    Click: **Feet**

    Click: **OK** *(to exit)*

Look at the status bar: The coordinate display has changed to show two instead of four places after the decimal.

Sizing Your Drawing

Create your AutoCAD drawing geometry in *real-world units*. In other words, if the object is 10" long, make it exactly 10" long in the drawing database. If it is a few millimeters long, you create the drawing to those lengths. You can think of the decimal units as representing whatever decimal measurement system you are using. For this drawing, the units will represent decimal feet, so 10 units will equal 10 feet in the drawing. After you have created the drawing geometry, you can decide on the scale at which you want to plot your final printed drawing on the sheet of paper. The ability to create drawings from which you can make accurate measurements and calculations on the computer is one of the powerful features of CAD. Also, you can plot the final drawing to any scale, saving time because you don't have to remake drawings just to change the scale.

For your plot plan, you will need a larger drawing area to accommodate the site plan shown in Figure 1.51.

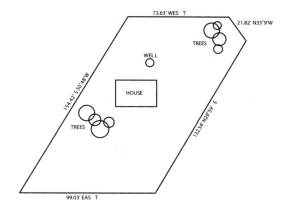

Figure 1.51   Plot Plan

Using Limits

The *Limits* command sets the size of your drawing area, where the grid is displayed. You can also turn off Limits if you do not want to preset the size of the drawing. You will use the command window.

Command: *LIMITS [Enter]*

Reset model space limits:

Specify lower left corner or [ON/OFF] <0.00,0.00>: *[Enter] (to accept default of 0,0)*

Specify upper right corner <12.00,9.00>: *300,225 [Enter]*

The default space in which you create your drawing geometry or model is called model space. It is where you accurately create real-world models. In Tutorial 5, you will learn to use paper space, where you lay out views, as you do on a sheet of paper. You can set different sizes for model space and paper space with the Limits command.

Show your new larger area on your display.

📇 Click: *View tab, Navigate panel, All (from the Zoom flyout)*

Move the crosshairs to the upper right-hand corner of the screen. You will see that the status bar displaying the coordinate location of the crosshairs indicates that the size of the graphics window has changed to reflect the limits of the drawing.

A larger grid spacing value will help you better relate to the sizes in your drawing.

Command: *GRID [Enter]*

Specify grid spacing(X) or [ON/OFF/Snap/Major/aDaptive/Limits/Follow/Aspect] <0.50>: *10 [Enter]*

Tip: *Double-clicking the middle mouse button with the cursor positioned inside the drawing area is a quick way to zoom all.*

To draw the site boundary, you will use absolute and polar coordinates as appropriate. You will be using surveyor angles to specify the directions for the lines. The AutoCAD surveyor angle units, are given in bearings.

A *bearing* specifies the angle to turn from the first direction stated toward the second direction stated. For example, a bearing of *N29'59"E* means to start at the direction North and turn an angle of 29'59" toward the East. Type letter *'d"* instead of a degree symbol when you are entering bearings.

Now you are ready to start drawing the lines of the site boundary. Use the Draw panel from the ribbon Home tab.

> On your own, check that Dynamic Input is turned off. Use the status bar or press [F12] to turn it off if needed.

*Click: **Line button***

Specify first point: **50,30 [Enter]**

Specify next point or [Undo]: @ **99.03<E [Enter]**

Specify next point or [Close/Undo]: @ **132.54<N29d59'E [Enter]**

Specify next point or [Close/Undo]: @ **21.82<N35d9'W [Enter]**

Specify next point or [Close/Undo]: @ **73.63<W [Enter]**

Specify next point or [Close/Undo]: **C [Enter]**

Your screen should look like Figure 1.52.

Figure 1.52   The Started Plot Plan Drawing

Using Rectangle

The *Rectangle* command has several options: Chamfer, Elevation, Fillet, Thickness, and Width as well as a prompt for the corners of the rectangle. These options allow you to manipulate the appearance and placement of the rectangle before it is drawn. Chamfer and Fillet are options that change the corners of the rectangle (covered in Tutorial 3). Elevation and Thickness are options best used in 3D modeling. The Width option allows you to specify a width for the lines making up the rectangle.

A rectangle will represent a house on the plot plan. You will use coordinate values to place a rectangle roughly in the center of your plot plan. You will use the Width option to make wider than normal lines.

 Click: **Rectangle button**

Specify first corner point or [Chamfer/Elevation/Fillet/Thickness/Width]: *W [Enter]*

Specify line width for rectangles <0.00>: *.5 [Enter]*

Specify first corner point or [Chamfer/Elevation/Fillet/Thickness/Width]: *120,95 [Enter]*

Specify other corner point or [Area/Dimensions/Rotation]: *150,115 [Enter]*

Your drawing should be similar to the one in Figure 1.53.

Tip: *You can also draw a rectangle by picking the corners directly from the screen using your mouse.*

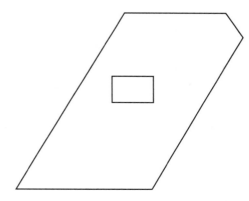

Figure 1.53   Rectangle Added for Top View of House

Having completed the site boundary, you should now save the drawing.

Click: **Save button**

Your file is saved to the name you previously assigned.

Drawing Circles

You will draw a circle to represent the location of the well on the plot plan. You draw circles using the *Circle* command located on the Draw panel.

> Click: ***Circle button***

Specify center point for circle or [3P/2P/ Ttr (tan tan radius)]: *145,128 [Enter]*

As you move the cursor away from the center point, a circle continually re-forms, using the distance from the center to the cursor location as the radius value. You will type the value to specify the exact size for the circle's radius.

> Specify radius of circle or [Diameter]: *3 [Enter]*

> Before continuing, check that the Grid Display is the only Status bar mode which is turned on. It can be difficult to draw freehand with other modes turned on. Some of the other modes, like Transparency will not make any difference. You will learn more about these modes in Tutorial 4.

> For now the only buttons that should appear highlighted is Grid Display.

Next, you will draw some circles to represent trees or shrubs in the plot plan. You will specify the locations for the trees by picking them from the screen.

> Click: ***Circle button***

> Specify center point for circle or [3P/2P/Ttr (tan tan radius)]: ***click on a point for the center of circle 1 (as shown in Figure 1.44)***

> Specify radius of circle or [Diameter]: ***move the crosshairs away until the circle appears similar to that shown in Figure 1.54, then click***

> On your own, draw the remaining circles representing trees using this method, so that you are pleased with their appearance.

Your drawing should look like that in Figure 1.54.

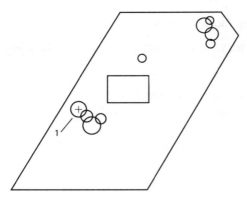

Figure 1.54   **Circles for the Well and Trees Added**

Tip: *Try typing the alias, "C" to start the Circle command. You might find it to be faster than picking from the menu. Remember you can also right-click and select to restart commands.*

Adding Text

Use the Text (*formerly Dtext*) command to add single lines of text, words, or numbers to a drawing. Text, or Single Line Text, is located on the ribbon Home tab, Annotation panel, under Text.

Unless you specify otherwise, text is added to the right of a designated starting point. You can use the Justify option to center text about a point or add it to the left of a point. For now, just add text to the right of the starting point.

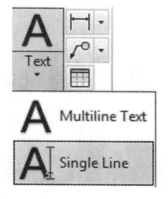

A̲ₗ Click: **Single Line button** *from the Home tab Annotation panel*

Specify start point of text or [Justify/Style]: **select a point at about coordinates 90,25**

Specify height <0.20>: **3 [Enter]**

Specify rotation angle of text <E>: **[Enter]**

You should see the typing cursor at the location you selected for the text start point indicating the software is now ready to accept typed-in text.

99.03' EAST

Figure 1.55   The Typing Cursor

Type: **99.03' EAST [Enter] [Enter]**

You can type the text just as you would with a word processing program as shown in Figure 1.55. The Text command does not wrap text, so you must designate the end of each line by pressing [Enter]. To end the Text command, press [Enter] at the beginning of a blank line (a null reply to the prompt). (You must use the keyboard, not the return button on your pointing device.)

Tip: *There is a tab named Annotate on the ribbon. There is also a panel named Annotation on the ribbon Home tab. If you have trouble finding the commands in the next section, make sure you are selecting them as directed. The tab and panel contain many of the same tools.*

Tip: *To determine the actual text height necessary, you must know the size of paper and scale you will use to plot the final drawing. In Tutorial 5 you will learn to use paper space to set up scaling and text for plotting. For now, if you are unsure about what text height to use, move the crosshairs on the screen and read the coordinate display on the toolbar. Use the lengths shown to get an appropriate size for your text. You can also use the rubberband line that appears during the text height portion of the Text command to set the height visually.*

Tip: *If you make a mistake before exiting the Text command, backspace to erase the text. (After exiting the Text command, you can double-click the line of text to make corrections.)*

Using Special Text Characters

You will add the text labeling the length and angle for the right-hand lot line. When you are using the standard AutoCAD fonts, the special text item %%d creates the degree symbol. Type the line of text with %%d in place of the degree symbol. When you have finished typing in the text and press [Enter], %%d will be replaced with a degree symbol. (You will use more special text characters in Tutorial 7.) You will also specify a rotation angle for the text so that it is aligned with the lot line. This time, try typing the command.

Command: ***TEXT [Enter]***

Specify start point of text or [Justify/Style]: ***click slightly to the right of the right-hand lot line***

Specify height <3.00>: ***[Enter]***

Specify rotation angle of text <E>: ***N29d59'E [Enter]***

Type: ***132.54'N29%%d59'E [Enter] [Enter]***

Once you press the final [Enter], the text should align with the lot line in your drawing.

Copying Text

Next you will learn how to copy a text object and edit it to quickly create labels for other items in your drawings. This is generally faster than placing text items one by one.

Click: Home tab, Modify panel, Copy button

Select objects: ***click on the bottom text object 99.03' EAST [Enter]***

Specify base point or [Displacement] <Displacement>: ***click on the middle of that text object***

Specify second point or <use first point as displacement>: ***click above the upper line as shown in Figure 1.56***

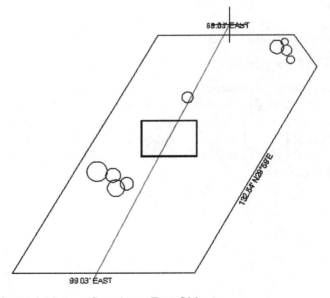

Figure 1.56   Copying a Text Object

Specify second point or [Exit/Undo] <Exit>: *continue on your own to place the copied text items as shown in Figure 1.57*

Press: [Enter] to end the command

Figure 1.57   Copied Text Placed in Drawing

In Place Text Editing

Next you will change the text so that the drawing displays the correct information.

Double-click: on the text in the rectangle so that it appears in the text editor as shown in Figure 1.58

Type: HOUSE [Enter]

On your own, change the text identifying the trees, well locations, and remaining bearings and distances.

Press [Enter] to exit the command when done editing.

Figure 1.58   Double-Click Text

Moving and Rotating Text

Rotating and moving text is easy with the text object's grips.

Figure 1.59   **Click to Show the Grip**

Click: **on the text along the left lot line** *so that its grip appears as shown in Figure 1.59*

Click: **in the small grip box at the left of the text so that it appears "hot" or active**—*its color should change*

Right-click: **with your cursor over the grip** *to show the grip editing menu*

Click: **Rotate**

On your own, use the mouse to rotate the text into alignment with the left lot line and click to select the desired angle.

Press: **[Esc]** *to unselect the grips*

Notice that as you rotate items, the further away you move the mouse from the grip, the easier it is to control the rotation angle.

You can move items directly using the grips without selecting from the menu. To do this,

Click: **the grip to make it active; then move it to a new location using your mouse**

On your own, position the remaining text items for the plot plan.

Setting the Text Style

The *Style* command allows you to create a style specifying the font and other characteristics for the shapes of the text in your drawing. A *font* is a set of letters, numbers, punctuation marks, and symbols of a distinctive style and design. The AutoCAD software supplies several *shape-compiled fonts* that you can use to create text styles. In addition to these shape-compiled fonts, you can also use your own True Type, Type 1 Postscript, or Unicode fonts. Some sample True Type fonts are provided with the AutoCAD software.

The Style command allows you to control the appearance of a font so that it is slanted (oblique), backwards, vertical, or upside-down. You can also control the height and proportional width of the letters.

To create a style, you will select Text Style by expanding the Annotation panel on the ribbon Home tab.

Figure 1.60   The Annotation Flyout

*Click: **Text Style** from the Home tab, Annotation panel, as shown in Figure 1.60*

The dialog box shown in Figure 1.61 appears on your screen. It is divided into four different sections: Style Name, Font, Effects, and Preview. All of the text in a drawing has a style applied to it. So far, your drawing has been using the style called Standard, which is the default.

You can create a new style and set it as the current style to be used for any subsequently entered text.

Figure 1.61   Text Style Dialog Box

*Click: **New***

*Type: **MyStyle** in the New Text Style dialog box*

*Click: **OK***

Tip: Keep in mind that if you use a font in your drawing and another person is going to open that drawing on a different computer system, they must have that font or a different font will be substituted. As different fonts have different horizontal spacing, this can cause the text to be misaligned. Stick to easy to read, common fonts, like Arial or Romans.shx font. Romans is part of AutoCAD, so every user should have it.

Font Area

Your system may have many fonts available in addition to the standard AutoCAD shape-compiled fonts.

> Click: **to expand the box below Font Name**

> Click: **on one of the fonts listed** *and note the changes in the Preview area of the dialog box*

The text in the Preview box will be underlined in red if it is a True Type font, as in Figure 1.62.

Figure 1.62   **Preview Area Shows Selected Font Shape**

An AutoCAD shape-compiled font that works well for engineering drawings is the Roman Simplex (romans.shx) font.

> On your own, scroll through the list until you see the romans.shx font, preceded by the calipers symbol, and select it.

The Font Style option only allows changes to True Type fonts, not to shape-compiled fonts (**.shx*) so it appears grayed out.

Size Area

Warning: Setting the text height in the Text Style dialog box causes you not to be prompted for the height of the text when you use the Text command.

Leaving the text height for a style set to zero, causes the software to prompt for the height when you place text. This way you can set the height when you place the text.

> **Leave the default text height set to 0.00.**

The Annotative selection in the Size area allows the text to be scaled automatically to show correctly at different layout scales. This is a very useful feature which you will learn more about in Tutorial 5. For now leave Annotative unchecked. Try clicking on the circled letter I next to it, to get more information and then return to the Text Style dialog box.

Effects Area

Upside down, Backwards, and Vertical are effects that can be applied to the font.

> Click: **to select Upside down,** *so that it appears checked*

Notice that the preview now shows the lettering upside down.

Click: **to deselect Upside down** *(remove the check)*

Entering a value for Width Factor allows you to make compressed and expanded letters.

On your own, change the Width Factor to 2 and notice the change in the preview area. The letters should appear stretched out. Change the value to .8 and look at the preview. This time the letters should appear compressed.

Return the Width Factor to a value of 1.00.

Change the Oblique Angle to 20 *(20d)*.

The letters in the preview should now appear slanted. Italic (oblique) letters are often sloped at about 18 degrees and never much more than 20 degrees. Try to use only one angle for all of the slanted letters within the same drawing for the best appearance.

Return the Oblique Angle to 0 (0d)

Apply the Changes to the Style

Once a style has been created, if you make changes you can update the style to reflect those. This is handy if you decide to switch the appearance of lettering after it is in the drawing. To ensure that the changes you have entered are applied to your new style.

Click: **Apply button**

To change an existing style, first select it from the list of styles, make the changes, and then apply them.

Setting Current Style

Any new text added to your drawing will apply the current text style until you set a different style as current.

Click: **Set Current**

Click: **Close** *(to exit the dialog box)*

You will now add a title to the bottom of the drawing.

Command: **TEXT [Enter]**

Specify start point of text or [Justify/Style]: **J [Enter]**

Enter an option [Align/Fit/Center/Middle/Right/TL/TC/TR/ML/ MC/MR/BL/BC/BR]: **C [Enter]**

Specify center point of text: **select a point near the middle bottom of the drawing**

Specify height <3.00>: **[Enter]**

Specify rotation angle of text<E>: **E [Enter]** *(be sure that your rotation angle is set to E)*

Type: **PLOT PLAN [Enter] [Enter]**

You can use the Help command to discover how the Justify options of the Text command work.

*Click: **Help button***

The Help window appears on your screen.

*Click: **Users Guide > Annotate Drawings > Notes and Labels > Create Text > Create Single-Line Text***

Scroll down to see the help for aligning text (Figure 1.63).

Figure 1.63   Help Window Information for Text Justification

Take a minute to familiarize yourself with them. You can return to this help screen whenever you want more information about how a specific command works.

*Click: **to close the Help window***

Setting a Style Current

You can quickly make a style current using the Text Style drop-down list as shown in Figure 1.64.

Figure 1.64   Text Style Drop-Down List

Click: **to show the Text Style drop-down list**

Click: **Standard** *from the list of styles*

Now new text added to the drawing will use the style named Standard.

Using Mtext

Unlike Text, the Mtext command automatically adjusts text within the width you specify. You can also create text with your own text editor and then import it with the Mtext command. As with Text, you can easily edit Mtext by double-clicking it to use the DDEdit command.

A *Click:* **MultilineText button**

Current text style: "Standard" Text height: 3.00

Specify first corner: ***click to the right of the plot plan drawing*** *where you want to locate the corner of the notes; a window area forms*

Specify opposite corner or [Height/Justify/Line spacing/Rotation/Style/ Width/Columns]: ***click to set the second corner of the window***

The ribbon changes to show the In-Place Text Editor (Figure 1.65).

Figure 1.65   The In-Place Text Editor

The ruler along the top of the area you selected for text entry allows you to size the area where the text will appear in your drawing. The pointers on the left side of the ruler control the indent and margin. Holding down your mouse button and dragging the right end of the ruler controls the width of the box (corresponding to the width of the text area). The large blank area of the dialog box is where you will type in the notes for the plot plan.

Type: **NOTES: [Enter] MINIMUM SET BACK FROM ALL LOT LINES OF 20' REQUIRED.**

Tip: *If you want to enter only the width of the text you will type in, type W at the prompt instead of specifying the corners of the box, and then type the width you want to specify.*

You can use the standard Windows Control key combinations to edit text in the Text Formatting dialog box.

[Ctrl]-C	Copy selection to the Clipboard
[Ctrl]-V	Paste Clipboard contents over selection
[Ctrl]-X	Cut selection to the Clipboard
[Ctrl]-Z	Undo and Redo
[Ctrl]-[Shift]-[Spacebar]	Insert a nonbreaking space
[Enter]	End the current paragraph and start a new line

Special Symbols

It is easy to add special symbols within a block of text using the Symbol flyout as shown in Figure 1.66. If you know the symbol's code, you can type it directly, but remembering the codes for symbols that you use infrequently can be difficult. Using the flyout, you can quickly select a symbol from the list.

Figure 1.66   Symbol Flyout

Formatting

To change the current font, style of text (bold or italic), or color of text, use the text formatting options. These appear similar to that of your word processor. Experiment with them on your own.

You can also cut and paste text between the In-Place Text Editor and your word processor.

Stacked Text for Fractions

You can create stacked fractions or stacked text with the Mtext command. To do so, separate the text to be stacked with either a forward slash (/), number sign (#), or the caret (^). Using / draws a line between the numerator and denominator of fractions.

*Type: **5/8** into the Multiline Text entry area at the end of the typed notes*

*Select: the **5/8** text so it appears highlighted*

Pull-down the Formatting Panel drop-down list as in Figure 1.67.

*Click: **Stack***

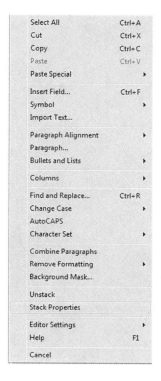

Figure 1.67

Highlight the 5/8 text and right-click to show the context menu.

*Click: **Stack Properties***

Figure 1.68

The Stack Properties dialog box appears as shown in Figure 1.68. This dialog box provides a variety of options for making stacked fractions.

*Click: **Cancel** to close the Stack Properties dialog box.*

Highlight the 5/8 text and right-click to show the context menu.

*Click: **Unstack***

On your own, delete the 5/8 text.

*Click: **Close Text Editor** (from the upper right of the ribbon area)*

The notes are placed in your drawing, similar to Figure 1.69.

Figure 1.69

Spell Checking Your Drawing

You can use AutoCAD's spell checker to detect spelling errors in your drawing.

Click: **Annotate tab, Check Spelling button**

Figure 1.70

The Check Spelling dialog box appears on the screen as shown in Figure 1.70.

Click: **Selected Objects** *from the pull-down list in the Where to check area.*

Click: **Select objects button** *to the left of the Where to check area.*

Select objects: **click on the minimum set back note [Enter]**

Figure 1.71   **Spelling Error**

If the text contains spelling errors, the Check Spelling dialog box will appear, as shown in Figure 1.71 and the incorrect item will be located and enlarged on your screen to make it easier to correct. If your drawing does not contain any misspellings, the message "Spelling check complete" will appear.

Click: ***Close***

Saving Your Drawing

Now, save your drawing.

Click: ***Save button***

The default file name is always the current drawing name. When you started the new drawing, you named it *plotplan.dwg*. The drawing is saved on the default drive unless you specified a different drive.

If you have already saved your drawing, the close box causes an immediate exit. If you have not saved your changes and want to, click on Save Changes in the dialog box. This will save your drawing to the file name *plotplan.dwg* that you selected when you began the new drawing.

You have completed the plot plan drawing.

Click: ***to close the AutoCAD program***

You should now see the Windows desktop.

Transferring Files

Use your operating system to copy or transfer files from one drive to another. To transfer the file named *plotplan.dwg* from the hard drive to a portable USB drive, use Windows Explorer.

Double-click: ***Computer*** *icon on your Windows desktop*

The Windows Explorer opens. You can use it to copy your saved Auto-CAD files from the local hard drive to a specified drive.

The various directories and drives on your computer or the contents of the current directory show on the right side of the dialog box. To change

Warning: *The appearance of Windows Explorer may depend on your operating system version and your individual settings*

Tip: *Use the Windows File Explorer to check that your file has copied to the destination correctly.*

the directory, position the arrow cursor over the name of the directory you want to select (in the list on the left) and double-click. If you need to step back out of a subdirectory to a directory one level closer to the root, or main, directory, click on the Back button. If you need to select a different drive, click on its name (*a:, b:, c:,* etc.) from the list at the left. Select your hard drive and the Work directory where your files are stored.

Click once to select and then right-click on the plotplan.dwg file.

On your own use this menu to copy the file to the drive where you want to save the file.

You see a box showing the file being copied.

You have completed Tutorial 1.

Key Terms

absolute coordinates	default directory	graphics window	shape-compiled font
alias	default units	grid	Sheet Set Manager
angle brackets	docked	highlight	Standard toolbar
architectural units	drag	implied Crossing mode	status bar
bearing	drawing session	implied Windowing mode	surveyor units
Cartesian coordinate system	engineering units	menu bar	template
case-sensitive	file extension	origin	title bar
command aliasing	floating	polar coordinates	toggle
command prompt	floating window	real-world units	tool tip
command window	flyout	relative coordinates	tool palette
context-sensitive	font	scientific units	toolbar
context-sensitive menu	fractional units	scroll bars	transparent command
coordinate values	graphics cursor (cross-hairs)	selection set	UCS icon

Key Commands

Circle 3 Points	Multiline Text	Style
Circle Center Radius	New Drawing	Undo
Copy	OOPS	Units
Dynamic Text	Rectangle	Window Cascade
Erase	Redo	Window Tile Horizontally
Grid	Redraw All	Window Tile Vertically
Help	Save	Zoom All
Limits	Single Line Text	
Line	Snap	

Exercises

Redraw the following shapes. If dimensions are provided, use them to create your drawing, showing the exact geometry of the part. The letter M after an exercise number means that the dimensions are in millimeters (metric units). If no letter follows the exercise number, the dimensions are in inches. The Ø symbol indicates that the following dimension is a diameter. Do not include dimensions on the drawings.

Exercise 1.1   Baseplate

Exercise 1.2   Rectangular Bracket

Exercise 1.3   Site Boundary
Tip: *Solve angle relative to 0° toward East or use Help to set Polar into relative mode.*

Exercise 1.4   Filter Plate

Exercise 1.5   Gasket

Exercise 1.6   Spacer

4 PLATE - 1020 STEEL
   2 REQUIRED - FULL SIZE

Exercise 1.7   Guide Plate

Exercise 1.8   Amplifier

Exercise 1.9   Dorm Room
Reproduce this drawing using Snap and Grid set to 0.25. The numerical
values are for reference only. Use Text to label the items.

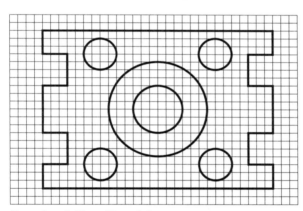

Exercise 1.10   Template
Draw the shape using one grid square equal to 1/4" or 10 mm.

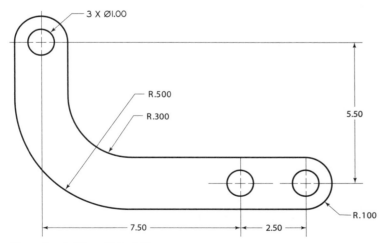

Exercise 1.11   Bracket
Redraw the following shape. Use the dimensions to create your
drawing showing the exact geometry of the part.

BASIC CONSTRUCTION TECHNIQUES

Introduction

You usually create drawings by combining and modifying several different basic shapes called *primitives*, such as lines, circles, and arcs, to create more complex shapes. This tutorial will help you learn how to use the AutoCAD® software to draw some of the most common basic shapes. As you work through the tutorial, keep in mind that one of the advantages of using CAD over drawing on paper is that you are creating an accurate model of the drawing geometry. In Tutorial 3, you will learn to list information from the drawing database. Information extracted from the drawing is accurate only if you created the drawing accurately in the first place.

Starting

Before you begin, **launch the AutoCAD 2012 program.**

If you need assistance, refer to Getting Started 1 and 2 of this guide.

Opening an Existing Drawing

This tutorial shows you how to add arcs and circles to the subdivision drawing provided with the datafiles that came with this guide. In Tutorial 3 you will finish the subdivision drawing so that the final drawing will look like Figure 2.1.

Wannabe Heights Estates

Figure 2.1

To open an existing drawing, you use the Application icon, Open selection or click the button that looks like an open folder from the Quick Access toolbar.

 Click: Open button

The Select File dialog box appears on your screen. Use the center portion, which shows the default directory and drive, to select

2

Objectives

When you have completed this tutorial, you will be able to

1. Open existing drawings.

2. Work with new and existing layers.

3. Draw, using the Arc and Circle commands.

4. Set and use running Object snaps.

5. Change the display, using Zoom and Pan.

6. Use Dynamic View.

7. Draw ellipses.

the location where your datafiles have been stored. You should have already created a directory called *c:\datafile2012*, and copied all the datafiles for this book into it. If you have not done so, you may want to review the Getting Started chapters. If the correct directory is not showing in the Look In box, use the Up One Level icon or expand the choices by clicking on the downward arrow for the Look In box. Use the scroll bars if necessary to scroll down the list of directories and open the appropriate one so the files appear in the dialog box as in Figure 2.2. Scroll down the list of files until you see the file named *subdivis. dwg*. When you select a file, a preview of the file appears in the box to the right. (Older files may not show a preview.)

Tip: *If you do not see a pre-view, pick Views from the dia-log box's menu bar and make sure that Preview is checked.*

Figure 2.2

Tip: *Use the buttons at the left of the dialog box to show the History (recently used files), My Documents folder contents, or Favorites you have added. To add a favorite, find the folder and then right-click the Favor-ites button. Pick Add Current Folder from the pop-up menu that appears. To add a folder as a button, pick Tools, Add Current Folder to Places.*

Menu choices at the top right of the Select File dialog box let you select different views to be displayed in the file list and other useful tools, such as a Find selection to search for files.

Click: **Tools, Find**

Type: **subdivis (in the Named area)**

Click: **Find Now button (from upper right of dialog box)**

The Find dialog box displays the location for the file named *Subdivis. dwg*, as shown in Figure 2.3. You can type in a portion of the name to match if you cannot remember the entire name or click the Date Modi-fied tab if you want to search by date and time the file was created.

Figure 2.3

*Double-click: **Subdivis.dwg (from the list at the bottom)***

You return to the Select File dialog box.

*Click: **Open***

When you have opened the file, it appears on your screen, as shown in Figure 2.4. Note that it opens with its own defaults for Grid, Snap, and other features. These settings are saved in the drawing file. When you open a drawing, its own settings are used.

Figure 2.4

Saving as a New File

The Save As command allows you to save your drawing to a new file name and/or different drive or directory. You can select this command from the Application icon or from the Quick Access toolbar.

Don't use the Save command, because that will save your changes into the original datafile.

 Click: **Save As button**

The Save Drawing As dialog box appears.

Figure 2.5

On your own, select the drive and directory *c:\work* and specify the name for your drawing, *subdivis.dwg*, similar to Figure 2.5..

The new file name is the same as the previous file name, but the directory is different. This creates a new copy of drawing *subdivis.dwg* saved in the directory *c:\work*.

The original file *c:\datafile2012\subdivis.dwg* remains unchanged on your drive. When you use the Save As command and specify a new file name, the software sets the newly saved file as current.

Using Layers

You can organize drawing information on different layers. Think of a *layer* as a transparent drawing sheet that you place over the drawing and that you can remove at will. The coordinate system remains the same from one layer to another, so graphical objects on separate layers remain aligned. You can create a virtually unlimited number of layers within the same drawing. The Layer command controls the color and linetype associated with a given layer. Using layers allows you to overlay a base drawing with several different levels of detail (such as wiring or plumbing schematics over the base plan for a building).

By using layers, you can also control which portions of a drawing are plotted, or remove dimensions or text from a drawing to make it easier to add or change objects. You can also lock layers, making them inaccessible but still visible on the screen. You can't change anything on a locked layer until you unlock it.

Current Layer

The *current layer* is the layer you are working on. Any new objects you draw are added to the current layer. The default current layer is Layer 0.

If you do not create and use other layers, your drawing will be created on Layer 0. You used this layer when drawing the plot plan in Tutorial 1. Layer 0 is a special layer provided in the AutoCAD program. You cannot rename it or delete it from the list of layers. Layer 0 has special properties when used with the Block and Insert commands, which are covered in Tutorial 10.

Layer POINTS is the current layer in *subdivis.dwg*. There can be only one current layer at a time. The name of the current layer appears on the Layer toolbar.

Controlling Layers

The Layer Control feature on the Layers panel on the Home tab of the ribbon is an easy way to control the visibility of existing layers in your drawing. You will learn more about creating and using layers in this tutorial. For now, you will use layers that have already been created for you.

Click: **on layer name POINTS from the Layers panel**

The list of available layers pulls down, as shown in Figure 2.6. Notice the special layer 0 displayed near the top of the list.

Figure 2.6

Click: **on the layer name CENTERLINE from the Layer Control list**

It becomes the current layer shown on the toolbar. Any new objects will be created on this layer until you select a different current layer. The Layer Control now should look like Figure 2.7, showing the layer name CENTERLINE.

Figure 2.7

Use the Line command you learned in Tutorial 1 to draw a line off to the side of the subdivision drawing.

Note that it is green and has a centerline linetype (long dash, short dash, long dash). The line you drew is on Layer CENTERLINE.

Erase or Undo the line on your own.

Controlling Colors

Each layer has a color associated with it. Using different colors for different layers helps you visually distinguish different information in the drawing. An object's color also may control which pens are used during plotting.

There are two different ways of selecting the color for objects on your screen. The best way is usually to set the layer color and draw the objects on the appropriate layer. This method keeps your drawing organized. The other method is to use the Color Control feature on the Properties panel. To select the Color Control pull-down feature,

Click: ByLayer, from the Properties panel to pull down the Color Control

Tip: *If your panels are minimized, you may need to click to expand the options.*

Click to expand color choices

Figure 2.8

Note that the standard colors (yellow, red, green, blue, etc.) are shown. You can also choose Select Color to view the full color palette.

Click: Select Color

The Select Color dialog box shown in Figure 2.9 appears on your screen, giving you a full range of colors from which to choose.

Tip: *On a black background, color 7 used for layer 0 appears as white; on a white background it appears black.*

Figure 2.9

The three tabs of the Select Color dialog box allow you to choose among different methods to determine the color for your drawing entities. The True Color tab allows you to set color to either RGB, which stands for Red, Green, Blue, the primary colors of light, or HSL, which stands for the Hue, Saturation, and Luminance of the color. The Color Books tab lets you select from among different standard ink manufacturer's predefined colors so that you can match print colors very closely to the colors you choose on your screen. In this text you will use Index Color (AutoCAD Color Index) as the method for selecting color.

*Make sure the **Index Color** tab is selected.*

The default option for the Color (and also for the Linetype) command is BYLAYER. It's the best selection because, when you draw a line, the color and linetype will be those of the current layer. Otherwise, the color in your drawing can become very confusing. You will click Cancel to exit the Select Color dialog box without making any changes. The colors for your new objects will continue to be determined by the layer on which they are created. Layers can have associated linetypes, as well as colors, as Layer CENTERLINE does.

*Click: **Cancel***

Layer Visibility

One of the advantages of using layers in the drawing is that you can choose not to display selected layers. That way, if you want to create projection lines or even notes about the drawing, you can draw them on a layer that you will later turn off, so that it isn't displayed or plotted. Or you may want to create a complex drawing with many layers, such as a building plan that contains the electrical plan on one layer and the mechanical plan on another, along with separate layers for the walls, windows, and so on. You can store all the information in a single drawing, and then plot different combinations of layers to create the electrical layout, first-floor plan, and any other combination you want. Next, use the Layer Control to lock Layer POINTS, freeze Layer TEXT, and turn off Layer EXISTING_ROAD.

*Click: **on Layer CENTERLINE** to show the list of layers*

The list of layers pulls down. Refer to Figure 2.10 as you make the following selections.

*Click: **the On/Off icon,** which looks like a lightbulb, to the left of Layer EXISTING_ROAD*

*Click: **any blank area of the screen** away from the Layer list to return to the drawing*

Note that the blue roadway lines have been turned off so that they no longer appear. Invisible (off) layers are not printed or plotted, but objects on these layers are still part of the drawing.

Figure 2.10   **Layer Control**

Freezing Layers

Freezing a layer is similar to turning it off. You use the *freeze* option not only to make the layer disappear from the display, but also to cause it to be skipped when the drawing is regenerated. This feature can noticeably improve the speed with which the software regenerates a large drawing. You should not freeze the current layer because that would create a situation where you would be drawing objects that you couldn't see on the screen. The icon for freezing and thawing layers looks like a snowflake when frozen and a shining sun when thawed.

Click: **to expand the Layer Control** *list*

Click: **the Freeze/Thaw icon** *to the left of Layer TEXT*

Click: **any blank area in the graphics window** *to return to the drawing*

Layer TEXT is still on, but it is frozen and therefore invisible. A layer can both be turned off and frozen; the effect is similar. You should either freeze a layer or turn it off, but there is no point in doing both. Your screen should now be similar to Figure 2.11.

Figure 2.11

Locking Layers

You can see a *locked layer* on the screen, and you can add new objects to it. However, you can't make changes to the new or old objects on that layer. This is useful when you need the layer for reference but do not want to change it. For example, you might want to move several items so that they line up with an object on the locked layer but prevent anything on the locked layer from moving. You will lock layer POINTS so that you cannot accidentally change the points already on the layer.

Click: **the Lock/Unlock icon** *to the left of Layer POINTS*

Now, Layer CENTERLINE is the current layer. (If for some reason it is not the current layer, set it current at this time.) Layer TEXT is frozen and does not appear. Layer EXISTING_ROAD is turned off and does not appear. Layer POINTS is locked so that you can see and add to it, but not change it.

On your own, try erasing one of the circled points in the drawing.

A message appears, stating that the object is on a locked layer. The object won't be erased.

Making Object's Layer Current

The Make Object's Layer Current button is located above the Layer Control pull-down (Figure 2.11). This command lets you select an object and then click on the icon to make that object's layer current.

*Click: **a black lot line** (white if your background color is black), representing a lot boundary*

Note that the Layer Control now shows LOTLINES, the layer of the line you selected. This name is only temporary, for if you drew a new line, the layer name changes back to the current layer (CENTER-LINE). This is useful when you are unsure which layer a particular object is on.

Figure 2.12

Next you will use the Make Object's Layer Current button to set LOTLINES as the current layer.

Make sure a black lot line is still highlighted

 Click: Make Object's Layer Current icon

The current layer is changed to LOTLINES, and any new objects will be added to this layer. In the command prompt is the message: LOTLINES is now the current layer.

Now you will change the current layer back to CENTERLINE by using the Layer Previous button. If you are not sure which button to select, hover your mouse over the buttons to show the tooltips.

*Click: **Layer Previous button***

Layer CENTERLINE returns as the current layer.

Using Layer

The Layer command lets you create new layers and control the color and linetype associated with a layer. You can also use Layer to control which layers are visible or plotted at any one time and to set the current layer. Remember, only one layer at a time can be current. New objects are created on the current layer. Use the Layer Properties Manager icon from the Layer panel to create new layers and set their properties. (Its command alias is LA.)

Click: **Layer Properties Manager button**

The Layer Properties Manager appears on the screen, showing the list of existing layers (Figure 2.13).

Tip: *Locked layers appear transparent by default.*

Tip: *You can right-click on a heading in the Layer Properties Manager, and select Maximize Column Headings from the pop-up menu that appears.*

Figure 2.13

Notice that the layers you earlier turned off, locked, or froze are identified with those icons. Next you will create a layer named EASEMENTS which you will use later in Tutorial 3. It will have a hidden linetype and the color cyan (a light blue shade)

Click: **New Layer icon** *(located at the top middle of the dialog box)*

A new layer appears with the default name Layer1, which should be highlighted as shown in Figure 2.14.

Tip: *You can resize the Layer Properties Manager by dragging on its corners.*

Figure 2.14

By default it has the same properties as the currently selected layer (CENTERLINE). You will change the layer name, color and linetype for the new layer next. Layer names can be as long as 255 characters. Layer names can contain almost any characters, except for restricted operating system characters like comma (,) and others like <>/":*|'=. Letters, numbers, spaces, and the characters dollar sign ($), period (.), number sign (#), underscore (_), and hyphen (-) are valid. While Layer1 is still highlighted,

Type: **EASEMENTS [Enter]**

Next, set the color for layer EASEMENTS. To the right of the layer names are the various layer controls mentioned previously. Each column title is labeled with the name of the function: On (light bulb), Freeze (sun), Lock/Unlock (lock), Color (small color box), Linetype, Lineweight, Plot Style, Plot, and Description. You can resize these columns to show more or less of the names by dragging the line between the name headings.

To change the color for layer EASEMENTS,

Click: **on the Color column box corresponding to layer EASEMENTS**

The Select Color dialog box containing color choices pops up on the screen as shown in Figure 2.15.

Make sure that the Index Color tab is uppermost.

Figure 2.15

Color in Layers

The Select Color dialog box allows you to specify the color for objects drawn on a layer. You will select the color cyan for the easement layer that you are creating. The color helps you visually distinguish linetypes and layers in drawings. You also use color to select the pen and pen width for your printer or plotter.

The Select Color dialog box has the choices BYLAYER and BY-BLOCK on the right side. As you are specifying the color for layer EASEMENTS only, you can't select these choices, so they are shown grayed. Move the arrow cursor over the Standard Colors boxes, where cyan is the fourth color from the left.

Click: **cyan from the Standard Colors boxes to the left of the ByLayer button**

The name of the color that you have selected appears in the Color: box at the bottom of the screen. (If you select one of the standard colors, the name appears in the box; if you select one of the other 255 colors from the palette, the color number appears.)

Click: **OK**

Now the color for layer EASEMENTS is set to cyan. Check the listing of layer names and colors to verify that cyan has replaced green in the Color column to the right of the layer name EASEMENTS.

Linetype in Layers

The linetype column allows you to set the linetype drawn for the layer. You will select the linetype HIDDEN for your layer named EASEMENTS.

Click: on Center in the Linetype column across from layer EASEMENTS

The Select Linetype dialog box appears on your screen.

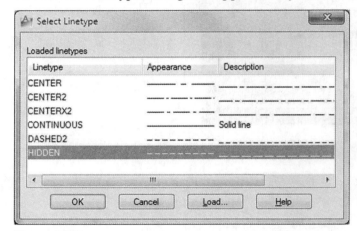

Figure 2.16

Click: **HIDDEN** *as shown in Figure 2.16*

Click: **OK**

You return to the Layer Properties Manager. Layer EASEMENTS should have the properties set as shown in Figure 2.16.

Click: [X] from its upper left to close the Layer Properties Manager

CENTERLINE should still be the current layer on the Layer toolbar, showing a green square to the left of the layer name. You will use the EASEMENTS layer you created later in this tutorial.

Using layers to control the color and linetype of new objects that you create will work only if BYLAYER is active as the method for establishing object color, object linetype, and lineweight.

On your own, examine the Color Control, Linetype Control, and the Lineweight Control on the Properties panel. All three should be set to BYLAYER.

Now that you know the basics of using and creating layers, you will begin creating the curved sections of the road centerline for the subdivision. The straight-line sections that the curves are tangent to have been drawn to get you started.

Using Object Snap

The object snap feature accurately selects locations based on existing objects in your drawing. When you click points from the screen without using object snaps, the resolution of your screen makes it impossible for you to select points with the accuracy stored in the drawing database. You have learned how to click accurately by snapping to a grid point. *Object snap* makes it possible for you to click points accurately on your drawing geometry by snapping to an object's center, endpoint, midpoint, and so on. Whenever prompted to select a point or location, you can use an object snap to help make an accurate selection. Without this command, locating two objects with respect to each other in correct and useful geometric form is virtually impossible. Object snap is one of the most important CAD tools. Their are several different ways to access and use the Object Snaps.

Right-click: **the Object Snap button** on the Status bar

A menu of Object Snap modes and in Figure 2.17.

Figure 2.17

Tip: *You can also activate an object snap by typing the three-letter name any time you are prompted to enter points or select objects. Refer to the Command Summary for the three letter codes.*

Object Snap can operate in two different ways. The first is called *override mode*. With this method, you select the object snap during a command. The object snap acts as a modifier within the command string to *target* the next point you select. You activate object snaps from within other commands by clicking the appropriate icon from the Object Snap toolbar. The object locations they select are indicated by small circles on the icons. When you activate an object snap in this manner, it is active for one click only. Remember, you can use this method only during a command that is prompting you to select points or objects.

A special feature called AutoSnap™ is active when Object Snap is in use. It displays a marker and description (SnapTip) when the cursor is placed near or on a snap point. This feature helps you to determine what location on the object will be selected.

The second method for using Object Snap is called *running mode*. With this method, you turn on the object snap and leave it on before you invoke any commands. When a running mode object snap is on, the marker box and SnapTip will appear during any future command when you are prompted for a point location, object selection, or other click. The SnapTip will tell you which object snap location is being targeted.

Click: **Settings** *from the menu (see Figure 2.17)*

The Drafting Settings dialog box you used to set the snap and grid appears on your screen. Notice it has three tabs: Snap and Grid, Polar Tracking, and Object Snap. Object Snap should be on top.

Click: **Clear All** *(to unselect any current modes)*

Click: **Node**

A check appears in the box when it is selected, as shown in Figure 2.18. Node snaps to objects drawn with the AutoCAD Point command. The symbol next to the Node setting represents the AutoSnap marker shape that will appear in the drawing.

Figure 2.18

Click: **Options** *(from the lower left of the dialog box)*

The Options dialog box appears on your screen as shown in Figure 2.19. You can use it to change Marker size, color, and settings. You may want to make the Marker box smaller or larger, depending on your drawing's complexity and size.

Figure 2.19

On your own, try using the slider to make the box smaller and then larger. Next, you may want to change the Marker color to a more noticeable color, such as red. When you have finished,

*Click: **OK** (to exit the Options dialog box)*

*Click: **OK** (to exit the Drafting Settings dialog box)*

*Click: **Object Snap button** to turn it on, if it is not already on*

On your own, make sure that **Ortho mode, Polar tracking, and Object snap tracking** are **off**.

Object Snap is a very useful tool and you will use it frequently throughout the rest of this guide. It can be very important to turn it on and off as needed. Notice that the Object Snap button on the Status bar is highlighted, meaning it is active. You may click the Object Snap button to toggle the use of object snap on or off, similar to the Snap Mode and Grid buttons. Check your status bar to make sure that the Object Snap button is turned on. (It appears highlighted.)

Now you are ready to start creating arcs at accurate locations in the drawing. When you are prompted to select, look for the marker box on the crosshairs. When it's there, you know that Snap to Node is being used to select the points that were set previously in the drawing.

Using Arc

The Arc command is on the ribbon Home tab, Draw panel, or you can type ARC at the command prompt. There are eleven different ways to create arcs. To see the options, click on the small triangle next to show the Arc flyout as shown in Figure 2.20.

Figure 2.20

Each Arc command option requires that you input point locations. The icons on the buttons help show you which points that option expects for input. You can define those point locations by manually typing in the coordinate values or locating the points with the cursor and pressing the click button on your pointing device. For the exercises presented in this tutorial, follow the directions carefully so that your drawing will turn out correctly. Keep in mind that if you were designing the subdivision, you might not use all the command options demonstrated in this tutorial. When you are using the AutoCAD software later for design, select the command options that are appropriate for the geometry in your drawing.

Arc 3 Points

The 3 Points option of the Arc command draws an arc through three points that you specify. The dots located on the icon represent the three points of definition. This means that three point locations will be necessary for drawing that arc. Remember, to specify locations you can click them or type in absolute, relative, or polar coordinates. You will draw an arc using the 3 Points option. The Snap to Node running object snap will help you click the points drawn in the datafile.

Click: **3 Point** *button*

Specify start point of arc or [Center]: ***select point 1, using the AutoSnap marker as shown in Figure 2.21***

As can be seen in Figure 2.21, the AutoSnap marker for Node appears when the cursor is near a node point.

Figure 2.21

Now you will continue with selecting the points.

Specify second point of arc or [Center/End]: ***select point 2***

The cursor enters drag mode, whereby you can see the arc move on the screen as you move the cursor. Many AutoCAD commands permit dynamic specification, or dragging, of the image on the screen.

Move the cursor around the screen to see how it affects the way the arc would be drawn. Recall your use of this feature to draw circles in Tutorial 1.

Specify end point of arc: ***select point 3***

The third point defines the endpoint of the arc. The radius of the arc is calculated from the locations of the three points. Your drawing should now show the completed arc, as shown in the upper part of Figure 2.22.

Figure 2.22

Tip: *You can type the option letters at the command prompt to select an arc creation method. Pressing the right mouse button pops up a menu that allows you to pick the same options for the Arc command that you selected previously. Pressing the space bar or [Enter] key ro restart the arc command uses Arc in a more general way, where you must select the command options by typing in the option letter(s).*

Arc Start, Center, End

Next, you will draw an arc by specifying the start, center, and endpoints. Figure 2.22 shows the points used to create this arc.

Click: ***Start, Center, End** button from the Arc flyout*

Specify start point of arc or [Center]: ***select point 4** as the start point*

Specify center point of arc: ***select point 5** to act as the arc's center*

Specify end point of arc or [Angle/chord Length]: ***select point 6** to end the arc*

The arc is drawn counterclockwise from the start point. Notice that now Start, Center, End is the top button on the Arc flyout. When you are using a flyout, the last item you clicked appears as the top flyout button, so options you use frequently take only one click.

Figure 2.22 shows the point locations needed to draw a *concave arc.* If the start point were located where the endpoint is, a *convex arc* outside the centerlines would have been drawn. When you have added the arc correctly, your arc should look like that in the lower part of Figure 2.23.

On your own, try drawing another arc with the Arc Start, Center, End option, this time clicking point 6 first, then the center, and then point 4.

Note that this arc is drawn counterclockwise, resulting in a convex arc.

Undo this backward arc by typing U [Enter] at the command prompt.

Figure 2.23

Arc Start, End, Angle

Arc Start, End, Angle draws an arc through the selected start and endpoints by using the included angle you specify. Next, draw an arc with the Start, End, Angle option, referring to Figure 2.23. This time you will use dynamic entry.

> *Click:* **to turn on Dynamic Input** *from the Status Bar*

 Click: **Start, End, Angle button** *from the Arc flyout*

Specify start point of arc or [Center]: ***select point 7***

Specify end point of arc: ***select point 8***

Specify included angle: ***59d12'30" [Enter]***

The arc is defined by the *included angular value* (often called the *delta angle* in survey drawings) from the start point to the end point. Positive angular values are measured counterclockwise. Negative angular values are measured clockwise. (Type d for the degree symbol when typing in surveyor angles. Use the single quote and double quote for minutes and seconds.)

Arc Start, Center, Length

Arc Start, Center, Length draws an arc specified by the start and center points of the arc and the chord length. The chord length is the straight-line distance from the start point of the arc to the endpoint of the arc. You can enter negative values for the chord length to draw an arc in the opposite direction. Figure 2.24 shows a diagram describing the geometry of this type of arc.

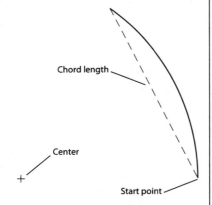

Figure 2.24

You will draw the next arc by using Arc Start, Center, Length. Figure 2.25 shows the dynamic entry to use for the chord length.

Figure 2.25

Click: *Start, Center, Length button* from the Arc flyout

Specify start point of arc or [Center]: *select point 9*

Specify center point of arc: *select point 10*

Specify length of chord: *169.4253 [Enter]*

Your new arc should look like the one shown in Figure 2.26.

Figure 2.26

Arc Start, End, Radius

Draw the next arc using Start, End, Radius. The locations of the start and end points are at 11 and 12.

Click: ***Start, End, Radius button*** *from the Arc flyout*

Specify start point of arc or [Center]: ***select point 11***

Specify end point of arc: ***select point 12***

Specify radius of arc: ***154.87 [Enter]***

Your drawing should be similar to that in Figure 2.27.

Figure 2.27

Continuing an Arc

Arc Continue allows you to join an arc to a previously drawn arc or line. You will give it a try off to the side of the subdivision drawing and then erase or undo it, as it is not a part of the drawing. To draw an arc that is the continuation of an existing line,

Click: ***Line button***

On your own, draw a line anywhere on your screen.

Click: ***Continue*** *from the Draw panel, Arc flyout*

The last point of the line becomes the first point for the arc. The cursor is in drag mode, and an arc appears from the end of the line. You are prompted for an endpoint.

Specify end point of arc: ***select an endpoint***

Next you will use Arc Start, Center, End to draw another arc. Then you will continue an arc from the endpoint of that arc.

Click: ***Start, Center, End*** *from the Draw panel, Arc flyout*

Specify start point of arc or [Center]: ***select a start point***

Specify center point of arc: ***select a center point***

Specify end point of arc or [Angle/chord Length]: ***select an endpoint***

Figure 2.28

*Click: **Continue** from the Draw panel, Arc flyout*

Specify end point of arc: ***select an endpoint***

Your drawings should look similar to those in Figure 2.28.

On your own, erase or undo the extra continued arcs and lines that you created.

Using Arc at the Command Line

To select the Arc command, you can also type the command alias, A, at the command prompt. When you start the Arc command this way, the default is the 3 Points option you used earlier. If you want to use another option, you can type the command option letter at the prompt. You will start the Arc command by typing its alias. You will then specify the start, end, and angle of the arc by typing the command option at the prompt. Refer to Figure 2.27 for the points, 13 and 14, to select.

Command: ***A [Enter]***

The command Arc is echoed at the command prompt, followed by

Specify start point of arc or [Center]: ***click point 13***

Specify second point of arc or [Center/End]: ***E [Enter]***

Specify end point of arc: ***click point 14***

Specify center point of arc or [Angle/Direction/Radius]: ***A [Enter]***

Specify included angle: ***30d54'04" [Enter]***

*Click: **to turn Dynamic Input button off***

The arc is added to your drawing. However, it may be hard to see because of the small size of the arc relative to the size of the screen and drawing.

Using Zoom

The Zoom commands change the size of the image on your display. The Zoom flyout is on the ribbon View tab, Navigate panel (Figure 2.29).

To zoom in on an area of the drawing, you can select Zoom In from the Zoom flyout.

*Click: **Zoom In button***

Your drawing is enlarged to twice its previous size on the screen (Figure 2.30).

Tip: *After you draw an arc, restarting the command and then pressing the space bar or [Enter] also engages the Continue option. You can use this method to continue a line from the previously drawn arc or line.*

Figure 2.29

Figure 2.30

Next you will zoom out, using the Zoom Out button from the flyout.

Click: Zoom Out button

Your drawing should return to its original size on the screen. The Zoom In and Zoom Out options use the Scale feature of the Zoom command to zoom to a scale of 2X (twice the previous size) and 0.5X (half the previous size).

Zooming Using Scale Factors

You can also use *scale factors* to zoom when you click the Scale option of the Zoom command. Scale factor 1.00 shows the drawing limits (where the grid is shown). Scale factor 0.5 shows the drawing limits half-size on the screen. Typing X after the scale factor makes the zoom scale relative to the previous view. For example, entering 2X causes the new view to be shown twice as big as the view established previously, as you saw when using Zoom In. A scale factor of 0.5X reduces the view to half the previous size, as you saw when using Zoom Out. Zoom Scale uses the current left corner or (0,0) coordinates as the base location for the zoom. Typing XP after the scale factor makes the new zoom scale relative to paper space. A scale factor of 0.5XP means that the object will be shown half-size when you are laying out your sheet of paper. You will learn more about paper space in Tutorial 5.

You will select the Zoom command by typing its alias at the command prompt.

Command: *Z [Enter]*

Specify corner of window, enter a scale factor (nX or nXP), or [All/Center/Dynamic/Extents/Previous/Scale/Window/Object] <real time>: *2X [Enter]*

The view is enlarged to twice the previous size.

Repeat the Zoom command.

Command: *[Enter] (to restart the last command)*

Specify corner of window, enter a scale factor (nX or nXP), or [All/Center/ Dynamic/Extents/Previous/Scale/Window/Object] : *.5 [Enter]*

The drawing limits appear on the screen at half their original size. The area shown on the screen is twice as big as the drawing limits. Now, restore the original view.

Command: *[Enter] (to restart the last command)*

Specify corner of window, enter a scale factor (nX or nXP), or [All/Center/ Dynamic/Extents/Previous/Scale/Window/Object] : *1 [Enter]*

Zoom Window

To use Zoom Window, create a window around the area that you want to enlarge to fill the screen. This lets you quickly enlarge the exact portion of the drawing that you are interested in. You will select this command using the Zoom flyout. Note that the Zoom command has an apostrophe in front of it at the command prompt to show that the command is transparent. This means that you can select it during execution of another command. You will zoom in on the area shown in Figure 2.31.

Click: *Zoom Window icon*

Specify first corner: *select point A*

Specify opposite corner: *select point B*

Figure 2.31

The defined area is enlarged to fill the screen as shown in Figure 2.32.

Figure 2.32

Zoom Previous

To return an area to its previous size, you will click Zoom Previous from the Standard toolbar.

Click: **Zoom Previous button**

Your drawing is returned to its original size. Areas can be repeatedly zoomed, that is, you can zoom in on a zoomed area; in fact, you can continue to zoom until the portion shown on the display is ten trillion times the size of the original.

Zoom Realtime

An easy way to zoom your drawing to the desired size is to use the Zoom Realtime feature on the Standard toolbar.

Click: **Zoom Realtime button**

Select an arbitrary point in the middle of your drawing and hold down the click button of your pointing device while dragging the cursor up and down. When you move the cursor upward, you zoom in closer to the drawing; when you move the cursor downward, you zoom out farther from the drawing.

Press ESC or ENTER to exit, or right-click to use the shortcut menu.

Zoom Realtime can quickly be selected at any time by right-clicking and clicking it from the short-cut menu.

Zoom All

Zoom All returns the drawing to its original size by displaying the drawing limits, or displaying the drawing extents (all of the drawing objects), whichever is larger. Select the Zoom All icon from the Zoom flyout.

 Click: **Zoom All button**

      The drawing should return to its original size, that is, as it was before you began the Zoom command. Experiment on your own with the other options of the Zoom command and read about them in the Help window.

Using the Scroll Wheel to Zoom

The scroll wheel on your mouse also provides Zoom functions. Try these out now.

    Roll the scroll wheel forward

The view of the drawing is enlarged on your screen.

    Roll the scroll wheel towards yourself.

The view zooms out and appears smaller.

    Double-click the scroll wheel.

The drawing fills the screen.

Zoom Dynamic

Another way to zoom in and move around in a large drawing quickly is to use the Zoom Dynamic.

Click: **Zoom Dynamic**

      The *view box* appears on your screen, as shown in Figure 2.33.

Figure 2.33

Tip: *If you open a drawing that you've saved with the view zoomed in, you can use Zoom All or double-click the scroll wheel to show the full drawing.*

Move your mouse to position the view box.

The box shows an X in the center, indicating it is in position mode. As you move your mouse around, the view box moves with your mouse movements..

Position the view box at the location you desire and click the mouse.

Now an arrow appears at the right edge of the box and as you move your mouse, the size of the box is enlarged or reduced as shown in Figure 2.34.

Figure 2.34

Try reducing the box and then click the mouse button.

You return to the position mode, so that you can move the box around again.

When you are satisfied with the location of the box, right-click the mouse and select Enter.

The area enclosed in the box fills the graphics window,

Using Pan Realtime

The Pan command lets you position the drawing view on the screen without changing the zoom factor. Unlike the Move command, which moves the objects in your drawing to different locations on the coordinate system, the Pan command does not change the location of the objects on the coordinate system. Rather, your view of the coordinate system and the objects changes to a different location on the screen.

Press and hold the scroll wheel and move your mouse

Doing this, you can drag your drawing around on the screen. The drawing should move freely about the drawing area until you let go of the scroll wheel, at which point it will stop.

You can also select to use the Pan command from the ribbon,

 *Click: **Pan button** from the View tab, Navigate panel*

Press and hold the left mouse button to position the drawing on the screen.

Press: [Esc] or [Enter] to exit the command

Double-click the scroll wheel to Zoom to the drawing extents.

Your drawing should now fill the drawing window.

Using Circle Options

In Tutorial 1 you learned to use the Circle command by specifying a center point and a radius value. You can also use the Circle command to draw circles by specifying any two points (Circle 2 Point), any three points (Circle 3 Point), or two tangent references and a radius (Circle Tan Tan Radius). You will use the Endpoint object snap mode to make circles that line up exactly with the ends of the existing lot lines.

*Right-click: **Object Snap button** from the status bar*

*Click: **Settings** from context menu that appears*

*Click: **to turn on Endpoint** in the dialog box*

*Click: **OK***

The Endpoint and Node running mode object snaps are now turned on. When you see the AutoSnap marker appear on the endpoint of a line, the crosshairs will snap to the marker point. If you see the Node marker, move the crosshairs until the endpoint you want is highlighted.

*Click: **LOTLINES** from the Layer Control to make it current*

Circle 2-Point

You will draw a circle using Circle 2-Point. Points 1 and 2 will be endpoints of the circle's diameter, as shown in Figure 2.35.

Figure 2.35

Click: **2-Point button from the Circle flyout**

Specify first end point of circle's diameter: **select point 1**

Specify second endpoint of circle's diameter: **select point 2**

The circle has been defined by the two selected endpoints defining its diameter. Your screen should look like Figure 2.36.

Figure 2.36

Circle 3-Point

To draw a circle using Circle 3-Point, specify any three points on the circle's circumference. Refer to Figure 2.36 for the points to select.

Click: **3-Point** *from the Circle flyout, Home tab Draw panel*

Specify first point on circle: **select point 3**

Specify second point on circle: **select point 4**

Because you are in drag mode, you see the circle being created on your screen as you move the cursor.

Specify third point on circle: **select point 5**

The three points on its circumference have defined the circle. Your screen should look like Figure 2.37.

Figure 2.37

Next you will draw a circle tangent to two angled centerlines. First, you will change the current layer and zoom in on points 1 and 2, shown in Figure 2.37.

*Click: **CENTERLINE** from the Layer Control list to make it current*

*Click: **Zoom Window button***

Specify first corner: ***click point 1***

Specify opposite corner: ***click point 2***

The area should be enlarged on your screen, as shown in Figure 2.38.

*Click: **Object Snap button** to turn it off*

The Object Snap button should now appear unselected, meaning that all running mode object snaps are temporarily turned off. You should do so because sometimes object snaps can interfere with the selection of points and the operation of certain commands. You will use the Circle Tangent, Tangent, Radius option, which uses the Tangent object snap. This will not work well unless other object snaps are turned off.

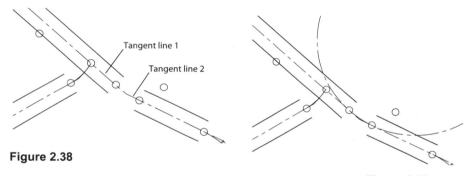

Figure 2.38

Figure 2.39

> **Tip:** *You can quickly zoom in using the scroll wheel on your mouse. To position the area near the center of the drawing window, hold down the scroll wheel to use Pan.*

Circle Tangent, Tangent, Radius

Circle Tangent, Tangent, Radius requires that you specify two objects to which the resulting circle will be *tangent*. Then give the radius of the resulting circle. This method is frequently used in laying out road centerlines. It involves selecting the two straight sections of the road centerline to which the curve is tangent and then specifying the radius.

*Click: **Tan, Tan, Radius** from the Circle flyout on the Draw panel*

Note that the AutoSnap marker appears any time the cursor is near a line. Refer to Figure 2.38 for the lines to select. You can select either line first.

Specify point on object for first tangent of circle: ***click tangent line 1***

Specify point on object for second tangent of circle: ***click tangent line 2***

Specify radius of circle <34.0000>: ***267.3098 [Enter]***

A circle with a radius of 267.3098 is drawn tangent to both original lines, as shown in Figure 2.39.

You can also use Circle Tangent, Tangent, Radius to draw a circle tangent to two circles. You will try this by drawing two circles off to the side of the drawing and then adding a circle that is tangent to both of them.

On your own, draw two circles off to the side of your subdivision drawing.

Click: ***Tan, Tan, Radius** from the Circle flyout*

Specify point on object for first tangent of circle: ***select one of the circles you just drew***

Specify point on object for second tangent of circle: ***select the other circle***

Specify radius of circle <267.3098>: *150 [Enter]*

A circle with a radius of 150 is drawn tangent to both circles.

Circle Tangent, Tangent, Tangent

The Circle Tangent, Tangent, Tangent command lets you quickly define a circle that is tangent to three entities in the drawing.

Try it on your own by selecting the Tan, Tan, Tan button from the Circle flyout and then selecting three lot lines to draw a circle tangent to.

Now erase the extra circles on your own.

Using Ellipse

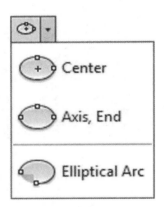

The command options for specifying an ellipse can be selected from the Ellipse flyout on the Home tab Draw panel.

Next, you will practice using the Ellipse command by drawing some ellipses off to the side of the drawing. You will erase them when you are through. To draw an ellipse by specifying three points,

Click: ***Axis, End button from the Ellipse flyout***

Specify axis endpoint of ellipse or [Arc/Center]: ***select a point***

Specify other endpoint of axis: ***select a point***

Specify distance to other axis or [Rotation]: ***select a point***

An ellipse is created on your screen, using the three points that you selected. The ellipse has a *major axis* (the longest distance between two points on the ellipse) and a *minor axis* (the shorter distance across the ellipse). The AutoCAD program determines which axis is major and which is minor by examining the distance between the first pair of endpoints and comparing it to the distance specified by the third point.

One way to describe an ellipse is to create a circle and then tip the circle away from your viewing direction by a rotation angle. This method requires you to specify the angle of rotation instead of the endpoint of the second axis.

You will draw an ellipse using two endpoints and an angle of rotation. See Figure 2.40 to determine the location of the points.

Tip: *If you get the message, Circle does not exist, the radius you specified may be too small or too large to be tangent to both lines.*

Tip: *The value shown as the default radius for the circle depends on the size of the last circle you drew.*

Figure 2.40

Click: **Axis, End button** *from the Ellipse flyout*

    Specify axis endpoint of ellipse or [Arc/Center]: ***select point 1***

Specify other endpoint of axis: ***select point 2***

This defined the distance between points 1 and 2 as the major axis (diameter) of the ellipse. This time at the command prompt, use the options to specify the rotation angle, as though tipping a circle.

    Specify distance to other axis or [Rotation]: ***R [Enter]***

    Specify rotation around major axis: ***35 [Enter]***

    On your own, **erase** the ellipses that you created.

The remaining construction methods for ellipses are similar to specifying the axes, but use radius values rather than diameter values. This way, when the center point of the ellipse is known, you can use it as a starting point. Refer to Figure 2.41 for the locations of the points in the next steps. This time type the command.

    Command: ***ELLIPSE [Enter]***

    Specify axis endpoint of ellipse or [Arc/Center]: ***C [Enter]***

The center of the ellipse is the intersection of the major and minor axes. You can enter a coordinate or use the cursor to select a point on the screen.

    Specify center of ellipse: ***select point 1***

Next, you provide the endpoint of the first axis. The angle of the ellipse is determined by the angle from the center point to this endpoint.

    Specify endpoint of axis: ***select point 2***

Now specify the distance measured from the center of the ellipse to the endpoint of the second axis, measured perpendicular to the first axis (or a rotation angle can be used).

    Specify distance to other axis or [Rotation]: ***select point 3***

The point that you selected determined whether the first axis is a major or minor axis. The ellipse is drawn on your screen.

Next, draw an ellipse by specifying a center point, one axis point, and an angle of rotation. Refer to Figure 2.42.

 Click: **Center from the Ellipse flyout**

    Specify center of ellipse: ***click point 1***

Specify endpoint of axis: ***click point 2***

Specify distance to other axis or [Rotation]: ***R [Enter]***

Specify rotation around major axis: ***30 [Enter]***

Before you go on, **erase** the ellipses you drew for when practice.

Use Zoom All to return to the original view.

Save your drawing at this time.

Tip: *Recall that AutoCAD keyboard entry is not case-sensitive. You can type uppercase, lowercase, or mixed-case letters. In this book your keyboard entry is shown uppercase to help you identify easily what you are supposed to type, but the program does not require uppercase letters.*

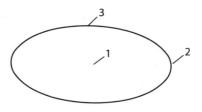

Figure 2.41

Tip: *Notice that when you pick the Center button from the Ellipse flyout, the "C" option is automatically selected at the command prompt : Specify axis endpoint of ellipse or [Arc/Center]: **C***

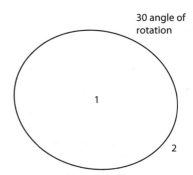

Figure 2.42

Tip: *If you have older Auto-CAD versions you can use the Save As command to save your drawing to the 2010, R14 or other formats. In the Save Drawing As dialog box, scroll through the Save Drawing Type list for the various options.*

When you have successfully saved your drawing,

> Click: **Application button, Exit AutoCAD**

You are now back at the Windows desktop.

You will finish the subdivision drawing in Tutorial 3.

Key Terms

chord length	freeze	minor axis	running mode
concave arc	included angular value	object snap	scale factor
convex arc	layer	override mode	tangent
current layer	locked layer	primitives	target
delta angle	major axis	regenerate	virtual screen

Key Commands

Aerial Viewer	Circle 3-Point	Layer Control	Snap to Node
Arc 3 Points	Circle Tan, Tan Radius	Mtext	Text
Arc Continue	Circle Tan, Tan, Tan	Object Snap	Zoom In
Arc Start, Center, End	Color Control	Open Drawing	Zoom Out
Arc Start, Center, Length	DText	Pan Realtime	Zoom Previous
Arc Start, End, Angle	DSViewer	Running Object Snap	Zoom Realtime
Arc Start, End, Radius	Ellipse	Save As	Zoom Scale
Circle 2-Point	Layer	Snap to Endpoint	Zoom Window

Exercises

Redraw the following shapes. If dimensions are given, create your drawing geometry exactly to the specified dimensions. The letter M after an exercise number means that the dimensions are in millimeters (metric units). If no letter follows the exercise number, the dimensions are in inches. Do not include dimensions on the drawings. The Ø symbol means diameter; R indicates a radius.

Exercise 2.1M Bracket

Exercise 2.2 Gasket

Exercise 2.3M Flange

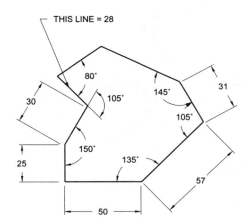

Exercise 2.4M Puzzle

Draw the figure shown according to the dimensions provided. From your drawing determine what the missing distances must be (Hint: use DIST).

Exercise 2.5 Plot Plan

Exercise 2.6 Link

POWER SUPPLY

Exercise 2.7 Power Supply
Draw this circuit, using the techniques you have learned.

EXERCISES **93**

Exercise 2.8 Gasket

Exercise 2.9 Shape

Exercise 2.10M Lever Crank

BASIC EDITING AND PLOTTING TECHNIQUES

Introduction

Next you will learn how to modify some of the basic shapes that you've drawn to create a wider variety of shapes required for technical drawings. As you work through the tutorial, keep in mind that one of the advantages of using CAD over drawing on paper is that you are creating an accurate model of the drawing geometry. You will see how to use this accurate drawing database to find areas, lengths, and other information.

In this tutorial you will finish drawing the subdivision that you started in Tutorial 2. A drawing has been provided with the datafiles that accompany this guide. You will start from it, in case the drawing that you created in Tutorial 2 has some settings that are different from the datafile. You will trim lines and arcs, and add fillets, multilines, and text ' to finish the subdivision drawing. When you've finished the drawing, you will plot your final result.

Starting

Launch the AutoCAD 2012 software.

Starting from a Template Drawing

A template drawing is one designed to be used as the basis for new drawings. Any AutoCAD settings, preferences, and drawn objects in the template become part of the new drawing, while the original template remains unchanged. Files that can be used as templates have the extension *.dwt*. There is really no difference between them and drawings except for the file extension. Any drawing can be saved as a template file using Save As and then changing the file type to Drawing Template File (*.dwt*).

In order to continue with the subdivision drawing, you will start a new file, using the drawing file *subdiv2.dwt* as a template.

Click: New button *from the Quick Access toolbar*

The Select Template dialog box should be showing, similar to that in Figure 3.1. You should see a list of premade templates to choose from; these are stored in the *Template* folder that was created when the software was installed.

Click: *to pull down the selections in the Look in box*

The Look in area lists the storage devices connected to your computer.

Choose the location of the *c:\datafile2012* folder so you can see the files in it as shown in Figure 3.1.

Objectives

When you have completed this tutorial, you will be able to

1. Modify your drawing, using the Fillet, Chamfer, Offset, and Trim commands.

2. Create and edit polylines and splines.

3. List graphical objects, locate points, and find areas from your drawing database.

4. Change properties of drawing objects.

5. Create multilines and multiline styles.

6. Print or plot your drawing.

Tip: *You can pick Application icon, Options and use the File tab of the Options dialog box to set a different default directory location for the template files.*

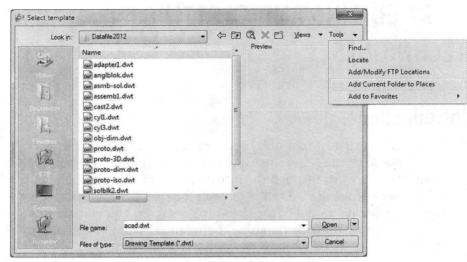

Figure 3.1

Click: **Tools** *to show the menu as shown in Figure 3.1*

Click: **Add Current Folder to Places**

The Datafile2012 folder is added to the list of places at the left of the dialog box as shown in Figure 3.2. This gives you a quick way to access the folder the next time you need it.

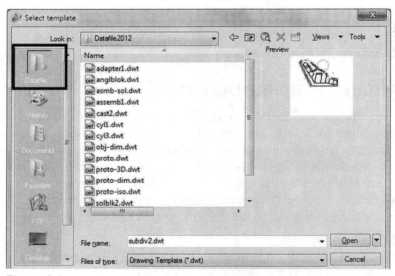

Figure 3.2

Select: **subdiv2.dwt**

Click: **Open (or double-click the on the file name)**

You should see the drawing on your screen with the AutoCAD default name "*Drawing#*". The *.dwt* file extension signals the software to create a copy of the drawing so that the actual *subdiv2.dwt* datafile will not be changed.

Click: **Save As button** *from the Quick Access toolbar*

Change to the c:\work directory.

For the file name,

Type: **MYSUBDIV [Enter]**

Now the drawing is saved with the new name MYSUBDIV in your *c:\ work* directory. The drawing on your screen should be similar to Figure 3.4.

Figure 3.3

Use Zoom Window to enlarge the area with the large circle

When you have finished zooming, your screen will look like Figure 3.4.

Figure 3.4

Using Trim

The Trim button is located on the ribbon Home tab, Modify panel. Trim removes part of an object in two steps. First, you are prompted to select the objects that you will use as cutting edges. The cutting edges are drawing objects that you will use to cut off the portions that you want to trim. The selected cutting edge object must cross the object that you want to trim at the point to trim it. Press [Enter] to indicate that you have finished selecting cutting edges and want to begin the second step. After you press [Enter], you are prompted to select the portions of the objects that you want to trim. Click on the portions you want to remove.

You can also hold down the shift key while selecting an object to extend that object to the cutting edge that you have selected.

The Trim command has several options.

The **Fence** option lets you select items to trim by drawing a "fence" (an open ended series of line segments) across them.

The **Crossing** option lets you select the items to trim with a crossing box.

The **Project** option gives you three choices for the projection method used by the command.

    View Trims objects where they intersect, as viewed from the current viewing direction.

    None Trims objects only where they intersect in 3D space.

    UCS Trims objects where they intersect in the current User Coordinate System.

The **Edge** option lets you decide whether to trim objects only where they intersect in 3D space or where they would intersect if the edge were extended. The Project and Edge options are very useful when you are working with 3D models as you will be in Tutorial 11.

The **Erase** option lets you erase unwanted items without leaving the Trim command.

The **Undo** option lets you undo the last trim without exiting the command; it's similar to the Undo option you used with the Line command.

You will use the Trim command from the Modify panel to remove the excess portion of the circle. Refer to Figure 3.4.

 Click: **Trim button**

    Current settings: Projection=UCS, Edge=None

Select cutting edges . . .

Select objects or <select all>: **select lines 1 and 2**

Select objects: **[Enter]**

Note: *The cutting edges selected will be highlighted. The command line reports that the projection mode set to UCS and the edge mode set to no extension.*

You have finished selecting the cutting edges. Next, select the portion of the circle to be removed.

Select object to trim or shift-select to extend or [Fence/Crossing/Project/ Edge/eRase/Undo]: **click on the circle near point 3**

Select object to trim or [Fence/Crossing/Project/Edge/ eRase/Undo]: **[Enter]** to end the command

When you are done, your figure should be similar to Figure 3.5.

Figure 3.5

Refer to Figure 3.6 to understand how the cutting edge works in relation to the object to be trimmed.

When lines come together, as at a corner, you can select one or both of the lines as cutting lines, as shown in Figure 3.6, parts 1 and 3. Again, the cursor location determines which portion of the line is removed.

Next restore the previous zoom factor and zoom in on the other circles to show them clearly.

Click: **Zoom All button** (or double-click the scroll wheel)

On your own, enlarge the area shown in Figure 3.7.

Figure 3.7

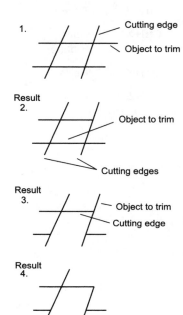

Figure 3.6

Tip: *When you zoom in on an area, circles may not be shown correctly. On the screen, circles are approximated with a number of straight-line segments. Type REGEN [Enter] at the command prompt, or the alias, RE, to cause the display to be recalculated from the drawing database to show the circular shapes correctly.*

Tip: *You can use most typical Windows shortcuts within Auto-CAD. Try some of these:*

Ctrl+C	*Copy to clipboard*
Ctrl+N	*New*
Ctrl+O	*Open*
Ctrl+P	*Print*
Ctrl+S	*Save*
Ctrl+V	*Paste*
Ctrl+X	*Cut to clipboard*
Ctrl+Y	*Redo*
Ctrl+Z	*Undo*

Next, you will trim the excess portions of the other circles. The arcs that remain when you have finished trimming will form the lot line and the cul-de-sac for the road.

Click: **Trim button**

Current setting: Projection=UCS Edge=None

Select cutting edges ...

Select objects or <select all>: *select lines 1 and 2 (see Figure 3.7)*

Select objects: *[Enter]*

Select object to trim or shift-select to extend or [Fence/Crossing/ Project/ Edge/eRase/Undo]: *click on the circle near point 3*

Select object to trim or shift-select to extend or [Fence/Crossing/ Project/ Edge/eRase/Undo]: *[Enter]*

Command: [Enter] (to restart the Trim command)

Select objects or <select all>: *select lines 4 and 5*

Select objects: *[Enter]*

Select object to trim or shift-select to extend or [Fence/Crossing/ Project/ Edge/eRase/Undo]: *click on the circle near point 6*

Select object to trim or shift-select to extend or [Fence/Crossing/Project/ Edge/eRase/Undo]: *Hold down Shift key and click near point 8 to extend the line across the circle so that you can see how the extend feature works*

Select object to trim or shift-select to extend or [Fence/Crossing/Project/ Edge/eRase/Undo]: *[Enter]*

Command: *[Enter] (to restart the Trim command)*

Select objects or <select all>: *select the circle near point 7*

Select objects: *[Enter]*

Select object to trim or shift-select to extend or [Fence/Crossing/ Project/ Edge/eRase/Undo]: *click on the line near point 8*

Select object to trim or shift-select to extend or [Fence/Crossing/Project/ Edge/eRase/Undo]: *[Enter]*

Figure 3.8

When you have finished trimming the circles, your screen should look like Figure 3.8. If it doesn't, change the drawing on your own so that it looks like the picture.

Double-click the scroll wheel to Zoom out to the extents of the drawing.

Using Offset

The Offset command creates a new object parallel to a given object. The Offset command is on the ribbon Home tab, Modify panel. You will use Offset to create parallel curves 30 units from either side of the curved centerlines that you drew in Tutorial 2.

Click: Offset button

To offset an object, you need to determine the *offset distance* (the distance away from the original object) or the *through point* (the point through which the offset object is to be drawn). Refer to Figure 3.9 for the points to select,

Specify offset distance or [Through/Erase/Layer] <Through>: ***30 [Enter]***

Select object to offset or [Exit/Undo] <Exit>: ***select curve 1***

Specify point on side to offset [Exit/Multiple/Undo]: ***click below the curve, like location A***

Select object to offset or [Exit/Undo] <Exit>: ***select curve 1***

Specify point on side to offset [Exit/Multiple/Undo]: ***click above the curve, like location B***

Once you have defined the offset distance, the prompt *Select object to offset:* is repeated, allowing you to create additional parallel lines that have the same spacing.

On your own, repeat the steps just described to create lines offset 30 units from either side of the remaining curved centerlines so that your drawing looks like that shown in Figure 3.9. Use the scroll wheel to Zoom and Pan as necessary so that you can better see the smaller curves when making selections. You can Zoom and Pan during other commands.

Figure 3.9

If you select the wrong item to offset, either erase the incorrect lines when you have finished or press [Esc] to cancel the command and then start again. When you have finished using the Offset command, press [Enter] to end the command. Note that the new objects created by the Offset command are on the same layer as the object that you selected to offset. Which layer is current doesn't matter; the newly offset object will be on the same layer as the original object that you selected.

Trimming the Remaining Lines

On your own, refer to Figure 3.9 and select curve 2 as the cutting edge.

Be sure to press [Enter] or the return button when you have finished selecting cutting edges.

Trim off the portions of the centerline that extend past the cutting edge by clicking the points labeled 1 and 2.

Repeat this process and trim all remaining centerlines where they extend beyond the centerline arcs.

Line 3 doesn't extend past any cutting edges, so it cannot be trimmed. Use the Erase command to remove it.

Now zoom in on the center area of the drawing so that you can trim the excess lines where the roadways join.

The center portion of the drawing will be enlarged on your screen.

Tip: Lines that do not cross the cutting edge cannot be trimmed. Use the Erase option of the trim command to erase objects that no longer cross the cutting edge.

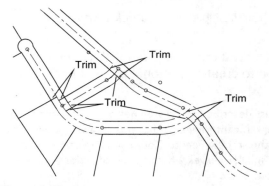

Figure 3.10

Tip: If you pick something to trim by mistake, you can type the option letter U (for Undo) and press [Enter] at the prompt. This restores the last object trimmed.

Selecting All Edges to Use with Trim

This time, instead of selecting one cutting edge at a time, you will press [Enter] to select all the lines in that area as cutting edges. Refer to Figure 3.10 to make your selections.

*Click: **Trim button***

Current settings: Projection=UCS Edge=None

Select cutting edges ...

Select objects or <select all>: *[Enter]*

All objects become selected as cutting edges.

Select object to trim or shift-select to extend or [Fence/Crossing/Project/ Edge/eRase/Undo]: *select the extreme ends of the lines you want to remove and continue doing so until all the excess lines are trimmed*

Select object to trim or shift-select to extend or [Fence/Crossing/Project/ Edge/eRase/Undo]: *[Enter]*

Experiment with the Fence and Crossing options on your own.

When you have finished trimming, Zoom out on your own to show the entire drawing on the screen. If you have some short line segments left that no longer cross the cutting edges, use Erase to remove them on your own. Your drawing should now look like that shown in Figure 3.13.

Figure 3.11

Changing Object Properties

Once you've drawn an object, changing the properties of the object or a group of objects may be useful. You will change the properties of the centerlines that you offset so that they are on the layer LOTLINES. The new offset lines are the edges of the road and should be on the same layer as the other lot lines.

A quick way to change objects to another layer is to use the Layer Control pull-down list. When you have objects selected and then choose a layer from the Layer Control list, the selected objects will be changed to the selected layer.

Click: *some, but not all, of the roadway edges that appear as centerlines so that they become highlighted with small grip boxes*

Click: *on the layer CENTERLINE to pull down available layers*

Click: *LOTLINES from the list of layers*

You will see the lines you selected change to the color and linetype for layer LOTLINES. Next you will press the escape key to unselect the lines.

Press: *[Esc]*

Notice that CENTERLINE once again shows as the current layer name in the Layer Control.

Tip: *You can double-click on an object to quickly bring up its properties.*

Using the Properties Panel

The Properties panel on the ribbon Home tab provides quick ways to change the color, lineweght, linetype, plot style, and transparency of an object. To do these things, you would perform similar steps as used to select an object and change its layer, only choose a different color or linetype Properties panel.

The Properties panel can also be used to list the information for a selected object.

*Click: **to expand the Properties panel***

Click on this arrow to show the Properties pallete

Figure 3.12

You can use the downward arrow in the lower right corner of the Properties panel to turn on the Properties palette, which provides more options for changing properties.

*Click: **the small arrow in the lower right of the Properties panel** to show the Properties palette*

The Properties palette appears on your screen as shown in Figure 3.13. It can dock to the edge of the screen or be floating, so you can position it anywhere on the screen. You can leave it open for continued use.

The Properties Palette

The Properties palette lets you change the linetype, layer, lineweight, color, transparency and geometric and other properties of the objects you select.

Currently there is no object selected, so the palette only reports general properties of the drawing.

*Click: **the roadway edges that have not been changed yet** (they appear green and with a centerline pattern)*

The grip boxes for the objects you select will appear when they are selected. The information reported in the Properties palette changes to show the information for the objects you selected.

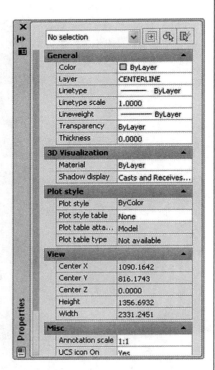

Figure 3.13

You will use the palette to change the objects you selected from layer CENTERLINE to layer LOTLINES.

*Click: **on layer CENTERLINE** to the right of the word Layer*

The list of layers appears, as in Figure 3.14.

Figure 3.14

*Click: **LOTLINES** from the list*

*Press: **[Esc] [Esc]** to unselect the arcs*

On your own, select any of the remaining offset lines still on layer Centerline and change them to layer Lotlines.

*Click: **the Close button [X]** in the upper left corner to close the Properties palette*

In your drawing, the lines you selected change to black (or white, depending on your configuration) and linetype CONTINUOUS, as set by layer LOTLINES's properties.

*Click: **to preselect one of the drawing lines on layer LOTLINES***

*Click: **Make Object's Layer Current button***

The layer name LOTLINES now appears as the current layer (with no objects selected) as shown in Figure 3.15.

Figure 3.15

Tip: *You can right-click the title bar on the Properties palette and select Auto-hide. This will cause the Properties palette to only show the narrow toolbar title unless you hover your mouse over it, which causes it to expand. This only works when the palette is not docked. You can also make the Properties palette transparent, in a similar way.*

Tip: *You can resize the width of the Properties palette by moving your cursor over its vertical edges and then clicking and dragging when you see the cursor change to a double headed arrow symbol.*

Tip: *Be sure to save your drawing whenever you have finished a major step and you are satisfied with it. Take a minute to use the Save icon from the Quick Access toolbar and save your drawing on your own.*

On your own, use Zoom Window to enlarge the center area of the drawing, as shown in Figure 3.16.

Figure 3.16

Using Fillet

The Fillet command connects lines, arcs, or circles with a smoothly fitted arc, or *fillet*. The Fillet command is on the Modify panel.

 Click: ***Fillet button***

Current settings: Mode = TRIM, Radius =0.0000

Select first object or [Undo/Polyline/Radius/Trim/Multiple]: ***R [Enter]***

Typing R indicates that you want to enter a radius.

Specify fillet radius <0.0000>: ***10 [Enter]***

You are prompted to select the two objects. Refer to Figure 3.16 to select the lines.

Select first object or [Undo/Polyline/Radius/Trim/Multiple]: ***select line 1***

Select second object or shift-select to apply corner: ***select line 2***

A fillet should appear between the two lines, as shown in Figure 3.17.

Figure 3.17

Tip: *If you use a radius value of 0 with the Fillet command, you can use the command to make lines intersect that do not meet neatly at a corner. This method also works to make a neat intersection from lines that extend past a corner. You can also do so with the Chamfer command (which you will learn next) by setting both chamfer distances to 0.*

Command: *[Enter]*

The previous command restarts when you press [Enter] or the spacebar at the blank command prompt. In this case, it returns to the original Fillet prompt, which allows you to repeat the selection process, drawing additional fillets of the same radius, or to type a command letter to select other fillet options. You will use the Multiple option to create multiple fillets of the same radius without having to restart the command. Create fillets between the lines shown in Figure 3.16.

> Current settings: Mode = TRIM, Radius = 10.0000
>
> Select first object or [Undo/Polyline/Radius/Trim/Multiple]: *M [Enter]*
>
> Select first object or [Undo/Polyline/Radius/Trim/Multiple]: *select line 3*
>
> Select second object or shift-select to apply corner: *select line 4*
>
> Select first object or [Undo/Polyline/Radius/Trim/Multiple]: *continue to fillet lines 5 through 10 on your own and end the command*
>
> Zoom out to the drawing extents. Erase any extra line segments left from using Fillet

You can use the Fillet command to fit a smooth arc between any combination of lines, arcs, or circles. Once you have defined the radius value, the direction of the fillet is determined by the cursor location used to identify the two objects.

Figure 3.18 shows some examples of how you can create fillets of different shapes by choosing different point locations. Each example starts with a line located directly above an arc, as shown in the column on the left. Clicking the objects where indicated yields the results shown in the column on the right.

You can also set the Fillet command so that it does not automatically trim the lines to join neatly with the fillet, which is the default. You do so by selecting the command option Trim (typing the letter T at the command prompt) and then typing N to choose the option No trim. Experiment with this method on your own.

Using Chamfer

The Chamfer command draws a straight-line segment between two given lines. *Chamfer* is the name for the machining process of flattening a sharp corner to create a beveled edge. Use the Help window to read about the options for the Chamfer command on your own. Chamfer is found on the ribbon Home tab, Modify panel.

> Use the Rectangle command to draw a rectangle, off to the side of the subdivision drawing, as shown in Figure 3.19 (about 500 by 250 units long).

Figure 3.19

Tip: *Holding down shift while selecting lines during the fillet command, creates a sharp corner between the two lines instead of making the rounded fillet.*

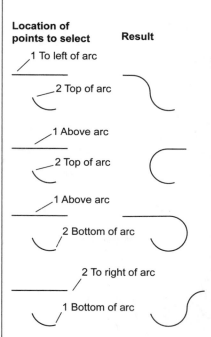

Figure 3.18

*Click: **Chamfer button***

(TRIM mode) Current chamfer Dist1 = 0.0000, Dist2 = 0.0000

Select first line or [Undo/Polyline/Distance/Angle/Trim/mEthod/Multiple]: ***D [Enter]***

Typing D indicates that you want to enter distance values.

Specify first chamfer distance <0.0000>: ***50 [Enter]***

Specify second chamfer distance <50.0000>: ***75 [Enter]***

The Chamfer command prompts you for selection of the first and second lines between which the chamfer is to be added. Refer to the upper part of Figure 3.20 to select the lines.

Select first line or [Undo/Polyline/Distance/Angle/Trim/mEthod/Multiple]: ***select the first line***

Select second line or shift-select to apply corner: ***select the second line***

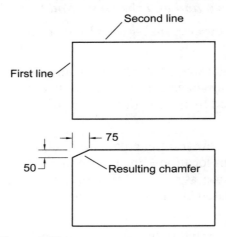

Figure 3.20

A chamfer should appear on your screen that looks like the one shown in the lower part of Figure 3.20. The distance that each end of the chamfer is from the corner defines the size of the chamfer. As with the Fillet command, once you have entered these distances, you can draw additional chamfers of the same size by typing the M option for Multiple and pressing [Enter] to enter the option. The command will then repeat until you press [Enter] to end the command.

On your own, use the commands that you have learned to erase the chamfered rectangle from your drawing. Use Zoom All to restore the original appearance and then save the drawing.

In Tutorial 1 you learned how to draw a rectangle with the Rectangle icon, which had the options Fillet and Chamfer. The same Fillet and Chamfer principles that you just learned apply to using the Rectangle icon. At this point you may find it useful to practice with the Rectangle icon and changing the Chamfer and Fillet dimensions offered in the command prompt. When you have finished practicing drawing rectangles, erase them before moving on to the next section.

Using Polyline

The Polyline command draws a series of connected lines or arcs that AutoCAD treats as a single graphic object called a *polyline*. The Polyline command is also used to draw irregular curves and lines that have a width. The Polyline command is on the ribbon Home tab, Draw panel.

You will use the Polyline command to create the shape for a pond to add to the subdivision drawing. Before continuing, check to see that LOTLINES is the current layer.

Click: **Polyline button**

Specify start point: **select any point to the right of the subdivision where you want to locate the pond**

Current line-width is 0.0000

Specify next point or [Arc/Halfwidth/Length/Undo/Width]: **select 9 more points**

To use the Close option similar to that of the Line command,

Specify next point or [Arc/Close/Halfwidth/Length/Undo/Width]: **C [Enter]**

Your screen should show a line made of multiple segments, similar to the one in Figure 3.22.

Figure 3.21

A shape drawn by using Polyline is different from a shape created by using the Line command, because the polyline is treated as one object. You cannot erase one of the polyline segments. If you try, the entire polyline is erased.

Other Polyline options allow you to draw an arc as a polyline segment (Arc), specify the starting and ending width (or half-width) of a given segment (Width, Half-width), specify the length of a segment (Length), and remove segments already drawn (Undo).

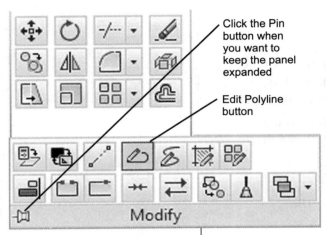

Click the Pin button when you want to keep the panel expanded

Edit Polyline button

Edit Polyline (PEDIT)

Once you have created a polyline, you can change it and its individual segments with Edit Polyline. The Edit Polyline (Pedit) command is on the Modify panel. You will use it to change the segmented line you just created to a smooth curve.

The Edit Polyline command provides two different methods of fitting curves: Fit and Spline. The **Fit** option joins every point you select on the polyline with an arc.

Click: *Edit Polyline button*

Select polyline or [Multiple]: *select any part of the polyline*

Enter an option [Open/Join/Width/Edit vertex/Fit/ Spline/Decurve/ Ltype gen/Undo]: *F [Enter]*

The straight-line segments change to a continuous curved line, as shown in Figure 3.22.

Fit curve connects all the vertices of a 2D polyline by joining each pair of vertices with an arc. You will use the Undo option of the command to return the polyline to its original shape.

Enter an option [Close/Join/Width/Edit vertex/Fit/Spline/Decurve/ Ltype gen/Undo]: *U [Enter]*

The original polyline returns on your screen. Now try the Spline option.

Enter an option [Close/Join/Width/Edit vertex/Fit/Spline/Decurve/ Ltype gen/Undo]: *S [Enter]*

A somewhat flatter shape replaces the original polyline (Figure 3.23). The **Spline** option produces a smoother curve by using either a cubic or a quadratic B-spline approximation (depending on how the system variable Splinetype is set). Splines work like a string stretched between the first and last points of your polyline. The vertices on your polyline act to pull the string in their direction, but the resulting spline does not necessarily reach those points. Among other things, splined polylines are useful for creating contour lines on maps.

Now try the **Width** option.

Enter an option [Close/Join/Width/Edit vertex/Fit/Spline/Decurve/ Ltype gen/Undo]: *W [Enter]*

Specify new width for all segments: *5 [Enter]*

The splined polyline is replaced with one with a 5 unit width. To exit the Edit Polyline command,

Enter an option [Close/Join/Width/Edit vertex/Fit/Spline/Decurve/ Ltype gen/Undo]: *[Enter]*

Your drawing should look similar to Figure 3.24.

Figure 3.22

Figure 3.23

Tip: *If you have a polyline that has already been curved with Fit or Spline, Decurve returns the original polyline.*

Figure 3.24

Figure 3.25

Editing Polylines using Grips

You can quickly edit polylines using grips. The [Ctrl] key is used to cycle between the editing options.

*Click: **on the Polyline to show its grips***

*Click: **on one of the grips to activate it as the base grip**, as shown in Figure 3.25*

The stretch options is the default. Notice you can drag the grip around to change the shape of your polyline.

Specify stretch point or [Base point/Copy/Undo/eXit]: *[Ctrl]*

After you press [Ctrl], the prompt ** REMOVE VERTEX ** appears in the Command line. This lets you change your polyline shape by deleting one of the defining points.

Pick to remove vertex: ***click the mouse, removing the vertex***

The polyline changes so that it is not being pulled toward the deleted point.

Command: *U [Enter]*

The grip editing is undone and the polyline returns to its previous shape

Using Spline

The Spline command lets you create spline using different methods. Among these are quadratic or cubic (*NURBS*) curves. The acronym NURBS stands for nonuniform rational B-spline, which is the method used to draw the curves. These curves can be more accurate than spline-fitted polylines because you control the tolerance to which the spline curve is fit. Splines also take less space in your drawing file than spline-fitted polylines.

The Object option of the Spline command converts spline-fitted polylines to splines. (The variable Delobj controls whether the original polyline is deleted after it is converted.) The Spline command is on the Draw panel. You will draw a spline off to the side of the subdivision and then later erase it.

Tip: *You can use Edit Polyline to convert objects into polylines. At the Select polyline: prompt, pick the line or arc that you want to convert to a polyline. You will see the message Object selected is not a polyline. Do you want to turn it into one? <Y>:. Press [Enter] to accept the yes response to convert the selected object into a polyline and continue with the prompts for the Edit Polyline command. (You can use Explode to change a polyline back into individual objects.)*

Tip: *The Edit Polyline, Join option allows you to join arcs, lines, and polylines to an existing polyline.*

Click: ***Spline Fit*** *button*

> Current settings: Method=Fit   Knots=Chord

Specify first point or [Method/Knots/Object] : ***click any point***

Enter next point or [start Tangency/toLerance]: ***click any point***

Enter next point or [end Tangency/toLerance/Undo/Close]: ***click any point***

Enter next point or [end Tangency/toLerance/Undo/Close]: ***click any point***

Enter next point or [end Tangency/toLerance/Undo/Close]: ***click any point***

Enter next point or [end Tangency/toLerance/Undo/Close]: ***C [Enter]***

Specify tangent: ***[Enter]***

Pressing [Enter] at the tangency prompt causes the AutoCAD software to calculate the default tangencies. You can make the spline tangent to other objects by clicking the appropriate points at these prompts. The spline appears on your screen.

Click: ***Help button***

The Help window opens on your screen.

> On your own, navigate to the S section of the Command Reference area and choose to view the help for the Spline command. Scroll down to show the help for the Method option as shown in Figure 3.26. Study the information located in the help screen and close it when you are finished.

Method

Controls whether the spline is created with fit points or control vertices. The options differ depending on whether you select Options for Splines with Fit Points or Options for Splines with Control Vertices.

Fit
Draw a spline by specifying fit points.
Changing the Method updates the SPLMETHOD system variable.

Control Points
Draw a spline by specifying control vertices.
This is the preferred method if you are creating geometry to use with 3D NURBS surfaces. Changing the Method updates the SPLMETHOD system variable.

Object
Converts 2D or 3D quadratic or cubic spline-fit polylines to equivalent splines and (depending on the setting of the DELOBJ system variable) deletes the polylines.

Figure 3.26

Splines are very useful in creating freeform surfaces on 3D models. Experiment by drawing splines on your own. You can edit Splines by using the Splinedit command on the Modify tab, similar to how polylines are edited. You can also edit Splines using their grips.

Using Blend

The Blend command creates a spline to connect two existing lines or curves. You can find it on the ribbon Modify tab on the drop down where the Fillet and Chamfer commands are located.

On your own, draw a line and an arc similar to those shown in Figure 3.27A off to the side of your current drawing.

Click: **Blend Curve** *button*

Continuity = Tangent

Select first object or [CONtinuity]: ***click on the line***

Select second object: ***click on the arc***

A spline is created forming a blend between the line and the arc, as shown in Figure 3.27B.

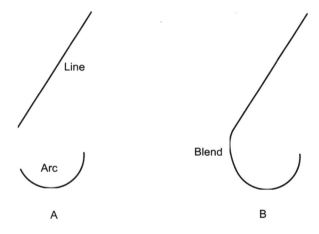

A B

Figure 3.27

When you have finished experimenting,

Erase all the splines and extra lines and arcs that you created.

Click: *to thaw layer TEXT*

Click: *TEXT to set it as the current layer*

Use the Dtext command (Single Line Text) to add the label POND to the pond. Use a text height of 30.

Save your drawing.

When you have finished, your screen should look like Figure 3.28.

Figure 3.28

Getting Information about Your Drawing

Because your AutoCAD drawing database contains accurate geometry and has been created as a model of real-world objects, you can find information about distances and areas, as well as locate coordinates.

Using List

The List command shows the information from the drawing database for the selection. Different information may be shown, depending on the types of and number of objects. Refer to Figure 3.28 as you select.

> Click: **List button** *from the Properties panel*

> Select objects: *click on line 1 [Enter]*

The text window appears on your screen. You can resize it by clicking on its corners and dragging it to a new size. You can also click on the title bar and drag it to a new location. Figure 3.29 shows the information listed for the selected line. You can use this information to make calculations or to label the lot lines of this subdivision.

Tip: *You can get the same information by opening the Properties palette.*

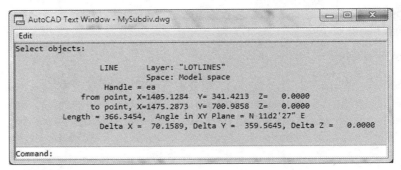

Figure 3.29

Close the text window by clicking on the close button in the upper right corner. This time try typing the command alias.

Command: LI [Enter]

Select objects: click on the polyline representing the pond

Select objects: [Enter]

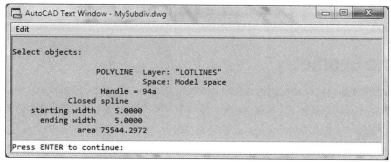

Figure 3.30

The text window again appears on your screen as shown in Figure 3.30. It contains information about all the vertices of the polyline. Keep pressing [Enter] until all the information has scrolled by or press [Esc} to exit from the command. At the beginning of the information listed, you will see the area and perimeter of the polyline. This information can be very useful for calculating the area of irregular shapes like the pond.

Figure 3.31

Locating Points

ID Point shows the coordinates of the location that you select. When you use this command in conjunction with object snaps, you can find the exact coordinates of an object's endpoint, center, midpoint, and other points. ID Point is located on the Utilities panel as shown in Figure 3.31.

Right-click: **Object Snap button and use the dialog box to select Endpoint** *(turn other modes off if they are on)*

Click: **to turn on Object Snap**

Click: **to expand the Utilities panel, choose ID Point** *(Figure 3.31)*

Specify point: **click on the left end of line 2**

The command window displays the coordinates of the point, X=912.5026, Y=334.8196, and Z=0.0000.

Measuring Geometry

The Measuregeom command finds distances, radius, angles, areas, or volumes. The measure flyout lets you select from Measuregeom command options.

Area

To measure an area you select points that enclose a boundary, or select a closed object. The default method begins by selecting points to define straight-line boundaries for the area you want to measure. When you are done selecting, press [Enter] to select Total. As you select locations you will see the area being shaded to provide feedback on what area you are defining. The area inside the boundary that you specify is reported. The Object option reports the area of a closed object, such as a polyline, circle, ellipse, spline, region, or a solid object. You could use this method to find the area of the pond instead of using List as you did previously. The Add and Subtract options let you define more complex boundaries by adding and subtracting from the first boundary selected. Next, you will find the area of lot 5. Using the Endpoint object snap will ensure the area selected for the calculation will be accurate.

Figure 3.32

Click: **Area button from the Measure flyout, Utilities panel**

Specify first corner point or [Object/Add area/Subtract area/eXit] <Object>: **click point a**

Specify next point or [Arc/Length/Undo]: **click b**

Specify next point or [Arc/Length/Undo/Total] <Total>: **click c**

Specify next point or [Arc/Length/Undo/Total] <Total>: **click d**

Specify next point or [Arc/Length/Undo/Total] <Total>: **[Enter]**

The area and perimeter values of lot 5 are listed in the command window: Area = 113884.6680, Perimeter = 1398.9121. The command stays active at the prompt so that you can make other measurements.

Tip: *When the DYN button on the status bar is on, you will also see these values in the dynamic cursor.*

Tip: *The area listed is in square units. If the drawing is in feet, the area will be in square feet. You can use the ribbon View tab, Palettes panel, Quick Calc button to convert to other units. To do so, use the Units Conversion area to set the Units (e.g., Area), what to convert from (e.g., square feet), and what to convert to (e.g., Acres). Type the area in the Value to convert box or cut and paste it from your Command area. The converted area will display in acres.*

Enter an option [Distance/Radius/Angle/ARea/Volume/eXit] <ARea>: *D [Enter]*

Specify first point: *click point a*

Specify second point or [Multiple points]: *click point d*

Distance = 278.0000, Angle in XY Plane = N 89d13'56" E, Angle from XY Plane = E Delta X = 277.9750, Delta Y = 3.7252, Delta Z = 0.0000. is reported at the command prompt. To exit the command,

Enter an option [Distance/Radius/Angle/ARea/Volume/eXit] <Distance>: *X [Enter]*

Click: EASEMENTS as the current layer before continuing

Using Multilines

Next, you will create a Multiline style so you can add multiple lines in one step. This feature is especially useful in architectural drawings (for creating walls) and in civil engineering drawings. For example, you can draw the centerline of a road and automatically add the edge of pavement and right-of-way lines a defined distance away. Multiline also allows you to fill the area between two lines with a color. The Multiline Style command lets you define up to 16 lines, called *elements*, to use when drawing multilines. You can save multiline styles with different names so that you can easily reuse them. Set the Justification option of the Multiline command to specify the top, middle, or bottom for locating the multiple pattern. You can also directly set the variable Cmljust to 0, 1, or 2, respectively.

Creating a Multiline Style

You will type the command name,

Command: *MLSTYLE [Enter]*

The Multiline Style dialog (Figure 3.33) appears showing the default style name, STANDARD. It is the current style.

Figure 3.33

To create a new style specifying the spacing, color, linetype, and name of the style, as well as the type of endcaps that will be used to finish off the lines,

*Click: **New button***

*Type: **EASEMENT** into the Create Multiline Style dialog box*

*Click: **Continue***

Figure 3.34

Use the New Multiline Style dialog box to set the spacing of the elements, as shown in Figure 3.34. The dialog box has two areas. You can use the Caps area to select different types of endcaps, including angled lines or arcs, to finish the multilines you create. You can also use this area to turn on Fill if you want the area between multiline elements to be shaded.

The Elements area is used to set the spacing, number, linestyle and color for the elements which make up the multiline. You will set the positive offset spacing to 15. To change the spacing for an element,

*Click: **on the top element shown in the list so that it becomes highlighted***

*Click: **in the input box to the right of the word Offset***

*Type: **15***

You should notice the offset value for the top element change 15. Next, set the offset spacing for the second element to –15.

*Click: **on the second element in the list***

*Click: **to highlight the text in the box to the right of the word Offset***

*Type: **–15***

When you have set the element spacing, your dialog box should look like Figure 3.34. Leave the color and linetype set to BYLAYER, as layer EASEMENTS is already set to cyan color and the DASHED linetype. When you have finished,

*Click: **OK** to return to the Multiline Styles dialog box*

The Save button saves a style to the library of multiline styles. When you click the Save button, the Save Multiline Styles dialog box appears on your screen. Multiline styles are saved to *acad.mln* by default in your support path. You can create your own file for your multiline styles, if you want, by typing in a different name. The Load button loads saved multiline styles from a library of saved styles. Rename lets you rename the various styles you have created. You can't rename the STANDARD style. When you have finished examining the dialog box,

Click: **Save**

On your own, navigate to your work directory and **save** the file.

Click: **Set Current**

Click: **OK** to exit the Multiline Styles dialog box

Drawing Multilines

You will add some multilines for to represent easements along the lot lines of the subdivision drawing. You will start the command by typing its name, MLine at the command prompt. The style, EASEMENT, that you created should be the current multiline style.

Command: **MLINE [Enter]**

Now you are almost ready to draw some multilines. Before you do, decide on the justification to use. You can choose to have the multilines you draw align so that the points you select align with the top element, with the zero offset, or with the bottom element. You will set the justification so that the points you pick are the zero offset of the multiline, in this case the middle of the multiline.

Justification = Top, Scale = 1.00, Style = EASEMENT

Specify start point or [Justification/Scale/STyle]: **J [Enter]**

Enter justification type [Top/Zero/Bottom] <top>: **Z [Enter]**

You will see the message Justification = Zero, Scale = 1.00, Style = EASEMENT. Now, you are ready to start drawing the easement lines. Refer to Figure 3.34 for the points to select.

Specify start point or [Justification/Scale/STyle]: **click point 1**

Specify next point: **click 2**

Specify next point or [Undo]: **click 3**

Specify next point or [Close/Undo]: **click 4**

Specify next point or [Close/Undo]: **click 5**

Specify next point or [Close/Undo]: **click 6**

Specify next point or [Close/Undo]: **click 7**

Specify next point or [Close/Undo]: **pick 8**

Specify next point or [Close/Undo]: **[Enter]**

Your drawing should look like Figure 3.35.

Tip: *Remember that the Endpoint running object snap should still be on.*

Tip: *If you want to trim a multiline, you must first use the Explode command to change it back into individual objects before you can trim it. Use the AutoCAD Help command for more information about using Explode.*

Tip: *When you type numbers divided by a "/" slash, a dialog box may appear. You can use it to set how fractions are stacked in the multiline text; either with a diagonal slash or horizontal bar. Selecting Don't show this dialog box again does just that. If autostacking is turned on, your fractions will stack automatically using which ever method you selected.*

Tip: *Right-clicking on the MText window brings up a shortcut menu that you can use to select many useful MText symbols that you can insert by picking Symbol from the shortcut menu.*

Tip: *You should save your drawing before you plot in case there is some problem with your plotter or printer.*

Wannabe Heights Estates

Figure 3.35

On your own, set TEXT as the current layer and use the Mtext (Multiline Text) command to add the following 15 unit tall text describing the location of the subdivision and the easements:

A SUBDIVISION LOCATED IN THE NE 1/4 OF THE SE 1/4 T.15, R.5E, SEC. 14, MPM

A 15' UTILITY EASEMENT IS RESERVED ALONG ALL EXTERIOR LOTLINES.

The completed drawing is shown in Figure 3.36.

Wannabe Heights Estates

Figure 3.36

Save your drawing now.

The Plot Dialog Box

Depending on the types of printers or plotters you have configured with your computer system, the Plot command causes your drawing to be printed on your printer or plotted on the device that you configured for AutoCAD use. The same command is used for printing and for plotting. Selecting Plot causes the Plot dialog box (Figure 3.37) to appear on your screen.

*Click: **Plot button** from the Quick Access toolbar*

Among the things that the Plot dialog box lets you choose are:

- The plotter or printer where you will send the drawing (Printer/plotter);

- The portion of your drawing to plot or print (Plot area);

- The scale at which the finished drawing will be plotted (Plot scale);

- Where your plot starts on the sheet (Plot offset);

- Whether to use inches or millimeters as the plotter units;

- The pen or color, line weight, line fill, screening, dithering selections for the plotter or printer (Plot style);

- Whether the plot is portrait or landscape orientation.

Tip: *To use the Plot command directly from the command prompt, type a hyphen (-) in front of the command (-plot). This also works for other commands.*

Figure 3.37

Because there are so many factors, some of them are not always displayed. To see the additional options,

*Click: **More Options icon** from the lower right of the dialog box*

The dialog box switches to show more options as shown in Figure 3.38.

When you are using the Plot dialog box, be careful not to change too many things about the plotter at once. That way you can see the effect that each option has on your plot.

Plot Device

Use the printer/plotter area to select from the plotters that you have configured. If no printers or plotters are listed, you must use the Plot and Publish tab from the Options dialog box to add a new printer or plotter configuration, or use the Windows operating system to install a printer. Refer to Getting Started 1 and 2 for details about configuring your output device.

To select a listed device, pull down the list of printers and click to highlight the name of the device you will use for your print. The options displayed for paper size and other items depend on your particular output device. If an item in the Plot dialog box appears grayed instead of black, it is not available for selection. You may not be able to choose certain items, depending on the limitations of your printer or plotter.

> Make sure that your plotter or printer name is selected in the Printer/Plotter Name area of the dialog box.

Plot Style Table (Pen Assignments)

A plot style table lets you assign properties such as color, line weight, line fill, screening, and dithering for your printer or other output device. There are two main methods used to assign the plotting properties: color dependent plot styles (*.ctb*), and named plot styles (*.stb*).

As you might guess, a color dependent plot style uses object color to determine the plot properties. A named plot style assigns a plot style property to objects or layers similar to the way the object color can be assigned. Plot style tables are independent of the output device selected. If a particular device does not have that property, say screening for example, that property is just skipped. This way a single plot style (or set of styles) can be used with a variety of printers or plotters. Plot styles are saved separately from the drawing. Changing the plot style changes how any drawing that uses that style will be output. For this example, you will use the default style named *acad.ctb*, which is a color dependent plot style. Refer to Figure 3.38.

Edit icon

Figure 3.38

Click: ***to expand the menu in the Plot style table area of the dialog box***

Click: ***acad.ctb***

Assign this plot table to all layouts?

Click: ***Yes***

Click: ***Edit icon*** *(see Figure 3.38)*

The Plot Style Table Editor appears as shown in Figure 3.39. You can use it to set the parameters for the appearance of the plotted lines in the drawing. You will not change any of these settings at this time. You will learn more about plotting in Tutorial 5.

Figure 3.39

Click: ***Cancel***

What to Plot

The Plot area portion of the dialog box lets you specify what area of the drawing will be printed or plotted:

- **Display** selects the area that appears on your screen as the area to plot.

- **Extents** plots any objects that you have in your drawing.

- **Limits** plots the predefined area set up in the drawing with the Limits command.

- **View** plots a named view that you have created with the View command. (If you have not made any views, this option will not appear.)

- **Window** lets you go back to the drawing display and create a window around the area of the drawing that you want to plot. You can do so by picking from your drawing or by typing in the coordinates.

You will pick Limits to choose the area that was preset in the drawing (where the grid showed in model space.) If you have not set up the size with Limits, then Extents is often useful as it selects the largest area filled with drawing objects as the area to print. The What to Plot selections are shown in Figure 3.40.

Figure 3.40

Click: Limits

Paper Size

Click: **the pull-down list under Paper Size**

A pull-down list similar to the one shown in Figure 3.41 appears so you can select the paper size. The paper sizes that you can select depend on your printer. US Standard 8.5 x 11 paper is called size A; 11 x 17 paper is size B. (Smaller values indicate the image area that your printer can print on the sheet.) Max is the maximum size of paper that your printer will handle.

Tip: *If you use the generic AutoCAD printer driver, DWF6 ePlot.pc3, you will see the paper sizes in shown in Figure 3.41.*

Figure 3.41

Click: **A size sheet (8.5 x 11) or your printer's closest size**

Drawing Orientation

Portrait orientation is a vertical sheet layout, and landscape is horizontal. Plot upside-down flips the direction that the plot starts on the sheet by 180 degrees. Certain options may not be available with your model of printer. If so, they will be grayed out. For this drawing,

Click: **Landscape**

Plot Scale

You set the scale for the drawing by entering the number of plotted inches for the number of drawing units in your drawing. If you do not want the drawing plotted to a particular scale, you can fit it to the sheet size by selecting Fit to Paper. Most of the time an engineering drawing should be plotted to a known scale.

*Click: to uncheck **Fit to Paper**. Custom should appear in the Scale box.*

On your own, type in 1 inches = 250 units

Doing so will give you a scale of 1"=250' for your drawing, because the default units in the drawing represent decimal feet.

Plot Offset

You can use the Plot offset area of the dialog box to move the drawing to the right on the paper by using a positive value for X, and to move the drawing up on the paper by specifying a positive value for Y. You should be aware that moving the origin for the paper may cause the top and right lines of the drawing not to print if they are outside the printer limits. Center the plot automatically calculates X and Y values to center the plot on the paper.

*Click: **Center the plot** (so the check box is selected)*

Plot Preview

You may preview your drawing as it will appear on the paper in the Preview window. If you have a very detailed drawing, obtaining a preview may take some time. The subdivision drawing is not too large to preview in a reasonable amount of time.

*Click: **Preview***

If a message appears stating "The annotation scale is not equal to the plot scale. Do you want to continue?" Click Continue.

Your screen should look similar to Figure 3.42. The drawing orientation is set to landscape.

The cursor should take on the appearance of a magnifying glass with a plus sign above it and a minus sign below it. It is set on Zoom Realtime, allowing you to zoom in or out from the drawing.

The following message should be at the command line:

Click and drag vertically to zoom, ESC or ENTER to exit, or right-click to display shortcut menu.

The toolbar across the top of the Preview window offers different Zoom options, Pan, and Close.

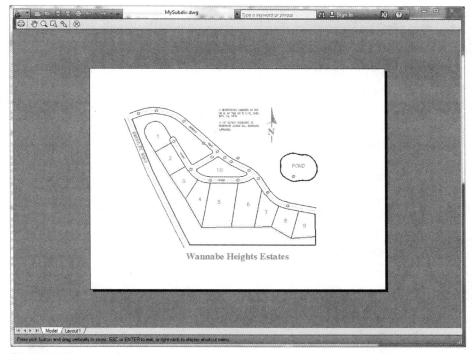

Figure 3.42

> On your own, select different commands to familiarize yourself with them. If the drawing appears to fit the sheet correctly, click Close Preview Window from the toolbar or press [Esc]. When you have returned to the Plot dialog box, click OK to plot your drawing.

You will learn more about annotation scale in Tutorial 5.

You will see a prompt similar to the following, depending on your hardware configuration: Effective plotting area: 10.50 wide by 8.00 high. Plotting viewport 1.

If the drawing does not fit the sheet correctly, review this section and determine which setting in the Plot dialog box you need to change. You should have a print or plot of your drawing that is scaled exactly so that 1" on the paper equals 250' in the drawing.

When you have a successful plot of your drawing, you have completed this tutorial. To exit this session,

> *Click:* ***Application icon, Exit***

Key Terms

chamfer	elements	offset distance	through point
cutting edges	fillet	polyline	

Key Commands

Area	Fillet	Multiline Style	Spline
Blend Curve	List	Offset	Trim
Chamfer	Locate Point	Plot	
Change Properties	Measure Geometry	Polyline	
Edit Polyline	Multiline	Print	

Exercises

Redraw the following shapes. If dimensions are given, create your drawing geometry exactly to the specified dimensions. The letter M after an exercise number means that the given dimensions are in millimeters (metric units). If no letter follows the exercise number, the dimensions are in inches. Don't include dimensions on the drawings.

3.1 Clearance Plate

3.2M Bracket

3.3 Roller Arm

3.4 Outside Caliper

3.5 Roller Support

3.6 Special Cam

Hint: *Create construction geometry to locate the center of the upper arc of radius 1.16. Turn on the Object Snap modes for Endpoint and Intersection. Then offset the outer left-hand arc a distance of 1.16 to the outside. Draw a circle with radius 1.16 and its center at the left endpoint of the .56 horizontal line. Where the offset arc and the new 1.16 circle intersect will be the center of the needed arc.*

3.7 Slotted Ellipse
Draw the figure shown (note the symmetry). Do not show dimensions.

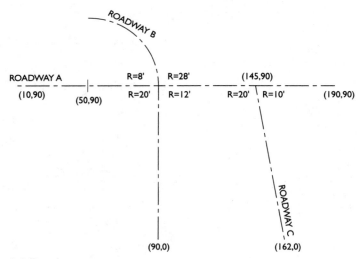

3.8 Roadway
Shown is a centerline for a two-lane road (total width is 20 feet). At each intersection is a specified turning radius for the edge of pavement. Construct the centerline and edge of pavement. Add text only if requested by your instructor.

3.9 Circuit Board

Draw the following circuit board, using Polylines with the width option to create wide paths.

3.10M Shaft Support

NOTE: THE THREE
SLOTTED FEATURES
AT THE RIGHT ARE
EQUAL & SYMMETRICAL

PULLER BASE
CAST IRON

3.11M Puller Base

WALKWAY
CONCRETE
DIMENSIONS IN FEET

3.12 Concrete Walkway
Hint: *Construct the straight centerlines first. Then use a circle to construct the top R20 arc. Use Circle, TTR to construct the right-hand arc, tangent to the upper arc and a vertical line 459 from the left end. Trim the lines and offset them to finish.*

GEOMETRIC CONSTRUCTIONS

Introduction

This tutorial will help you expand your skills by introducing several techniques used to construct accurate geometry. You will use object snaps to select locations, such as intersections, endpoints, and midpoints of lines, from your existing drawing geometry. You will also use object snap tracking to draw objects at specific angles or in geometric relationships to existing drawing objects. This tutorial shows how to apply the drawing commands to create shapes for technical drawings. You will create four drawings: a wrench, a coupler, a geneva cam and a gasket and use editing commands to create the drawing geometry quickly.

You will do many of the steps on your own, using the commands you have learned in the previous tutorials. Pay careful attention to the directions, being sure that you complete each step before going on.

Starting

Launch the AutoCAD® 2012 software.

Click: **New button**

Double-click: **acad.dwt** *template*

Setting the Units and Limits

You will create the wrench drawing using decimal inch measurements. For example, 4.5 units in your drawing will represent 4.5 inches on the real object. Although the AutoCAD software's decimal units can stand for any measurement system, here you will have them stand for inches. When you create drawing geometry, make the objects in your drawing the actual size. Do not scale them down as you would when drawing on paper. Keep in mind that one advantage of the accurate CAD drawing database is that you can use it directly to control machine tools to create parts. You would not want your actual part to turn out half-size because you created a half-size drawing of the part. When you plot the final drawing, you specify the ratio of plotted inches or millimeters to drawing units to produce scaled plots.

> On your own, use the Limits command to set up a larger drawing area whenever necessary and then Zoom All so that you see this larger drawing area on your screen.

> Decimal units should be the default. If they are not, use the Units command and set them to decimal now.

> Check to make sure that the limits for the drawing area are set to 12.0000 X 9.0000.

> Use Zoom All to fit the drawing limits to your screen.

4

Objectives

When you have completed this tutorial, you will be able to

1. Draw polygons and rays.

2. Use object snaps to pick geometric locations.

3. Load linetypes and set their scaling factors.

4. Use the Copy, Extend, Rotate, Move, Mirror, Array, and Break commands.

5. Build selection sets.

6. Edit an Array.

7. Use grips to modify your drawing.

8. Use 2D drawing constraints to define the geometry of a shape.

Turn on Grid display and Snap mode (both should be set to 0.5 inches).

Turn off all other modes on the Status bar, except for Grid and Snap.

Save your drawing in your *c:\work* directory as *wrench.dwg*.

Drawing the Wrench

You will start the wrench drawing by making some lines to use for construction. Later, you will change them into centerlines. Refer to Figure 4.1.

Figure 4.1

On your own, use **Line** to draw a horizontal line **7.5** units long near the middle of your graphics window. You may want to turn on Dynamic Input and use it to specify the line lengths.

The line does not have to be at the exact center because you can easily move your drawing objects later if they do not appear centered. You will learn how to move objects in this tutorial.

Draw two vertical lines that are **3.00** units long and **4.5** units apart, as shown in Figure 4.1. The exact location of the vertical lines on the horizontal construction line is not critical, as long as they are 4.5 units apart.

Remember, you cannot select accurately just by clicking from the screen, so use Snap, an object snap, offset or type exact values.

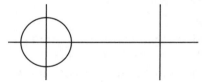

Figure 4.2

Click: ***Circle button***

Use Snap to draw a **1-inch radius circle** with its center at the intersection of the horizontal line and the left vertical line.

Using Copy Object

Just like it sounds, Copy makes copies of an object or group of objects within the same drawing. The original objects remain in place, and during the command you can move the copies to a new location. You can click Copy quickly from the ribbon, Home tab, Modify panel. Next, copy the circle to create a second one in your drawing.

 Click: ***Copy button***

Select objects: ***select the circle***

Select objects: ***[Enter]***

Pressing [Enter] indicates that you have finished selecting objects and

Tip: *Draw one line and then use the Offset command you learned in Tutorial 3, with an offset distance of 4.5, to create the other line.*

Tip: *Getting the cursor to select the circle with Snap on might be difficult. Using implied Windowing or Crossing would allow you to easily select the circle. You might also find that turning Snap off makes selecting the circle easier. Be sure to turn it back on again before selecting the base point or -displacement, or you may not pick the exact center point.*

want to continue with the command. Be sure that Snap is on again so you can accurately select the center point of the circle, which you created on the snap increment.

> Specify base point or [Displacement/mOde] <Displacement>: **select the center point of the circle**

The cursor switches to drag mode so that you can see the object move about the screen as you are prompted for the second point of displacement. You can define the new location by typing new absolute or relative coordinate values or by clicking on a location from the screen.

The second circle must be centered at the intersection of the horizontal and right vertical lines, which should be a snap location.

> Specify second point or [Array] <use first point as displacement>: **click on the right intersection**

> Specify second point or [Exit/Undo] <Exit>: **[Enter]**

You will work with the mOde options and Array options of the copy command later in the tutorial. Don't forget that it is easy to use Help to look up information on all of the command options. Your drawing should now look like Figure 4.3.

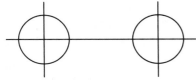

Figure 4.3

Next, use the Offset command on your own to offset the horizontal construction line a distance of 0.5 units to either side of itself to create the body of the wrench.

Your resulting drawing should look like Figure 4.4.

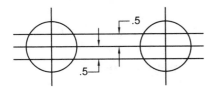

Figure 4.4

Now use the Trim command to trim the lines that you created with the Offset command so that they intersect neatly with the circles.

When you have finished, your drawing should look like Figure 4.5.

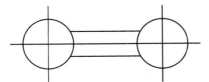

Figure 4.5

Effective Use of Layers

Recall that layers behave like clear overlay sheets in your drawing. To use layers effectively, choose layer names that make sense and separate the objects you draw into logical groups. You will create a centerline layer and then use it to change the middle lines of the wrench onto that layer so that they take on its color and linetype properties.

Click: Layer Properties button

The Layer Properties Manager appears on the screen, as in Figure 4.6.

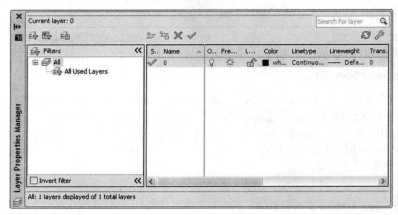

Figure 4.6

One layer name should be listed in the Name column, 0. Layer 0 is a special layer that is provided in AutoCAD. You cannot rename it or delete it from the list of layers. Layer 0 shows a green check indicating it is the current layer.

You will create a layer named, appropriately enough, Centerlines, for drawing the centerlines and set its color to green and linetype to center and make it the current layer.

Click: **New Layer button** located near the top middle of the dialog box

A new Layer1 should be highlighted in the list of layer names.

Type: **Centerlines [Enter]**

Click: **on the Color box corresponding to layer Centerlines**

Click: **Green** (Color 3 from the list of standard colors)

Click: **OK**

Now the color for layer Centerlines is set to green.

Click: **on Continuous** in the Linetype column for layer Centerlines

The Select Linetype dialog box shown in Figure 4.7 appears. Note that only one choice of linetype, CONTINUOUS, is available. Before you can select a linetype, you must load it. You need do so only one time in the drawing, and you do not need to load all the linetypes. To keep your drawing size small and get a shorter list of linetypes in the dialog box, load only the linetypes that you use frequently in your drawing. You can

Tip: *Draw one line and then use the Offset command you learned in Tutorial 3, with an offset distance of 4.5, to create the other line.*

always load other linetypes as needed during the drawing process. You will select Load, the second button from the right at the bottom of the dialog box, to load the linetypes you want to use.

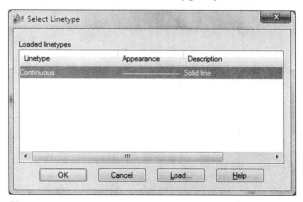

Figure 4.7

Click: **Load**

Loading the Linetypes

The Load or Reload Linetypes dialog box appears, as shown in Figure 4.8. To the right of the File button is the name of the default file, *acad.lin*, in which the predefined linetypes are stored. You can also create your own linetypes, using the Linetype command. You can store your custom linetypes in the *acad.lin* file or in another file that ends with the extension **.lin*. Below the file name is the list of available linetypes and a picture of each.

Figure 4.8

Use the scroll bar at the right of the list to move down the items until you see the selection CENTER.

Click: **CENTER** *so that the name becomes highlighted*

Click: **OK** *to exit the Load or Reload Linetypes dialog box*

Click: **Center** *so that it is the highlighted selection in the Select Linetype dialog box*

Click: **OK** *to exit the Select Linetype dialog box*

The centerline pattern is selected for the layer and is ready for use as shown in Figure 4.9.

Tip: *Objects that have had their color or linetype set to something other than BYLAYER will not be affected by changing the color or linetype of the layer they are on. In general, using layers to set the color and linetype is better.*

Figure 4.9

> *Double-click: **Centerlines** so that it appears with a green check mark indicating that it is the current layer*

> *Click: **X** to close the Layer Properties Manager*

Changing Properties

You will use the new layer you created to control the linetype and color of the centerlines.

> *Click: **the middle horizontal line and the two vertical lines***

Small squares, called grips, show on the endpoints and midpoints of each line as shown in Figure 4.10.

> *Click: **to pull down the list of layers** as shown in Figure 4.10*

> *Click: **Centerlines***

Figure 4.10

The lines change to have the properties of that layer—the color green and linetype center. To remove the hot grips from your screen so that your drawing looks like Figure 4.11,

Press: *[Esc]*

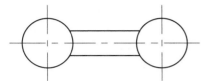

Figure 4.11

Setting the Global Linetype Scaling Factor

The *global linetype scaling factor* (LTScale command) is a value that you set to adjust the lengths of the lines and dashes used to make up various linetypes. This is very important for giving your drawings the correct appearance. Linetype patterns are stored in a file with the *.lin* file extension, which is external to your drawing. The lengths of the lines and dashes are set in that external file. But when you are working on large-scale drawings and the distances are in hundreds of units, a linetype with the dash length of 1/8 unit will not appear correctly. To adjust the linetypes, you specify a factor by which the length of the dashes in the *.lin* file should be multiplied. The global linetype scaling factor adjusts the scaling of all the linetypes in your drawing as a group.

When you are working on a large drawing such as the subdivision plat that you created in Tutorials 2 and 3, increase the scale for the dashed lines of the linetype to make the dashes visible. When you are working on a drawing that you will plot full scale, generally you should set the global linetype scaling factor to 1.00, which is the default. Setting the global linetype scaling factor to a decimal less than one (e.g., 0.75) results in a drawing with smaller dashes making up the linetypes. In general, the linetype scaling factor you set in your drawing should be the reciprocal of the scale at which you will plot your drawing. When you learn about paper space in Tutorial 5, you will see that you can set the linetype scaling factor both in model space, where you are working now, and for the paper space layout. (When using multiple viewports, you can also set the linetype scale differently in each viewport.)

You will type the command to set the global linetype scale at the command prompt.

Command: *LTSCALE [Enter]*

New scale factor <1.0000>: *.75 [Enter]*

The centerlines should now cross in the center of each circle, as shown in Figure 4.12.

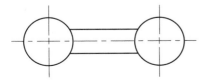

Figure 4.12

Tip: *If you have trouble with the lines returning to their previous LTscale property, press [Enter] after you type the value in the Properties palette before you close it.*

Tip: *The Dimcenter command creates correctly shown centerlines for circles. You will learn to use it in Tutorial 6.*

Changing an Object's Linetype Scale

You can also use the Linetype Scale area of the Properties dialog box (CELTSCALE command) to set the linetype scale for any particular object, independent of the rest of the drawing. You should first adjust the general appearance of the lines using the global command LTSCALE and then use the next method if some lines still need further adjustment. The object linetype scale factor is multiplied by the global LTSCALE to determine the object's linetype scaling.

Next, you will set the linetype scale for the two vertical lines to 1.5, giving them a different linetype scale than the horizontal line. You will click the Properties button from the Standard toolbar in order to use the Properties palette.

Click: **the two vertical lines** *to select them (their grips show)*

Double-click: **one of the selected lines** *to show the Properties palette*

The Quick Properties palette appears on your screen as shown in Figure 4.13. You will customize this palette to show the LTSCALE property.

Figure 4.13

Click: **the Customize button** *near the upper right of the Properties palette*

The Customize User Interface dialog box appears as shown in Figure 4.14. The AutoCAD software is easy to customize to show the tools that you prefer. You will learn more about customization in Tutorial 10.

Notice that Color, Layer and Linetype appear checked, while Linetype scale and others are not selected in the right side of the dialog box. You can quickly turn on and off which items to show in the Quick Properties dialog box.

Ensure that Line is highlighted as the object type (Figure 4.14)

Click: **to check the box to the left of Linetype scale**

Click: **Apply**

Click: **OK**

Figure 4.14

You will use the next steps to set the linetype scaling factor for the vertical lines you pre-selected to 1.5.

*Click: **the two vertical lines** to select them if they are no longer selected*

*Double-click: **one of the selected lines** to show the Properties palette. (Notice it now has Linetype scale listed.)*

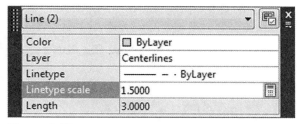

Figure 4.15

Highlight the text in the box to the right of Linetype Scale and overtype the new value.

*Type: **1.5 [Enter]***

*Click: **the Close button [X]** in the upper right of the Properties palette to close it*

*Press: **[Esc]** to unselect the object grips*

Save your drawing before continuing.

Now your drawing should look like Figure 4.16.

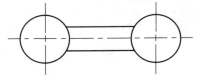

Figure 4.16

Now you are ready to add the fillets to your drawing, as shown in Figure 4.17. Refer to Tutorial 3 if you need to review Fillet.

Use the **Fillet** command, with a radius of **0.5**, to add the fillets on your own.

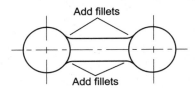

Add fillets

Add fillets

Figure 4.17

Using Polygon

The Polygon command draws regular polygons with 3 to 1024 sides. Polygons act as a single object because they are created as a connected polyline. A regular *polygon* is one in which the lengths of all sides are equal. The size of a polygon is usually expressed in terms of a related circle. Polygons are either *inscribed* in or *circumscribed* about a circle. A pentagon is a five-sided polygon. Figure 4.18 shows a pentagon inscribed within a circle and a pentagon circumscribed about a circle.

Inscribed   Circumscribed

Figure 4.18   **Examples**

You will add a pentagon to the right side of the wrench, circumscribed about a circle.

> *Expand the ribbon Home tab, Draw panel to show the Polygon button.*

 Click: Polygon button

Enter number of sides <4>: *5 [Enter]*

Specify center of polygon or [Edge]: *select the center point of the circle at the right end of the wrench drawing*

Enter an option [Inscribed in circle/Circumscribed about circle]<I>: *C [Enter]*

You are now in drag mode; move your cursor around and notice how the pentagon changes size as you do so. You may specify the radius of the circle, either by clicking with the pointing device or by typing in the coordinates. For this object you will specify a radius of one-half inch.

Specify radius of circle: *.5 [Enter]*

A five-sided regular polygon (a pentagon) is drawn on your screen. Your drawing should be similar to Figure 4.19.

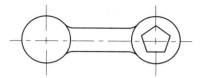

Figure 4.19

Drawing Hexagons

Hexagons are six-sided polygons and are a common shape in technical drawings. The heads of bolts, screws, and nuts often have a hexagonal shape. The size of a hexagon is sometimes referred to by its *distance across the flats*. The reason is that the sizes of screws, bolts, and nuts are defined by the distance across their flat sides. For example, a 16-mm hexhead screw would measure 16 mm across its head's flats and would fit a 16-mm wrench. The distance across the flats of a hexagon is not the same as the length of an edge of the hexagon. Figure 4.2020 illustrates the difference between the two distances. If a hexagon is circumscribed about a circle, the diameter of the circle equals the distance across the hexagon's flats. If a hexagon is inscribed in a circle, the diameter of the circle equals the distance across the corners of the hexagon.

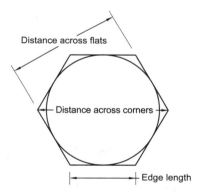

Figure 4.20

The Polygon command's Edge option draws regular polygons by specifying the length of the edge. This is helpful when you are creating side-by-side honeycomb patterns. Note that the software draws polygons counterclockwise. With the Edge option, the sequence in which you select points affects the position of the polygon (Figure 4.21).

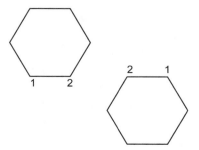

Figure 4.21

Next, you add the hexagon to the other side of the wrench.

Command: *[Enter] or right-click and select Repeat Polygon*

Enter number of sides <5>: *6 [Enter]*

Specify center of polygon or [Edge]: *click the center point of the left circle*

Enter an option [Inscribed in circle/Circumscribed about circle]<C>: *[Enter]*

Radius of circle: *.5 [Enter]*

A hexagon measuring 1.00 across the flats appears in your wrench. The final drawing should be similar to Figure 4.22.

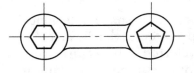

Figure 4.22

You have now completed your wrench. You will save this drawing and begin a new drawing for a coupler. You will close drawing Wrench so that it does not stay available on your screen.

Click: *Save button*

Click: *Application icon, Close to close the Wrench drawing*

In this next section, you will practice with additional drawing commands and with object snaps. You will start a new drawing and name it *coupler.dwg*.

Click: *New button*

Click: *acad.dwt as the template to use*

Click: *Open*

You return to the drawing editor.

On your own, turn on the **Grid** display if it is not already. Set **Snap** Mode to **.25** and turn it on.

Use **Zoom All** *so that the limits area fills the graphics window.*

Click: *Save button*

Choose: *c:\work directory*

Type: *coupler.dwg as the name of the new drawing*

Using Polar Tracking

When you are in a command (such as Line or Circle) that prompts for a location such as From or To, you can use polar tracking to align the cursor along a path defined by a polar angle from the previous point. Polar tracking works along preset angle increments of 90° by default or you can specify other angles. The angles can be measured relative to the previous line segment or absolutely from the default of zero degrees being horizontal to the right.

To see the effect of Polar tracking clearly,

 Click: **the Dynamic Input button** *to turn it off*

Next turn on polar tracking,

 Click: **Polar tracking button** *from the status bar or press [F10]*

  Like object snap, you will not notice any result until you select a command, such as Line or Circle, that prompts you to specify a location.

Next you will set the angle increment for polar tracking.

 Right-click: **Polar tracking button** *from the Status bar*

 Click: **Settings** *from the short-cut menu that appears near the cursor*

The Drafting Settings dialog box appears on your screen with the Polar Tracking tab uppermost, as shown in Figure 4.23.

Figure 4.23

Next, set the angle to use for polar tracking.

 Click: **45** *from the Increment angle pull-down list*

 Click: **Relative to last segment** *button (if not already selected)*

 Click: **Options button** *from the bottom left of the dialog box*

The Options dialog box shows on your screen as in Figure 4.24.

Tip: *Polar tracking measures distances from the last point selected, so it is considered relative. An absolute measurement would be from the 0,0 point of the World Coordinate System. You can right-click on the Polar tracking button and use the Drafting Settings dialog box to control whether angles are measured relative to the last point or absolutely. This is also true for Dynamic Input.*

Make sure that Display AutoTrack tooltip and Display polar tracking vector are checked.

Click: **OK**

Click: **OK**

Figure 4.24

You will use polar tracking along with the Line and Circle commands to create lines 1–4 for the coupler shown in Figure 4.25.

Figure 4.25

Check that the Polar tracking button on the status bar is turned on.

In the next steps, use your mouse scroll wheel to zoom in or out as necessary so you can see the lines easily.

Click: **Line button**

Specify first point: **3.75,6.5 [Enter]**

Press: [F7] to turn off the grid so you can see the tracking line clearly

A line will rubberband from coordinate point (3.75, 6.5) on your screen. Move the crosshairs around so that you see the rubberband line. As you get near 0 degrees, 45 degrees, and any other angle increments of 45 degrees, you will notice a tracking line appear on your screen.

> Position your cursor below the previous point, as shown in Figure 4.26, to draw a line .25 units long along the angle of 270 degrees. When you see the tooltip appear with the correct value **click to select the location and draw line 1**
>
> Specify next point or [Undo]: *use polar tracking to draw a line .25 units at a relative angle of 90 degrees (line 2)*
>
> Specify next point or [Undo]: *use polar tracking to draw a line 2.75 units at a relative angle of 270 degrees (line 3)*

To draw line 4, you will type the length at the command prompt because it is not a point on the current Snap increment.

> Specify next point or [Close/Undo]: *(use polar tracking at a relative angle of 90 degrees) .375 [Enter]*
>
> Specify next point or [Close/Undo]: *[Enter]*
>
> *Press: [F10] to turn Polar tracking off (or use the status bar button)*
>
> *Click: Circle button*
>
> Specify center point for circle or [3P/2P/Ttr (tan tan radius)]: *8,6.5 [Enter]*
>
> Specify radius of circle or [Diameter]: *.75 [Enter]*

When you have finished drawing these objects, your drawing should look like the one in Figure 4.27.

Figure 4.26

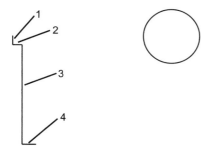

Figure 4.27

> *Click: to turn Snap mode off*

Next you will use object snaps to locate points accurately. Leaving Snap turned on may interfere with selection in the next steps.

Using Object Snaps

As you learned in Tutorial 2, you use object snaps to select locations accurately in relation to other objects in your drawing. Object snaps can operate in two different ways: override mode and running mode.

Remember, when an object snap is active, the AutoSnap™ marker box appears whenever the cursor is near a snap point. When you select a point, it will select the object snap point if the marker box is present, *whether or not the cursor is within the marker box.*

Tip: *Ortho mode restricts the cursor to horizontal or vertical movement. Ortho mode and polar tracking cannot be turned on at the same time. When you select Ortho mode, polar tracking is automatically turned off and vice versa, so that only one mode is available at any time.*

Showing a Floating Toolbar

You will show the floating Object Snap toolbar to make selecting object snaps easy. Recall that the object snaps are also on the Standard toolbar as a flyout selection. You can turn toolbars on by right-clicking any toolbar.

Click: **View tab, Windows panel** *(Figure 4.28)*

Figure 4.28

Click: **Toolbars** *to show the dropdown*

Click: **AutoCAD** *and then* **Object Snap** *from the list of Toolbars as shown in Figure 4.29.*

The Object Snap toolbar appears on your screen, as shown in Figure 4.30. You can position it anywhere on the screen or dock it to the edge of the graphics window. (If you used previous versions of AutoCAD, you may have wondered where these went.)

Figure 4.30

Object Snap Overrides

You will finish drawing the coupler, using object snap overrides to position the new lines and circles. (You may see other ways that you could use editing commands to create parts of this figure, but in this example object snaps will be used as much as possible. When you are working on your own drawings, use the methods that work best for you.)

Snap to Endpoint

The Endpoint object snap (END) locates the closest endpoint of an arc, line, or polyline vertex. You will draw a line from the endpoint of line 1, shown in Figure 4.26, to touch the circle at the quadrant point. The *quadrant points* are at 0°, 90°, 180°, and 270° of a circle or an arc. You will use the Endpoint and Quadrant object snaps to locate the exact points. You will use the Object Snap toolbar to select the object snaps as overrides. This means they only stay active for one click.

Click: **Line button**

Specify first point: *click Snap to Endpoint button*

Move your mouse near the endpoint of a line to notice the AutoSnap marker that appears.

Figure 4.29

Note: *You can switch to the AutoCAD Classic workspace, if you really prefer the old style menus and toolbars. But **don't** do it during these tutorials or you may have trouble following the instructions.*

Tip: *You can also type a three-letter code for the object snap at the Select objects prompt instead of picking an object snap mode from the toolbar. (The command-line equivalent of the Endpoint object snap is END.)*

Endp of: *place the cursor on the upper end of line 1 shown in Figure 4.31 and click the mouse when the AutoSnap Endpoint marker shows*

The new line starting point should have jumped to the exact endpoint of line 1. Next you will specify the second endpoint of the new line.

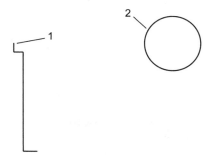

Figure 4.31

Snap to Quadrant

The Quadrant object snap attaches to the quadrant point on a circle nearest the position of the crosshairs. The command-line equivalent of Snap to Quadrant is QUA. The quadrant points are the four points on the circle that are tangent to a square that encloses it. They are also the four points where the centerlines intersect the circle. Next you will finish the line, using the Quadrant object snap to pick the quadrant point of the circle as the second endpoint for your line. You should still see the prompt for the next point of the Line command.

Specify next point or [Undo]: *click Snap to Quadrant button*

Qua of: *click on the circle near point 2 (Figure 4.31)*

Specify next point or [Undo]: *[Enter]*

Your drawing should be similar to Figure 4.32

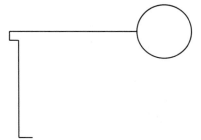

Figure 4.32

Tip: *Object Snap Overrides only stay active for one pick. When an object snap running mode is active, you can still use a different object snap during a command. The object snap override takes precedence over the object snap running mode for that pick.*

Snap to Center

The Center object snap finds the center of a circle or an arc. You will use it to create concentric circles by selecting the center of the circle that you have drawn as the center for the new circle you will add. The command-line equivalent for Snap to Center is CEN.

Click: **Circle button**

Specify center point for circle or [3P/2P/Ttr (tan tan radius)]: *click Snap to Center button*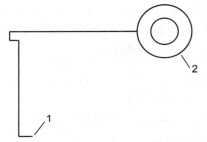

Cen of: *click on the edge of the circle*

The software finds the exact center of the circle and a circle rubberbands from the center to the location of the crosshairs. Note the marker that appeared when your cursor was on the circle. Remember, Object snap overrides stay active for only one pick. You are now prompted to specify the radius.

Specify radius of circle or [Diameter]<0.7500<: *.375 [Enter]*

The circle should be drawn concentric to the original circle in the drawing, as shown in Figure 4.33.

Figure 4.33

To position the next line from the endpoint labeled 1 in Figure 4.33 and tangent to the outer circle labeled 2, you will use the Endpoint object snap and then the Tangent object snap.

Click: **Line button**

Specify first point: *click Snap to Endpoint button*

Endp of: *click near the right endpoint labeled 1*

A line rubberbands from the endpoint of line 1 to the location of the crosshairs. Next, you will locate the second point of the line to be tangent to the circle.

Snap to Tangent

The Tangent object snap attaches to a point on a circle or an arc; a line drawn from the last point to the referenced object is drawn tangent to the referenced object. The command-line equivalent is TAN.

Specify next point or [Undo]: *click Snap to Tangent button*

Tan to: *click the lower right side of the circle when you see the AutoSnap Tangent marker near point 2*

Specify next point or [Undo]: *[Enter]*

Tip: *To draw a line tangent to two circles, pick Line. At the Specify first point prompt, pick Snap to Tangent and pick on one of the circles in the general vicinity of the tangent line you want to draw. You will not see a line rubberband. At the Specify next point prompt, pick Snap to Tangent again and pick the other circle. When you select the second object, the tangent is defined and will be drawn on your screen.*

Your drawing should be similar to Figure 4.34.

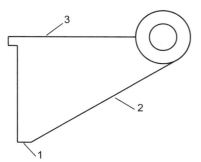

Figure 4.34

Again, using object snap, you will draw a line from the intersection of the short horizontal line and the angled line, perpendicular to the upper line of the object.

Snap to Intersection

Snap to Intersection finds the intersection of two graphical objects. The command-line equivalent for Snap to Intersection is INT.

Refer to Figure 4.34 when selecting your points.

Click: **Line button**

Specify first point: **click Snap to Intersection button**

Int of: **click so that the intersection of lines 1 and 2 is anywhere inside the target area**

A line rubberbands from the intersection to the current position of the crosshairs. To select the second endpoint of the line, you will use Snap to Perpendicular to draw the line perpendicular to the top horizontal line.

Snap to Perpendicular

The Perpendicular object snap attaches to a point on an arc, a circle, or a line; a line drawn from the last point to the referenced object forms a right angle with that object.

This time, use the Perpendicular object snap by typing its command-line equivalent, PER.

Specify next point or [Undo]: **PER [Enter]**

Per to: **click on line 3**

Specify next point or [Undo]: [Enter]

The line is drawn at a 90° angle, perpendicular to the line, regardless of where on the line you clicked. The drawing on your screen should be similar to Figure 4.35. Although this example draws a perpendicular line that touches the target line, it need not touch it. If you choose to draw perpendicular to a line that does not intersect at an angle of 90°, the perpendicular line is drawn to a point that would be perpendicular if the target line were extended.

Tip: *Note that when Snap to Intersection is on and the cursor passes over any object, the AutoSnap marker for intersection (an X) shows up with three dots to its right. These dots mean that if you select the line, you will be prompted for a second line or object that intersects with the first.*

Tip: *When you use 3D solid modeling in Tutorial 11, remember that when you are finding the intersection of two objects with Snap to Intersection, the objects must actually intersect in 3D space, not just apparently intersect on the screen. (One line may be behind the other in the 3D model.) To select lines that do not intersect in space, use the Apparent Intersection object snap. It finds the intersection of lines that would intersect if extended and also the apparent intersection of two lines (where they appear to intersect in a view).*

Tip: *Remember, in order to draw a perpendicular line, you must define two points. When you are defining a perpendicular from a line, no line is drawn until you define the second point. The reason is that infinitely many lines are perpendicular to a given line, but only one line is perpendicular to a line through a given point. Your perpendicular line will be drawn after you have selected the second point.*

Figure 4.35

Snap to Parallel

To use the Parallel object snap you identify an object that your choice
will be parallel to. Its command-line equivalent is PAR.

> *Click:* **Line button**
>
> Specify first point: **click Snap to Intersection button**
>
> Int of: **click point 4 shown in Figure 4.35**
>
> Specify next point or [Undo]: **click Snap to Parallel button**
>
> Par to: **hold your cursor over line 2 until you see the AutoSnap
> marker Parallel appear but do not click the mouse button**
>
> Specify next point or [Undo]: **move your cursor so that the line
> rubberbanding from point 4 is roughly parallel to line 2.**

You should see a parallel tracking line appear as shown in Figure 4.36.

Track along a parallel direction

Parallel: 4.3730 < 30°

Parallel symbol

Hover over this line until
parallel symbol appears

Figure 4.36

When it does,

> *Click:* **a point along the tracking line parallel to line 2 [Enter]**

Next you will undo the parallel line.

> **Command: U [Enter]**
>
> Use the techniques that you have learned to save your drawing now.

*Tip: The override object snaps
are available by right-clicking
and selecting Snap Overrides
from the short-cut menu that
appears on screen. OSnap
Settings is also available this
way.*

Practicing with Running Mode Object Snaps

You can also use object snap in the running mode, as you did in Tutorial 2 with Snap to Node. When you use object snaps this way, you turn the mode on and leave it on. Any time that a command calls for the input of a point or selection, the current object snap is used when you click. The running mode object snaps are very useful, as they reduce the number of times you must select from the menu to achieve the desired drawing results. You can use any of the object snaps in either the running mode or the override mode.

*Right-click: **Object Snap button** and use the short-cut menu to choose **Settings***

The Drafting Settings dialog box appears on the screen with the Object Snap tab uppermost.

*Click: **Clear All** to remove any current selections*

*Click: **Intersection***

*Click: **Object Snap On (F3) check box** so that it is selected*

A check appears in the box to indicate that you have selected Intersection. The Drafting Settings dialog box should appear as shown in Figure 4.37.

Figure 4.37

*Click: **OK** to exit the Drafting Settings dialog box*

Now Intersection is turned on. Anytime you are prompted to select, an AutoSnap marker box will appear when the cursor is near the intersection of two drawing objects.

More Object Snaps

The other object snaps are described next. Try them on your own until you are familiar with how they work.

Snap to Apparent Intersection (APPINT)

The Apparent Intersection object snap finds two different types of intersections that the regular Intersection object snap wouldn't find. One type is the point at which two objects would intersect if they were extended. The other type is the point at which two 3D lines appear to intersect on the screen, when they do not in fact intersect in space. The command-line equivalents for Snap to Apparent Intersection are APPINT and APP.

Snap to Nearest (NEA)

The Nearest object snap attaches to the point on an arc, circle, or line closest to the middle of the target area of your cursor. It will also find point objects that are within the target area.

A line drawn with the Nearest function may look like a line that could have been drawn simply using the Line command, but there is a difference. Many AutoCAD operations, such as hatching, require an enclosed area: All lines that define the area must intersect (touch). When you draw lines by clicking two points on the screen, sometimes the lines don't actually touch. They appear to touch on the screen, but when you zoom in on them sufficiently, you will see that they don't touch. They may only be a hundredth of an inch apart, but they don't touch. When creating an AutoCAD drawing, you should always strive to create the drawing geometry accurately. The Nearest function ensures that the nearest object is selected. The command-line equivalent is NEA.

Snap to Node (NOD)

The Node object snap finds the exact location of a point object in your drawing. You used it in Tutorial 2 to locate exact points that had already been placed in the drawing with the Point command. The command-line equivalent is NOD.

Snap to Insertion (INS)

The Insertion object snap finds the insertion point of text or of a block. (You will learn about blocks in Tutorial 10.) This method is useful when you want to determine the exact point at which existing text or blocks are located in your drawing. The command-line equivalent is INS.

Snap to Midpoint (MID)

The Snap to Midpoint object snap finds the midpoint of the selected object.

Warning: *When you have finished experimenting, return to the Drafting Settings dialog box and turn off any object snaps you may have left on.*

Tip: *The Locate Point (ID) command that you learned in Tutorial 3 lists the coordinates of a selected point. To find the exact insertion point of text or a block, pick Locate Point and then use the Insertion object snap and pick on the text or block. Similarly, you can find the coordinates of an endpoint or intersection by combining those object snaps with the Locate Point command.*

Tip: *You can turn on more than one object snap at the same time. For instance, you could select both Intersection and Nearest from the Drafting Settings dialog box. AutoSnap will show different marker boxes for each snap setting chosen.*

Tip: *You can right-click during selection operations to show the shortcut menu for object snap modes, including Midpoint between Two Points.*

Snap to Midpoint Between Two Points (MTP)

The Midpoint between Two Points snap finds the midpoint between two points you select.

Snap From (FROM)

The From object snap is a special object snap tool. It establishes a temporary reference point from which you can specify the point to be selected. Usually it is used in combination with other object snap tools. For example, you would use it if you were going to draw a new line that you want to start a certain distance from an existing intersection. To do so, click the Line command; when prompted for the starting point of your line, click the Snap From button. You will then be prompted for a base point. It is the location of the reference point from which you want to locate your next input. At the base point prompt, click Snap to Intersection. You will be prompted to select the intersection of two lines. Click on the intersection. As the result of your using Snap From, you will see the additional prompt of <Offset>. At this prompt, use relative coordinates to enter the distance you want the next point to be from the base point you selected.

Snap to Extension (EXT)

The Extension object snap also establishes a temporary reference. It displays a temporary extension line when you move the cursor over an object's endpoint, so that you can draw to an extension of the same line.

Object Tracking

Object Tracking is a unique snap tool allowing you to start a line with reference to other locations. For instance, if you have drawn a rectangle and want to draw a line from the middle of the rectangle, there is no snap for that point. With Tracking, you can start the line with reference to as many points as you select. Tracking will be covered in Tutorial 6.

Practice on your own with each of the object snaps. Hover the cursor over each of the remaining object snaps from the toolbar and read the tooltips explaining their functions. Undo any changes you make while practicing until your drawing appears as shown in Figure 4.38.

Figure 4.38

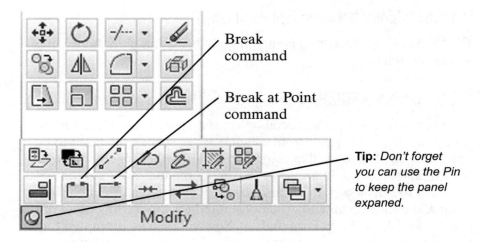

Break command

Break at Point command

Tip: *Don't forget you can use the Pin to keep the panel expaned.*

Using Break

The Break command erases part of an object (for example, a line, arc, or circle). The Break button is on the Modify panel. When using the Break command, you can specify a single point at which to break the object or specify two points on the object and the Break command will automatically remove the portion between the points selected. You also can select the object and then specify the two points at which to break it.

You will break the circle between intersection 1 and intersection 2 (Note that you could also accomplish the same thing by using Trim.)

You will use the First point option after selecting the Break button. Refer to **Figure 4.38** for the points to select.

Tip: Zoom in if necessary to see the intersections clearly.

Tip: The Break at Point icon allows you to break a selected object at a specified point without erasing any portion of it.

Turn on the running mode Object Snap for **Intersection** on your own.

Click: **Break button** *from the expanded Modify panel*

Select object: ***click the large circle***

Specify second break point (or First point): ***F [Enter]***

Specify first break point: ***click intersection 1***

Enter second point: ***click intersection 2***

When you select the second break point, the portion of the circle between the two selected points is removed. Your drawing should look like Figure 4.39. Save your coupler drawing.

Click: **Save button**

Figure 4.39

On your own, change your **Snap** setting to **0.25** before continuing.

Erase the lines labeled 1, 2, and 3 in Figure 4.39.

Draw a new line **0.5** units (two snap increments) from the previous leftmost line as shown in Figure 4.40 (labeled Boundary edge).

When you have completed this step, your drawing should be similar to Figure 4.40.

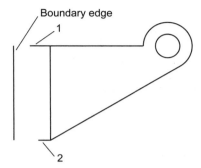

Figure 4.40

Using Extend

The Extend command extends the lengths of existing lines and arcs to end at a selected boundary edge. Its function is the opposite of the Trim command. Like Trim, Extend has two parts: First you select the object to act as the boundary, then you select the objects you want to extend. Extend is on the ribbon Home tab, Modify panel.

Similar to the Trim command, the command-line options for the Extend command are Project, Edge, and Undo. The default option is just to select the objects to be extended. You can use the Edge option to extend objects to the point at which they would meet the boundary edge if it were longer. This method is useful when the boundary edge is short and the lines to be extended would not intersect it.

The Project option allows you to specify the plane of projection to be used for extending. This option is useful when you're working in 3D drawings because it allows you to extend objects to a boundary selected from the current viewing direction or User Coordinate System. Often 3D objects may not actually intersect the boundary edge but just appear to do so in the view. You can use the Project option to extend them as they appear in the view. The Undo option lets you undo the last object extended, while remaining in the Extend command.

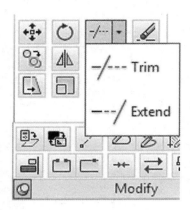

Now you will use the Extend command to extend the existing lines to meet the new boundary. Refer to Figure 4.40.

Click: **Extend button**

    Current settings: Projection=UCS Edge=None

Select boundary edges . . .

Select objects or <select all>: **select boundary edge**

Select objects: **[Enter]**

You have finished selecting boundary edges. To extend the horizontal lines, select them by clicking points on them near the end closer to the boundary edge. (If you click closer to the other end, you will get the message "No edge in that direction," and the lines won't be extended.)

    Select object to extend or shift-select to trim or [Fence/Crossing/Project/ Edge/Undo]: **select lines 1 and 2**

    Select object to extend or shift-select to trim or [Fence/Crossing/Project/ Edge/Undo]: **[Enter]**

The drawing will look like Figure 4.41 once the lines have been extended.

Figure 4.41

Using Rotate

The Rotate command allows you to rotate a drawing object or group of objects to a new orientation in the drawing. Rotate is on the ribbon Home tab, Modify panel. In this section, you will use Rotate to rotate objects in your drawing.

Click: **Rotate button**

    Current positive angle in UCS: ANGDIR=counterclockwise ANG-BASE=0

Select objects: **select the entire coupler using a Crossing window**

7 found

Select objects: **[Enter]**

You are prompted for the base point. You will select the middle of the object as the base point, as shown in Figure 4.42.

Tip: *The base point need not be part of the object chosen for rotation. You can use any point on the screen; the object rotates about the point you select. You may often find it useful to select a base point in the center of the object you want to rotate. As the object rotates, it stays in relatively the same position on the screen.*

Figure 4.42

Specify base point: click in the middle of the coupler

Specify rotation angle or [Copy/Reference]: *45 [Enter]*

Your coupler should be rotated 45 degrees, as shown in Figure 4.43. Positive angles are measured counterclockwise. A horizontal line to the right of the base point is defined as 0 degrees. You can also enter negative values.

Next you will restore the object to its original position before you continue.

Click: ***Undo button***

The coupler returns to its original rotation.

Using Move

The Move command moves existing objects from one location on the coordinate system in the drawing to another location. Do not confuse the Move command and the Pan command. Pan moves your view and leaves the objects where they were. Move actually moves the objects on the coordinate system. Move is on the Modify toolbar.

Click: ***Move button***

Select objects: *use Crossing or Window to select all of the coupler drawing*

Select objects: *[Enter]*

Specify base point or [Displacement] <Displacement>: *click the Snap to Endpoint button*

Endpoint of: select the upper left corner of the coupler

The cursor switches to drag mode so that you can see the object move about the screen, as shown in Figure 4.44.

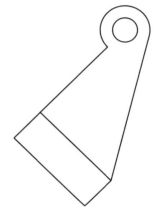

Figure 4.43

Figure 4.44

Specify second point or <use first point as displacement>: *select a point so the coupler is to the lower right of its old location*

Methods of Selecting Objects

There are many ways that you can select graphical objects for use with commands. For example, Window and Crossing. You can save lots of time when creating and editing drawings by the clever use of the selection methods. Generally, whenever you are asked to select objects, you can continue selecting until you have all the objects that you want highlighted in one selection set. You can combine the various selection modes to select the objects you want. The command then operates on the selection set you have built.

At any Select objects: prompt, you can type the option letters for the method you want to use. You may continue selecting, using any of the methods in the following table, until you indicate that you have finished building the selection set by pressing [Enter] or the return button. Then the command will take effect on the objects that you have selected.

Name	Option Letter(s)	Method
Clicking	none	Selects objects by positioning cursor and clicking the left mouse button
Select Window	W	Specifies diagonal corners of a box that only selects objects that are entirely enclosed
Select Crossing	C	Specifies diagonal corners of a box that selects all objects that cross or are enclosed in the box
Select Group	G	Selects all objects within a named group, prompts to enter group name
Select Previous	P	Reselects the previous selection set
Select Last	L	Selects the last object created
Select All	ALL	Selects all the objects in your drawing unless they are on a frozen layer
Select Window Polygon	WP	Similar to Window except you draw an irregular polygon instead of a box around the items to select
Select Crossing Polygon	CP	Similar to Window Polygon except that all objects that cross or are enclosed in the polygon are selected
Select Fence	F	Similar to Crossing except that you draw line segments through all the objects you want to select
Select Add	A	Use after Remove to add more objects to the selection set. Can continue with any of the other selection modes once Add has been chosen
Select Remove	R or Shift Click	Selects objects to remove from the current selection set; removal continues until Add or [Enter] is used; you can use Window, Crossing, etc., while selecting items to remove. Pressing shift and clicking on a selected object removes it from the current selection. (Do not select on a grip handle.)
Undo	U	During object selection, deselects the last item or group of items you selected
Control	[Ctrl]	After you click as close to the object as you can, press [Ctrl] to cycle through objects that are close together or directly on top of one another. Continue to press [Ctrl] until the object you want is selected.

Additional methods of selecting are Auto, Box, Subobject, Object, Single, and Multiple. Consult AutoCAD Help for the Select command for definitions of their use.

Select Similar

Select similar allows you to quickly select objects that are similar to one you have already selected. To see how this works,

*Click: to select **one of the straight lines** (its grips appear)*

*Right-click: **to show the short-cut menu** (Figure 4.45)*

Figure 4.45

*Click: **Select Similar***

All of the straight line segments become selected and their grips appear.

*Press: **[Esc]** to deselect the lines*

You can also set which properties of an object determine whether it is similar to the selected one, using the Selectsimilar command.

Command: ***[Enter]** to restart the command*

SELECTSIMILAR Select objects or [SEttings]: ***SE [Enter]***

The Select Similar Settings dialog box appears as shown in Figure 4.46.

Figure 4.46

The properties which you can select to determine similarity from are:

Color	objects with matching colors are similar.
Layer	objects on matching layers are similar.
Linetype	objects with matching linetypes are similar.
Linetype scale	objects with matching linetype scales are similar.
Lineweight	objects with matching lineweights are similar.
Plot style	objects with matching plot styles are similar.
Object style	objects with matching styles (text styles, dimension styles, table styles) are similar.
Name	referenced objects (blocks, xrefs, images) with matching names are similar.

Click: **Cancel to exit the dialog box**

Press: **[Esc] to exit the command**

Using Selection Filters

Selection filters are a special method of selecting objects. You can use them to select types of objects, such as all the arcs in the drawing or objects that you created by setting the color or linetype independently of the layer that they are on.

Command: **FILTER [Enter]**

The Object Selection Filters dialog box shown in Figure 4.47 appears on your screen. You can use this dialog box to filter the types of objects to select. You can save named filter groups for reuse.

Click: **in the Select Filter area to show the list, then click Arc**

Click: **Add to List**

Figure 4.47

Click: **Apply**

After choosing Apply, you return to the command prompt to select the objects in your drawing. Note the message,

Applying filter to selection.

Select objects: *use Crossing to select all of the objects*

You should see the message "Applying filter to selection. 1 found." Only the arc object matched the filter list. The lines of the drawing were filtered out.

Select objects: *[Esc] to cancel*

Command: *[Enter] to restart the FILTER command*

You should see the Object Selection Filters dialog box on your screen.

Click: *Clear List*

Click: *[X] Windows Close button to close the dialog box*

Using Quick Select

Use Quick Select (Qselect) to create a selection set which includes or excludes matching objects and properties. You can apply Quick Select to your entire drawing or to a previously created selection set. You can also append the Quick Select objects to the current selection set or replace the current selection. Quick Select is on the ribbon Home tab, Utilities panel and also the Properties palette. You can also right-click and choose Quick Select from the short-cut menu.

 Click: *Quick Select button from the Utilities panel*

You should see the Quick Select dialog box as shown in Figure 4.48.

Figure 4.48

You will use Quick Select to select the entire drawing except for the top arc.

Verify that the Apply to area shows Entire drawing.

*Click: **Arc** from the pull-down list to the right of Object type*

The Properties area now displays properties of the arc which you could select for further filtering. In the How to apply area you can choose "Include in new selection set" which creates a new selection set of only objects that match the filtering criteria. Selecting "Exclude from new selection set" creates a new selection set composed only of objects that do not match the filtering criteria. In the How to apply area,

*Click: **Exclude from new selection set***

Make sure that Append to current selection set is not selected.

*Click: **OK** to exit the dialog box*

All of the objects, with the exception of the top arc, should now be selected. Next you will use the color control to set the color for the selected objects to red.

*Click: **Red** from the Color Control on the Properties panel*

*Press: **[Esc]***

All but the arc should now appear in red on your screen.

Closing the Coupler Drawing

On your own, **close** the coupler drawing. **Discard** the changes to *coupler.dwg*.

Creating the Geneva Cam

You will create the geneva cam shown in Figure 4.49, using many of the editing commands you have learned in this tutorial. You will learn to use the Array command to create rectangular and radial patterns.

Tip: *The Quick Select icon appears at the top of the Properties palette to provide quick selection functions when changing properties.*

Figure 4.49

On your own, start a new drawing from the **acad.dwt** template.

Save the drawing to your **\work** directory with the name **geneva.dwg**.

Continuing on your own, set the **Snap** to **0.25.**

Check the status bar to be sure that **Snap** and **Grid** are turned on.

Use **Zoom All** if needed so that the grid area fills the graphics window.

Next you will use the Circle command to create the innermost circle of diameter 1.00. Locate the center of the circle at (5.5, 4.5).

Click: ***Circle button***

3P/2P/TTR/<Center point>: ***5.5,4.5 [Enter]***

Diameter/<Radius>: ***D [Enter]***

Diameter: ***1 [Enter]***

Use Offset or the Circle command to draw a **1.5-diameter** circle and a **4-diameter** circle **concentric** to the circle you just drew.

Your drawing should look like Figure 4.50.

Tip: *If you use Offset, remember to calculate the offset distance based on the diameters given. You will need to subtract the diameter of the inner circle from the diameter of the outer circle and then divide the result by 2 to find the value to use for the offset distance.*

Figure 4.50

Use Line to draw vertical and horizontal lines through the center of the circles.

Your drawing should look like Figure 4.51.

Figure 4.51

Next create lines parallel to the vertical centerline.

Click: ***Offset button***

Specify offset distance or [Through/Erase/Layer] <2.50000>: ***.25 [Enter]***

Select object to offset or [Exit/Undo] <Exit>: ***click the vertical centerline***

Specify point on side to offset or [Exit/Multiple/Undo] <Exit>: ***click on the right side of the line***

Select object to offset or [Exit/Undo] <Exit>: *click the same vertical centerline*

Specify point on side to offset or [Exit/Multiple/Undo] <Exit>: *click on the left side of the line*

Select object to offset or [Exit/Undo] <Exit>: *[Enter]*

Using Construction Line (Xline)

Construction Line, on the ribbon Home tab, Draw panel, creates a line (through a point that you select) that extends infinitely in both directions from the first point selected. The Ray command, on the Draw panel, draws a line which extends infinitely in only one direction.

Using the XLINE command, you can select options to draw a horizontal or vertical line, to bisect a specified angle, or to offset the construction line by a distance from the object. You will use the Angle option from the command prompt to specify an angle of 60 degrees and a point for the line to pass through.

 Click: *Construction Line button*

Specify a point or [Hor/Ver/Ang/Bisect/Offset]: *A [Enter]*

Enter angle of xline (0) or [Reference]: *60 [Enter]*

Specify through point: *5.5,4.5 or click the center point of the circles, using Snap*

Specify through point: *[Enter]*

Zoom to enlarge your view as needed.

The construction line appears in your drawing, as shown in Figure 4.52.

Tip: *You can keep a panel expanded by selecting to "pin" it, using the icon that looks like a push pin.*

Figure 4.52

The construction line will extend as far as you pan your view in both directions of extension. If you trim a construction line at one end, it becomes a ray, extending infinitely in only one direction. If you trim it at both ends, it becomes a line.

> Use Trim with the horizontal centerline as your cutting edge to trim off the lower portion of the construction line. When you are finished, the construction line only extends upward from the center point.

Next you will use the Circle command to add the construction circles to your drawing. The first two circles to add are concentric with the existing circles in the drawing, in other words, they have the same centerpoint.

> On your own, turn on **running object snap** for **Center** and **Intersection**.
>
> Click: **Circle button**
>
> Specify center point for circle or [3P/2P/Ttr (tan tan radius)]: *select the center of the circles using object snap*
>
> Specify radius of circle or [Diameter] <2.0000>: *2.57 [Enter]*
>
> Command: *[Enter] or right-click and select to restart the command*
>
> Specify center point for circle or [3P/2P/Ttr (tan tan radius)]: *select the center of the circles using the object snap Center to select the same center point as before*
>
> Specify radius of circle or [Diameter] <2.5700>: *1.25 [Enter]*

Next you will add two construction circles which you will later trim to form arcs.

> Command: *[Enter] to restart the Circle command*
>
> Specify center point for circle or [3P/2P/Ttr (tan tan radius)]: *Use object snap Intersection to select where the vertical centerline crosses the 1.25 radius construction circle identified a point A*
>
> Specify radius of circle or [Diameter] <1.2500>: *.25 [Enter]*

The small circle is added to your drawing between the two lines you offset. Your drawing should look like that in Figure 4.53.

Figure 4.53

Use the next steps to draw the final construction circle where the 60-degree ray and the outer circle intersect.

Command: *[Enter] to restart the Circle command*

Specify center point for circle or [3P/2P/Ttr (tan tan radius)]: ***click point 1 in Figure 4.53, using object snap Intersection***

Specify radius of circle or [Diameter]<.2500>: ***.90 [Enter]***

Your drawing should now look like Figure 4.54.

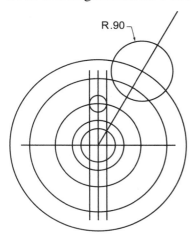

Figure 4.54

On your own, use **Trim** and **Erase** commands to remove the unwanted portions of the figure until your drawing looks like Figure 4.55.

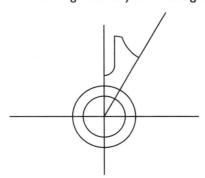

Figure 4.55

Using Mirror

The Mirror command makes a mirror-image copy of the objects you select around a *mirror line* that you specify. Mirror is on the Modify panel. Its button is the mirror image of a shape. The Mirror command also allows you to delete the old objects or to keep them.

To mirror an object, you must specify a mirror line, which can be horizontal, vertical, or slanted. A mirror line defines both the angle and the distance at which the mirror image is to be drawn. The mirrored image is drawn perpendicular to the mirror line. The mirrored object is the same distance from the mirror line as the original object is, but it's on the other side of the mirror line. The mirror line does not have to exist in your drawing; when asked to specify the mirror line, you can click two points from the screen to define it.

Tip: *Try using Crossing to select several objects to trim at one time. Use the Erase option of the Trim command to remove any objects that no longer cross a cutting edge.*

Figure 4.56

The vertical centerline will serve as the mirror line as you mirror the lines and arcs of the geneva cam. Refer to Figure 4.56 as you click on points. Be sure that Snap is turned on or use object snaps before clicking on the mirror line.

Click: ***Mirror button***

Select objects: ***click objects 1, 2, 3, and 4***

Select objects: *[Enter]*

Specify first point of mirror line: ***select the exact center of the concentric circles***

Your cursor is now dragging a mirrored copy of the objects.

Specify second point of mirror line: ***select a point straight below the center point***

Erase source objects? [Yes/No] <N> *[Enter]*

Your drawing should look like Figure 4.57.

Figure 4.57

Tip: *If you select objects that you do not want to mirror, you can remove them from the selection set. To do so, Shift-click on the objects while still at the Select objects: prompt. Press [Enter] when you have selected the objects you want.*

Tip: *An object can be mirrored about one of its own edge lines. Or, if you want, you can add mirror lines to the drawing and then erase them after completing the construction; or you can pick any two points from the screen that would define the line you want to specify.*

Using Array

The Array commands copy an object multiple times to form a regularly spaced rectangular or circular pattern, or a pattern along a path. When you need to create regularly spaced patterns, use Array to do it quickly.

A *rectangular array* has a specified number of rows and columns of the items with a specified distance between them.

A *polar array* copies the items in a circular pattern around a center point that you specify.

A *path array* evenly distributes copies along a specified path, or portion of the path.

Examples are: creating a circular pattern of holes in a circular hub, creating rows of desks in laying out a classroom, creating the teeth on a gear, or setting lamposts along a curved walkway. The Array command is on the ribbon Home tab, Modify panel shown in Figure 4.58.

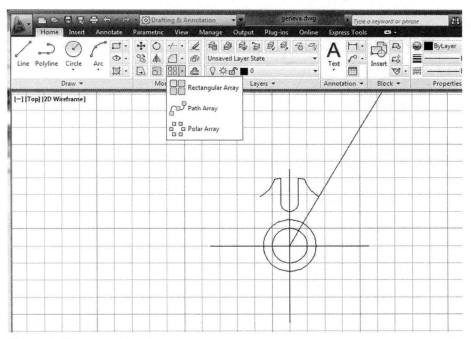

Figure 4.58

Click: ***Polar Array button***

The command prompt shows the options for a polar array.

Select objects: ***select lines 1-8 [Enter]***

Type = Polar Associative = Yes

Specify center point of array or [Base point/Axis of rotation]: ***click on the center of the circles*** *using object snap center*

At the next prompts, you can specify the Total number of items & Angle to fill, the Total number of items & Angle between items, or the Angle to fill & Angle between items.

Pick the center of the circles as the base point

You will use the Total number of items & Angle to fill. The copies can fill 360 degrees of the circle or some portion of 360 degrees.

> Enter number of items or [Angle between/Expression] <4>: *6 [Enter]*
>
> Specify the angle to fill (+=ccw, -=cw) or [EXpression] <360>: *[Enter]*
>
> Press Enter to accept or [ASsociative/Base point/Items/Angle between/Fill angle/ROWs/Levels/ROTate items/eXit]<eXit>: *[Enter]*

You can use the command prompt options to rotate the items as they are copied to preserve their orientation. You can find more information about the Array commands in the on-line help.

> On your own, use **Erase** to erase the angled ray from the drawing.
>
> The geneva cam is now complete; **save** it on your own.

Your drawing should look like that in Figure 4.59.

Figure 4.59

Editing Associative Arrays

When an associative array is created, its elements are linked to the arrayed object and can be easily accessed for later editing and updates. Associative arrays are the default. You can double-click on any part of the arrayed object to quickly edit it.

> *Double-click:* **on one of the arcs or lines of the array**

Notice that all of the arcs and lines are now grouped together as one object. After you double-click on an arrayed object, the Array Editor contextual tab appears on the screen as shown in Figure 4.60. You can also edit associative arrays using Quick Properties.

The leftmost item on the contextual tab shows the type of array, in this case a Polar one. Additional items on the contextual tab show: Items Panel, Item Count, where you can change the number of items in the array, Angle between Items, where you can specify the angle, Angle to Fill, which can be between 0° and 360°.

The Base Point area on the Properties panel lets you redefine the base point of the array. If you did not select the center of the circles as your base point, you could correct it here.

Rotate Items is used to control how objects rotate as they are arrayed.

Using Edit Source and Replace Item you can activate an editing state in

Tip: *If you did not select the correct objects and your drawing does not look like the figure, you can edit the source objects you selected to array or replace selected objects. Live previewing helps you see what the results will look like and then you can accept or change the selections as needed.*

which you can change the source objects (or replace the source objects) you selected to array.

Reset Array restores erased items and removes any item overrides.

Row Count lets you specify the number of rows in your array; while Row Spacing and Total Row Distance provide spacing options for the rows. This is more commonly used in rectangular arrays, but you can create a second "row" of items in your polar array. This will appear like a second ring.

> On your own, try changing the Row Count to 2. When you are finished change it back to 1.

Remaining options let you set the spacing and number for 3D arrays or arrays along a path. For now leave those items unchanged.

> Press: **[Esc]** to exit the Array Editor

Figure 4.60

Making Changes using Grips

A quick way to make changes to your drawing is by using the object's grips. Grips let you grab an object already drawn on your screen and use editing commands directly using your mouse.

You return to the drawing editor.

Activating an Object's Grips

> *Move the crosshairs over the upper vertical centerline of the geneva cam and click to select the line.*

The line becomes dashed and small boxes, called grips, appear at the endpoints, as shown in Figure 4.61. You can use them to stretch, move, rotate, scale, and mirror the object.

Tip: *To use the grips you must have a two- or three-button mouse. Use the Options dialog box to check that you have grips enabled. Pick on the Selection tab so that it becomes the uppermost tab in the dialog box. Select the box to the left of Enable Grips at this time if it is not already selected. You can also turn grips on or off and change their color and size using the Grip Size slider box.*

Figure 4.61

Selecting the Base Grip

Move the crosshairs to the grip at the upper end of the line and click to select it.

The selected grip changes to the highlighting color. This *base grip* will act as the base point for the command you will select using your mouse.

Using Stretch with Hot Grips

In the command line area, you should already see the prompt for the Stretch command.

STRETCH

Specify stretch point or [Base point/Copy/Undo/eXit]: *move the cross-hairs to a point above the old location of the endpoint and click*

The upper end of the line, where you picked the base grip, rubberbands from the position of the crosshairs. The point you selected should be stretched to the new stretched location. (You can also shorten objects with stretching.)

On your own, use turn off Object Snap mode for the next steps.

Using Move with Grips

On your own make a crossing box that crosses the entire geneva cam.

The grips appear as small boxes on all the selected objects.

Select the center of the circles as the base grip by moving the crosshairs over the box and clicking.

The base grip becomes highlighted. You will see the prompt for the Stretch command in the command line area.

Right-click: **to activate the Grips short-cut menu**

Click: **Move** *from the short-cut menu*

The command prompt shows the following options for the Move command. You will move the geneva cam down and to the left. The objects seem attached to the crosshairs during the move as shown in Figure 4.62.

MOVE

Specify move point or [Base point/Copy/Undo/eXit]: ***click a new location for the center grip down and to the left of the previous location***

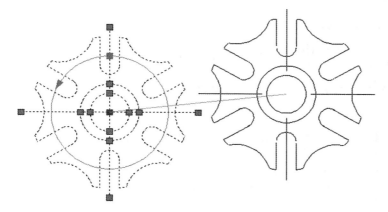

Figure 4.62

Using Move with the Copy Option

The grips should still be visible.

Click: **the grip at the center of the circles as the base grip**

Right-click: **to show the Grips short-cut menu**

Click: **Move**

Specify move point or [Base point/Copy/Undo/eXit]: ***C [Enter]***

A new prompt, similar to the previous one, appears.

MOVE (multiple)

Specify move point or [Base point/Copy/Undo/eXit]:

On your own, move the crosshairs to a location where you would like to make a copy of the object and click; repeat this procedure to make several copies.

When you are finished, press [Enter] or the return button and click Exit to end the command.

If you were to choose Copy from the short-cut menu instead of selecting Move, only the object that shares the Grips box that you selected would be copied.

On your own, use the grips and select **Copy** from the short-cut menu (without selecting Move first).

Use the **Erase** command to erase some of the copies if your screen is too crowded.

Press **[Esc]** to unselect any object grips you may have on

Tip: *If you want to cancel using the hot grips, press [Esc] twice.*

Tip: *You can also press [Enter] to cycle through the command choices that are available for use with hot grips.*

Using Rotate with Grips

Next you will use Crossing to select an entire geneva cam and activate its grips.

*Click: **above and to the left of one of the geneva cam copies***

*Click: **a point below and to the right of that geneva cam so that all of the drawing is selected***

The grips will appear on the objects in the drawing.

Turn Snap off [F9] so that you can see the effect of the rotation command clearly.

*Click: **the center of the circles as the base grip***

You will see the base grip change color. The Stretch command appears at the command prompt.

*Right-click: **to show the Grips short-cut menu***

*Click: **Rotate***

You will see the faint object rotating as you move the crosshairs around on the screen. You can click when the object is at the desired rotation or type in a numeric value for the rotation. Angles are measured with 0-degrees is to the right and positive values counterclockwise, unless you change the default.

ROTATE

Specify rotation angle or [Base point/Copy/Undo/Reference/eXit]: *45 [Enter]*

Now the object rotated 45°.

Using Scale with Grips

The Scale command changes the size of the object in your drawing database. Be sure that you use Scale only when you want to make the actual object larger. Use Zoom Window when you just want it to appear larger on the screen in order to see more detail.

On your own, activate the grips for the geneva cam, using implied Crossing.

When you have done this successfully, the grips will appear at the corners and midpoints of the lines, circles and arcs.

*Click: **the grip at the center of the circles as the base grip***

The grip becomes filled with the highlighting color. You will see the Stretch command in the command prompt area.

*Right-click: **to show the Grips short-cut menu***

*Click: **Scale***

SCALE

Specify scale factor or [Base point/Copy/Undo/Reference/eXit]:

As you move the crosshairs away from the base point, the faint image of the object becomes larger; as you get closer to the base point, it appears smaller. You can also type a scaling factor, similar to typing the

Tip: *To change the scale to known proportions, you can type in a scale factor. A value of 2 makes the object twice as large; a value of 0.5 makes it half its present size.*

rotation angle in the last steps. When you are happy with the new size of the object,

*Click the left mouse **button to accept the new size***

Using Mirror with Grips

On your own, activate the **grips** with implied Windowing again.

Select the **center grip** as the base grip.

Right-click: to pop-up the menu and select **Mirror**

The Mirror command uses a mirror line and forms a symmetrical image of the selected objects on the other side of the line. You can think of this line as rubberbanding from the base grip to the current location of the crosshairs. Note that, as you move the crosshairs to different positions on the screen, the faint mirror image of the object appears on the other side of the mirror line. You will see the prompt

MIRROR

Specify second point or [Base point/Copy/Undo/eXit]: *B [Enter]*

The Base point option lets you specify some other point besides the grip that you picked as the first point of the mirror line for the object.

Specify base point: ***click on a point to the left of the geneva shape***

Move the crosshairs on the screen and note the object being mirrored around the line that would form between the base point and the location of the crosshairs. When you are happy with the location of the mirrored object, click to select it. The old object disappears from the screen and the new mirrored object remains. End the command by pressing [Enter] or the return button.

Noun/Verb Selection

You can also use grips with other commands for noun/verb selection. *Noun/verb selection* is a method of selecting the objects that will be affected by a command first, instead of first selecting the command and then the group of objects. Think of the drawing objects as nouns, or things, and the commands as verbs, or actions. You will use this method with the Erase command to clear your screen.

*Click: **a point below and to the right of all your drawing objects***

Other corner: ***click a point above and to the left of the drawing objects***

You will see the grips for the objects that were crossed by the implied Crossing box appear in your drawing. The objects are now preselected and their grips show on the screen.

*Click: **Erase button***

As soon as you clicked the Erase button, the items that you had selected were erased.

On your own, save the now empty drawing as **gasket.dwg.** Leave it open as you will return to it after the next section.

Using the Path Array

The command Arraypath lets you quickly arrange copies of a set of objects along a chosen path.

To see this command in action, you will open your subdivision drawing and add a row of trees along the roadway edge.

On your own, open your drawing named **Subd_Plot.dwg** that you finished in Tutorial 3.

Click the Model tab to show only model space.

Create a new layer named TREES and assign it color green and linetype Continuous. Make this the current layer.

The subdivision drawing should appear on your screen similar to Figure 4.63. Next you will use the Tool Palettes to add a premade tree to your drawing. You will learn more about the Tool Palettes in Tutorial 10.

Figure 4.63

Click: **Tool Palettes** *from the View tab, Palettes panel*

Click: **Architectural** *to show it as the top tab on the palette*

Click and drag: **Trees - Imperial** *to add a tree to your drawing*

As you click on the tree symbol and drag it into your drawing, the top view of a tree moves with your cursor until you release the mouse button to place it. See Figure 4.64.

The tree is larger than it should be for the scale of the drawing. You can use the grip editing Scale command to resize it. It will be shown larger here to make it easy to see the effects of the Path Array command.

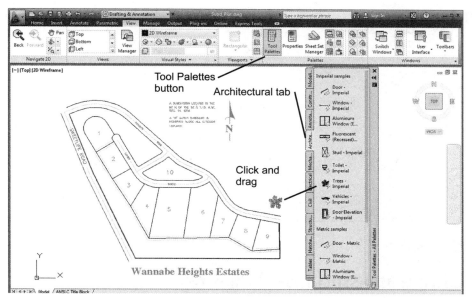

Figure 4.64

Tip: *Try some of the other items from the Tool Palettes off the side in your drawing. Right-clicking on many of the items provides a menu that you can use to select different views, or different styles of the object. For example, by right clicking on a tree once it is in your drawing, you can select a deciduous tree or the side view instead of a top view.*

On your own, use the **Spline** command to draw a curve that follows along the edge of the road as shown in Figure 4.65.

Figure 4.65

 Click: ***Path Array*** *from the Home tab, Modify panel*

   Select objects: ***click on the tree [Enter]***

Select path curve: ***click on the spline you drew***

Enter number of items along path or [Orientation/Expression] <Orientation>: ***10 [Enter]***

Specify the distance between items along path or [Divide/Total/Expression] <Divide evenly along path>: ***[Enter]***

Press Enter to accept or [ASsociative/Base point/Items/Rows/Levels/Align items/Z direction/eXit]<eXit>: ***[Enter]***

The tree is copied along the path curve as shown in Figure 4.66.

Figure 4.66

Editing an Associative Path Array

The default method for creating a Path Array is associative. This means the information for creating the array is retained, which allows for powerful editing features. In addition to similar options you can use while creating the array, after it is created you can change:

- the starting direction of the path.
- how the array objects are aligned to the path.
- the distance between items.
- how the objects are distributed along the path.
- the number of items.

Click: **on any of the trees in the array**

The entire array becomes highlighted and the Array context menu appears at the top of the screen as shown in Figure 4.67.

Figure 4.67

The trees are too large in proportion to the path. The scale of the original tree can be changed during array editing using Edit Source.

Edit Source lets you change the original item without losing the associativity of the array.

 Click: **Edit Source button**

A message appears on your screen.

Figure 4.68

Click: **OK**

You return to your drawing. Now you can edit the original tree.

Click: **the tree** to show its grips

Click: **the central grip** to use as the base grip

Right-click: **to show the short-cut menu**

Click: **Scale**

Specify scale factor or [Base point/Copy/Undo/Reference/eXit]: **.5 [Enter]**

The trees become half the previous size. To close the array editing state,

Click: **Edit Array, Save Changes**

Click: **on any of the trees in the array**

The array becomes highlighted and the Array context menu returns to the screen.

On your own, change the number of items to **20** as shown in Figure 4.69. After you have changed the number of items, press [Esc] to deselect the array.

Save and close this drawing. The empty drawing, **gasket.dwg, should still be on your screen. If it is not, check for it using View, Switch Windows or reopen the file if necessary.**

Figure 4.69

Tip: *You can move the path curve to a separate layer and freeze it, or make it non-plotting if you do not want to show the path in the finished drawing.*

Objects in the array can be aligned tangent to the path. Try the effect of the Align Items button on your own.

Using 2D Parametric Constraints

Another method you can use to define drawing geometry is to assign *parametric constraints* to define the shapes. Next you will draw the gasket shown in Figure 4.70 and use parametric constraints to define its geometry.

Figure 4.70

First, draw the general shapes for the gasket. The lines do not have to be perfectly straight, in fact, it is easier to see the effects of adding constraints if the drawing is not perfect.

> On your own, use a **polyline** to draw the four connecting lines, making sure to use the **Close** option to connect the final segment to form a closed polyline. Add the circles and two lines that will become the centerlines. Something like Figure 4.71 will work just fine.

Figure 4.71

*Click: **Parametric tab***

The ribbon changes to show the parametric tools as shown in Figure 4.72.

Figure 4.72

The constraints available for defining geometry are:

Horizontal: lines or pairs of points on objects must remain parallel to the X axis of the current coordinate system.

Vertical: lines or pairs of points on objects must remain parallel to the Y axis of the current coordinate system.

Perpendicular: two selected lines must maintain a 90 degree angle to one another.

Parallel: two selected lines must remain parallel.

Tangent: two curves (one can be a line) must maintain tangency to each other or their extensions.

Smooth: a spline must be contiguous and maintain *G2 continuity* with another spline, line, arc, or polyline.

Coincident: two points must stay connected or a point must stay connected to a curve or line (or its extension).

Concentric: two arcs, circles, or ellipses must maintain the same center point.

Collinear: two or more line segments must remain along the same line.

Symmetric: two selected objects must remain symmetric about a selected line or line defined by two points.

Equal: selected arcs and circles must maintain the same radius, or selected lines must maintain the same length.

Fix: points, line endpoints or curve points must stay in fixed position on the coordinate system.

In addition to constraining geometric features, you can also add the following size constraints.

Linear: specifies a distance between two points along the x- or y- axis.

Aligned: specifies a distance between two points.

Radius: specifies the radius for a curve.

Diameter: specifies the diameter of a circle.

Angular: specifies the angle between two lines.

You can also convert dimensions placed with the software's dimensioning commands (Tutorial 7), into dimensional constraints.

Next you will add some constraints to further define the geometry you have drawn.

Click: **Horizontal button** *from the Geometric palette of the Parametric tab*

The line changes to be horizontal if it was not already. The constraint marker for horizontal, which looks similar to the button appears along the line in the drawing as shown in Figure 4.73. Each segment of the polyline can be constrained individually.

Select an object or [2Points] <2Points>: *click the top line of the roughly rectangular shape*

 Click: **Perpendicular**

Select first object: *click the left line of the rectangular shape*

Select second object: *click the top line you constrained to horizontal*

The perpendicular constraint marker appears in the drawing and the lines adjust to become perpendicular.

On your own, select the polyline so that its grips appear. **Use grip editing** to move the vertices of the polyline. Notice that these lines now maintain the constrained relationships. When you are finished testing, press [Esc] to unselect the polyline. If you made any changes, use **Undo** to restore the original appearance.

Figure 4.73

 Click: **Parallel button** *from the Geometry panel of the Parameters tab*

Select first object: *click the right line of the rectangle*

Select second object: *click the left line of the rectangle*

The parallel constraint is added and the right line is adjusted to be parallel to the left one.

On your own, add a **perpendicular** constraint between the bottom line and the right line of the rectangle.

Add a **vertical** constraint to the line that will act as a vertical centerline.

Add a **horizontal** constraint to the line that will act as a horizontal centerline.

Your drawing should be similar to Figure 4.74. It may not be exactly the same depending on your first sketched shapes. Next you will make the rectangle symmetric about the centerlines you drew.

Tip: *If your lines do not stay connected like shown, you may not have created a closed polyline. If so, try adding a Coincident constraint to connect the endpoints of the lines.*

Tip: *If you do not get the result you are expecting, try selecting the items in the opposite order. When using constraints that create a relationship between two objects, the order of selection can make a difference. Generally the first object selected remains fixed and the second object selected adjusts to maintain the relationship. As more constraints are added, these relationships become more complex and the objects must satisfy a set of constraints.*

Figure 4.74

 Click: ***Symmetric button*** *from the Geometry panel of the Parameters tab*

Select first object: ***click the right line of the rectangle***

Select second object: ***click the left line of the rectangle***

Select symmetry line: ***click the vertical centerline***

The drawing adjusts so that the lines are equal distance from the vertical centerline.

 Click: ***Symmetric button*** *from the Geometry panel of the Parameters tab*

Select first object: ***click the upper line of the rectangle***

Select second object: ***click the lower line of the rectangle***

Select symmetry line: ***click the horizontal centerline***

The drawing adjusts again to satisfy this constraint condition. Next you will make the center of the smaller circle coincident with the vertical centerline.

Click: ***Coincident button*** *from the Geometry panel of the Parameters tab*

Select first point or [Object/Autoconstrain] <Object>: ***click the outer circle***

Select second point or [Object] <Object>: ***click the vertical centerline***

In the previous steps, selecting the circle automatically finds it center as the point to make coincident as shown in Figure 4.75.

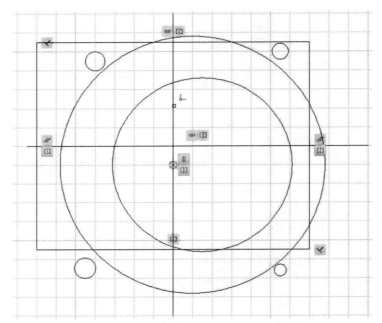

Figure 4.75

On your own, make the same circle center **coincident** with the horizontal centerline.

 *Click: **Concentric button** from the Geometry panel*

Select first object: ***click the inner circle***

Select second object: ***click the outer circle***

Now your drawing should look similar to Figure 4.76. The smaller circles are still unconstrained, so they may be in different locations. Also the size of the rectangles and circles are not fixed.

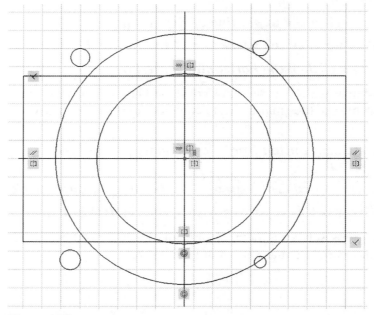

Figure 4.76

On your own, use the grips to resize the rectangle and circle. Notice that these stay symmetric as you resize the objects.

 Click: **Equal button** *from the Geometry panel*

Select first object or [Multiple]: ***click the top horizontal line***

Select second object: ***click the left vertical line***

Now the sides of the rectangle must be equal. You do not need to define the other two sides of the square, as their perpendicular, parallel, horizontal, and vertical constraints already define them.

It is generally not a good practice to *overconstrain* the geometry. Overconstraining means defining the same geometry in multiple ways. For example if you were to add an Equal constraint between the top line and the right side line of the rectangle. Based on the sides having perpendicular constraints and the bottom line being parallel to the top one, the left side length must be equal to the length of the right side, which has already been defined equal to the top.

Next you will constrain the size of the outer circle and the square.

 Click: **Linear** *from the Dimensional panel of the ribbon Parametric tab*

Specify first constraint point or [Object] <Object>: ***click the left endpoint of the upper horizontal line***

Specify second constraint point: ***click the right endpoint of the upper horizontal line***

Specify dimension line location: ***click above the line to place the dimensional constraint [Enter]***

The value for the linear dimension constraint shows. In this example Dimension text = 6.8014. You may have a different value. Next add a diameter dimension for the circle.

 Click: **Diameter from the Dimensional panel of the ribbon Parametric tab**

Select arc or circle: ***click on the outer circle.***

Specify dimension line location: ***click to place the dimension [Enter]***

Dimension text = 7.3891 *(You may see a different value)*

Figure 4.77 shows the drawing with these dimensional constraints added. Your values may be different.

Click: **Parameters Manager button**

The Parameters Manager appears on your screen as shown in Figure 4.77. The two dimensional constraints you added are shown there.

Tip: *The Equal constraint provides an option that allows you to select multiple objects to make equal to the first. To use it, pick the Equal constraint button and enter M at the prompt.*

Figure 4.77

You can use mathematical expressions to define dimensional constraints. You can also type values and have the drawing geometry update to match the value.

> *Click:* **in the input box in the Expression column** *across from the d1 linear dimension value*

> *Type:* **dia1*.85** *as shown in Figure 4.78 (if your dimension parameter are identified differently use the ones for your drawing)*

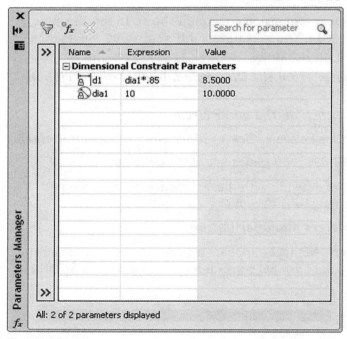

Figure 4.78

Now the size of the square is based on the size of the circle.

*Double-click: **on the diameter dimensional constraint in your drawing** (or you can type the value in the Parameters Manager)*

*Type: **10 [Enter]** for the circle diameter value*

The drawing automatically updates to the new size. Notice that the linear dimension for the square is now 8.5.

On your own, add **Equal** constraints to the four small circles.

Add a **Symmetry** constraints to the upper two circles using the vertical center-line as the symmetry line. Do the same for the two lower circles.

Next, add a **Symmetry** constraint to the two circles at the left using the horizontal line as the symmetry line. **Drag the upper left circle** into the upper left corner of the square, outside the circle. **Save** your drawing.

The other small circles, should move with it maintaining their symmetry. Your drawing should look similar to Figure 4.79.

Figure 4.79

On your own, use the Fillet command, with a Radius of .5 and the Polyline option to add rounded corners to the square.

Trim the circle and square.

Notice that this changes the constraints. As the geometry changes, some of the constraints no longer apply and are deleted automatically.

*Click: **Autoconstrain** from the Geometry panel of the Parameters tab*

*Select objects or [Settings]: **use a window to select the entire drawing [Enter]***

The software has automatically applied constraints it infers might be useful for the shape you have drawn.

Experiment on your own. Use the grips to resize some of the drawing objects.

How does it behave differently than the version you constrained in the tutorial?

Add constraints and dimensions until the shape updates as you think best when you click and drag the top arc to reshape the gasket.

You have completed Tutorial 4. Save your drawings or exit without saving your changes if you do not want the most recent versions of the drawings saved.

Parametric constraints will not be used in the following tutorials. As you work through the tutorials follow the directions, so that you will get the results shown in the figures. Keep in mind geometric and dimensional constraints are very useful tools.

Exit the AutoCAD software.

Key Terms

associative	global linetype scaling factor	mirror line	polygon
base grip		noun/verb selection	quadrant point
circumscribed	G2 continuity	parametric constraint	rectangular array
distance across the flats	grips	polar array	selection filters
	inscribed		

Key Commands

Array	Grips	Rotate	Snap to Intersection
Arraypolar	Linetype	Scale	Snap to Nearest
Break	LTScale	Snap From	Snap to Node
CELTScale	Mirror	Snap to Apparent Intersection	Snap to Parallel
Construction Line (XLine)	Move	Snap to Center	Snap to Perpendicular
Copy Object	Polygon	Snap to Endpoint	Snap to Quadrant
Extend	Quick Select	Snap to Extension	Snap to Tangent
FileDIA	Ray	Snap to Insertion	Stretch

Exercises

The letter M after an exercise number means that the given dimensions are in millimeters (metric units). If no letter follows the exercise number, the dimensions are in inches. Don't include dimensions on the drawings.

4.1M Gasket

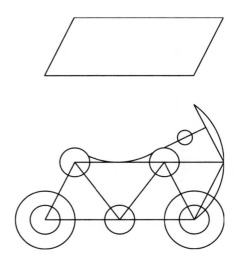

4.2 The Cycle

Starting with the parallelogram shown, use Object snaps to draw the lines, arcs, and circles indicated in the drawing. Use parametric constraints if directed by your instructor.

4.3 Starboard Rear Rib

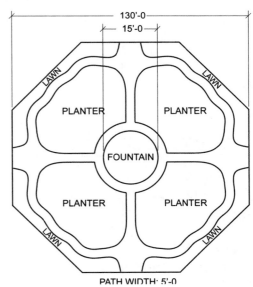

4.4 Park Plan

Create a park plan similar to the one shown here. Use Polyline and Polyline Edit, Spline to create a curving path. Note the symmetry. Add labels with Single line text.

4.5 Floor Plan
Draw the floor plan according to the dimensions shown. Add text, border, and title block.

4.6 Interchange
Draw this intersection, then mirror the circular interchange for all lanes.

4.7M Plastic Knob

4.8M Foundry Hook

4.9M Support

4.10 Hanger

4.11 Slotted Ellipse

Draw the figure shown (note the symmetry). Do not show dimensions.

4.12 Shift Lever

TEMPLATE DRAWINGS AND MORE PLOTTING

Introduction

One of the advantages of using the AutoCAD software is that you can easily rescale, change, copy, and reuse drawings. Up to this point, most of the drawings that you have created began from a drawing called *acad.dwt*. In *acad.dwt*, many variables are preset to help you begin drawing. A drawing in which specific default settings have been selected and saved for later use is called a *template drawing*. You can save any existing drawing as a template from which to start a new drawing.

You may want to create different template drawings to use for different sheet sizes and types of drawings. In this tutorial you will use a template for a C-sized sheet (22" X 17") to arrange views of the subdivision drawing for easy plotting. You will also make a drawing template containing default settings of your own from which you will start 8.5" X 11" drawings in succeeding tutorials.

Setting up template drawings eliminates repetitive steps and helps you work efficiently. The amount of time you spend creating one template is roughly the amount of time you will save on each subsequent drawing that you start from the template drawing. Your template drawing will contain your custom defaults for layers, limits, grid, snap, and text size and font for use in future drawings.

You will use paper space *layouts* to add views of your model space drawing as you want it to appear on the printed sheet. Using paper space layouts allows you to have more than one printed sheet format for a single model space drawing. You will also insert c:\work\mysubdiv.dwg into a new drawing as a *block* and use the settings there to plot it to scale.

Starting

Before you begin, **launch the AutoCAD 2012 program.**

Using a Standard Template

You will create a new drawing using a standard AutoCAD template file: the ANSI-C template with color-dependent plot styles. This is set up to plot on a 22" X 17" sheet of paper following guidelines from the American National Standards Institute (ANSI/ASME). It will be used to demonstrate features you can use to lay out plotted sheets.

Click: **File, New**

Click: **to change the file extension to .dwt** *from the pull-down at the bottom of the dialog box*

Objectives

When you have completed this tutorial, you will be able to

1. Use a template drawing for standard sheet sizes.

2. Insert a drawing into another drawing as a block.

3. Zoom drawing views to scale for plotting.

4. Create and save a template drawing for later use.

5. Create a system of basic layers for mechanical drawings.

6. Use layer groups and filters.

7. Preset Viewres, Limits, and other defaults in a template drawing.

8. Set up paper space layouts in a template drawing.

9. Set the style for drawing points.

10. Use the Divide command.

11. Plot drawings using a layout.

12. Create a Sheet Set.

The Select Template dialog box changes to show the template selections.

Use the Look in area to select the SheetSets folder *as shown in Figure 5.1*

The templates stored in the SheetSets subfolder of the default template location (set using the Files Tab of the Options dialog box) are listed alphabetically. You should see a list similar to that shown in Figure 5.1.

Tip: *To change the default template directory pick Application icon, Options, select the Files tab, and change the setting under Drawing Template File Location. To see the setting, pick the + (plus sign) to expand the list under Drawing Template Settings, and the items below it. You can use the Browse button at the right of the dialog box and click to select a new directory.*

Figure 5.1

Click: ***Manufacturing Imperial.dwt*** *from the list of available templates*

Click: ***Open*** *(or double-click the file name)*

A new drawing should appear on your screen with a border and standard title block for a C-sized sheet. You will save it with a new name to your *c:\work* directory.

Click: ***Save button***

Type: ***Subd_Plot*** *as the file name to save*

The file name Subd_Plot should show in the AutoCAD title bar. Notice that when you save a drawing created from a template it does not overwrite the template file. You supply a new name. This way you will not accidentally change your template file. Your screen should look similar to Figure 5.2.

Figure 5.2

Paper Space Layouts

Using paper space layouts allows you to arrange views of your drawing on a "sheet of paper." A *paper space layout* is used for things like borders, title blocks, text notes, and viewports. (A viewport is like a window that you can look through to see your model space drawing on the sheet of paper.)

Up to this point you have been working in *model space* to create your drawing geometry. As you have already seen in Tutorial 3, you can plot your drawing from model space if desired. A better method is to use paper space layouts to control the appearance of your plotted drawing.

The UCS icon has changed to show the paper space icon, which looks like a triangle. Also the ANSI C Title Block layout tab appears next to the Model tab on the status bar as shown in Figure 5.2.

Figure 5.3 illustrates the concept of using paper space layouts and model space drawings.

Figure 5.3

Page settings are used to control the plotter each time you plot the drawing. This way you do not have to reset the plotter requirements each time you print. You can also save the page settings and use that same named page setup with other drawings, or within a template file.

The paper space layout in this case already contains a border with zone numbers and letters which make it easy for you to refer to an area on the sheet when noting a revision or discussing the drawing with a client. It also contains a standard title block and revision block to which you can add your own text.

Printer Area

The white area on the screen (or shaded area in the illustration in Figure 5.3) represents the sheet of paper. The dashed line represents the limits of the printer. The distance from the edge that a printer can reach is different for each printer. The distance from the left edge isn't necessarily the same as it is from the right edge or the top and bottom edges. (When you preview a plot in the Plot dialog box, the outer line in the preview shows the printer limits.) The limits of a printer may also be different for each sheet size.

Viewport

The template drawing that you inserted does not contain any viewports. A viewport is like a hole through the paper that you can look through to see model space. Next, you will create a viewport on a layer named Viewport. You will set the color for the viewport to magenta, so that it stands out on your screen.

Click: *Layer Properties icon*

The Layer Properties Manager appears on your screen. You will use it to create a new layer named Viewport, with the color magenta, and give it a non-plotting status as shown in Figure 5.4.

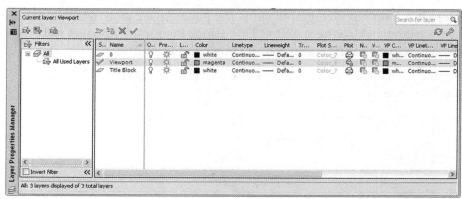

Figure 5.4

Click: *New button*

Type: *Viewport*

Click: *the color box corresponding to layer Viewport*

Click: *magenta from the top row of standard colors*

Click: *the icon in the Plot column row* associated with layer Viewport, so that the icon changes to a printer with a red crossed-circle
to set it to non-plotting

Double-click: *Viewport* layer to set it current

Click: *[X] from the upper left of the dialog box to close the Layer
Properties Manager*

Creating a Viewport

Next you will use the Vports command from the ribbon View tab,
Viewports panel to create a polygonal viewport. Paper space viewports
can be irregular shapes. You will draw this one to match the inside
border of the C-sized title block.

Tip: *Often you do not want to
plot the actual viewport objects
as they would appear as a box
around the view. To do this,
you can make the Viewport
layer non-plotting. On your
screen you will still see the
objects, but you will notice later
that this layer will not plot. This
can also be useful for notes,
construction lines and other
information you want to show,
but would not want to plot.*

Figure 5.5

Click: *Polygonal from the ribbon View tab, Viewports panel as
shown in Figure 5.5*

Specify start point: *click point 1 as shown in Figure 5.6*

Specify next point or [Arc/Length/Undo]: *click points 2-8 in order*

Specify next point or [Arc/Close/Length/Undo]: *C [Enter]*

Figure 5.6   Drawing the Viewport

You should now see the lines that make up the viewport colored magenta. This viewport allows you to access your model space drawing from paper space.

Switching to Model Space

To access model space inside a viewport, you can double-click inside the viewport. To return to the paper space layout, double-click outside of the viewport area. You can also type the alias MS at the command prompt to switch to model space. Type PS to switch back to paper space. Next, switch to model space,

> *Double-click:* **anywhere inside the viewport**

The viewport border becomes highlighted. The paper space icon no longer shows on the screen.

> Move your cursor around on the screen to notice that the crosshairs display while inside the viewport, but the pointer shows when you move outside the viewport.

This shows that you are in the mode where you can draw in model space, inside the viewport.

Another way to switch to model space is to use the Model tab. This changes your display so that the paper space layout is temporarily not visible. Often this is a useful way to work on your drawing.

> *Click:* **the Model tab** *from below the drawing area*

The screen appears blank as you do not have a drawing created yet. You no longer see the title block and border.

Inserting an Existing Drawing

You can insert any drawing into any other AutoCAD drawing. You will use Insert Block to insert the subdivision drawing that you finished in Tutorial 3 into the current template drawing so you can see the effects of using paper space viewports in the next steps.

When a drawing is inserted into another drawing it becomes a Block. In other words, all of the objects in the drawing are made into a single symbol or Block object. This object resides on the layer that was current when it was inserted. (Blocks can be converted back to individual objects on their original layers using the Explode command.) The Insert button is on the ribbon Home tab, Block panel.

First, make layer 0 the current layer.

> *Click:* **Layer 0** *from the Layer Control to set it as the current layer*
>
> *Click:* **Insert button** *from the Home tab, Block panel*

The Insert dialog box appears on your screen, as shown in Figure 5.7.

Figure 5.7

You will click the Browse button to insert an existing drawing. Only the portion of the drawing created in model space will be inserted.

Click: **Browse**

The Select Drawing File dialog box appears on your screen. You will select the file you created in Tutorial 3 named *mysubdiv.dwg*. You may need to change to the directory where it is located.

Click: **mysubdiv.dwg**

Click: **Open**

You return to the Insert dialog box. Note the check to the left of the Specify On-screen box under the Insertion point heading. If there is no check, click the box now.

This means you will return to your drawing to select the point where the subdivision drawing will be inserted. The Scale parameter is set to 1.0 for X, Y, and Z and the Rotation angle is set to 0. You can type a different value for the scale and rotation for inserted drawings if you want, or you can check to specify them on-screen. Typically you will insert drawings at the original size (a scale factor of 1.0 and the original rotation, 0-degrees).

Click: **OK** *(to return to the drawing)*

Specify insertion point or [Basepoint/Scale/Rotate]: **0,0 [Enter]**

The image of the subdivision does not show in the viewport because, at the current zoom factor, the subdivision is much too large for the viewport. In order to see the subdivision, you must zoom out within the viewport. To make the subdivision fit inside the drawing window,

Click: **Zoom All button** *(or try typing Z [Enter] A [Enter])*

Now the entire subdivision drawing should appear in the drawing area, as shown in Figure 5.8.

Tip: *If you have not completed mysubdiv.dwg from Tutorial 3, use the datafile subdiv2.dwg instead. It will not be complete, but you will be able to to see the effect of the commands.*

Figure 5.8

Showing the Drawing in the Layout

Next switch back to the layout tab to show the subdivision drawing in the layout containing the border and title block.

> *Click: **ANSI C Title Block layout tab***

The view switches back to the layout. Now you still do not see the subdivision drawing. Why? Because once again the view is zoomed in a way that only shows a blank portion of the drawing. To change this, first make sure you are inside the model space viewport,

> *Double-click: **inside the viewport area** to switch to model space*
>
> *Double-click: **the mouse scroll wheel** to zoom to drawing extents*

Figure 5.9

Setting the Viewport Zoom Scale

The next step is to set the scale for the drawing inside the viewport by establishing a relationship between the number of units in model space and the number of units in paper space. The standard scale area of the dialog box lets you choose from some likely relationships between paper space and model space. Figure 5.10 shows the Viewport Scale button on the status bar layout and view tools area. The Viewport Scale button is only visible when you are in model space, or from paper space when a viewport is selected.

*Double-click: **outside the viewport** to switch to paper space*

Notice the Paper/Model button on the status bar changes to display Paper

***Select the viewport** (it becomes highlighted and its grips show)*

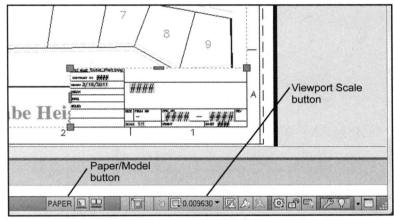

Figure 5.10   Status Bar Layout and View tools

*Click: **to expand the Viewport Scale list** as shown in Figure 5.11*

*Click: **1:100***

Tip: *Double-clicking on a drawing object quickly pops up the Properties dialog box. Viewports are drawing objects in paper space. Try double-clicking on the viewport and using the Properties dialog box to quickly set its scale.*

Figure 5.11

Your drawing should zoom inside the viewport similar to Figure 5.12. The scale that you would note in the title block for this drawing is 1"=100'. That is because the paper space sheet is set up in inch units. The model space subdivision was drawn with decimal units where 1 unit equals 1 foot. The drawing is now zoomed so that when it plots, one paper space unit will equal 100 model space units, or a scale of 1"=100'. The entire subdivision does not fit inside the viewport, so you will use the custom scale area of the dialog box to fit the entire subdivision inside the viewport. It is preferred to plot drawings at typical scales such as the ones available on the standard scales selection. Custom scales should be used for drawings only when necessary to show the drawing clearly.

Figure 5.12

You will create a custom scale to zoom the drawing inside the viewport, so that one unit in paper space equals 150 units in the subdivision in model space (a scale of 1"=150').

The Custom selection from the Viewport Scale list lets you add new scales to the list that you can select later. The viewport scale actually specifies the zoom XP scale factor. From model space, you can also type the Zoom command and set this scale factor from the command prompt. The zoom XP scale factor is a ratio. It is the number of units from the object in paper space divided by the number of units in model space. For example, if you want the model space object to appear twice its size on the paper, specify 2XP as the scale factor (2 paper space units/1 model space unit). You can also think of the zoom XP factor as the value or size of one model space unit when shown in paper space. To specify a scale of 1"=150' for the subdivision, you would set the XP scaling factor to 0.006667 (1 unit in paper space/150 units in model space).

You will use the status bar Viewport Scale selection to zoom the model space drawing so that one paper space unit equals 150 model space units.

Click: **to expand the Viewport Scale list** *from the status bar*

Click: **Custom** *from the bottom of the list*

Figure 5.13

The Edit Drawing Scales dialog box appears as shown in Figure 5.13. The scale you would like to choose 1: 150 is not listed, so you will add a new scale.

Click: **Add button** *from the upper right of the dialog box*

Type the following settings into the dialog box as shown in Figure 5.14:

Name appearing in scale list: *1"=150'*

Paper units: *1*

Drawing units: *150*

Figure 5.14

Click: **OK** *to exit Add Scale*

Click: **OK** *to exit Edit Drawing Scales*

Now the new scale name 1"=150' is added to the list.

*Double-click: **inside the viewport** to make it active*

*Click: **to expand the Viewport Scale list***

*Click: **1"=150'** from the list (it may be near the top of the list)*

Note the image is now smaller. The scale you would note for the drawing is now 1"=150'

Figure 5.15

You have set up the zoom scale for the viewport so that if you plot paper space at a scale of 1=1, the model space object is shown at a scale of 1"=150' on the paper. Remember, in the original subdivision drawing, each unit represented one foot.

Using Pan to Position the Drawing

Use the Pan command to drag the model space drawing around in the paper space viewport without changing the scale or the location of the drawing on the model space coordinate system. Once you have selected the Pan command, the cursor changes to look like a hand.

Check that you are in model space inside the viewport, before using pan to position the view.

Command: ***MS [Enter] (or use the status bar Model/Paper button)***

The viewport should be highlighted and the paper space icon does not show.

*Click: **Pan Realtime icon** (or press and hold the scroll wheel)*

Click a point near the top center of the subdivision and drag the image around until it is centered in the viewport as shown in Figure 5.16.

*Press: **[Esc]** to exit the Pan command*

Figure 5.16

The layout and viewing tools area of the status bar is shown enlarged in Figure 5.17. Note the Viewport Scale button now shows 1"=150', the name for the scale that you created. To the left of the Viewport Scale button is the Lock/Unlock Viewport button.

Tip: *You will learn more about the relationship between viewport and annotation scale in Tutorial 7*

Maximize/Minimize Viewport — Lock/Unlock Viewport — Viewport Scale — Toolbar Window Positions Lock/Unlock

Figure 5.17

Locking the Viewport Scale

In order to preserve the relationship between model space and paper space, be sure that if you use Zoom Window to enlarge your drawing, you use Zoom Previous, not Zoom All, to return to this Zoom XP size before you plot. Additionally, you can always return to this list and specify the scale factor again if needed. Develop a habit of checking the viewport scale before you plot a drawing.

You can use the layout and view tools area of the status bar to lock the viewport, so that its scale cannot be inadvertently changed by zooming.

   Click: ***Lock/Unlock Viewport button*** *so that it appears locked*

Creating a Second Floating Viewport

Viewports can be created in model space or in paper space. Model space viewports are called *tiled viewports* because their edges line up next to each other like floor tiles. Paper space viewports are called *floating viewports* because they can overlap each other or "float" on top of one another. Multiple paper space viewports can be printed on one layout sheet.

You can use floating viewports to create enlarged details, location drawings, or additional views of the same object. (You will learn more about this method when you create solid models in Tutorial 11.)

Switch back to paper space and set the layer before creating another viewport.

*Double-click: **outside the viewport border** to switch to paper space*

*Click: **to make the Viewport layer current** using the Layer Control*

*Click: **to turn off running Object Snap** from the status bar*

*Click: **Named Viewports button** from the View tab, Viewports panel*

*Click: **New Viewports tab***

The Viewports dialog box appears as shown in Figure 5.18.

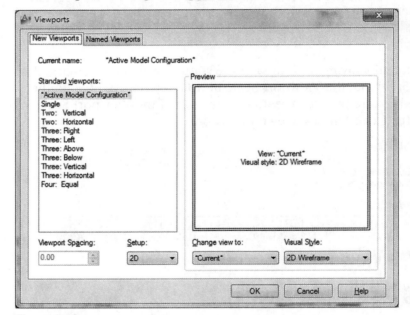

Figure 5.18

The left side of the dialog box shows options for standard viewport configurations you can select. Click on an item in the list below Standard viewports to see a preview of that arrangement in the preview pane. Later in these tutorials you will work with 3D drawings. For now, leave 2D selected in the Setup area and 2D Wireframe in the Visual Style area.

*Click: **Single** from the Standard viewports area*

Leave Setup set to 2D

Leave Change view to: set to *Current*

Leave Visual Style set to 2D Wireframe

*Click: **OK***

At the next prompts, you click a location for corners of the viewport.

Specify first corner or [Fit] <Fit>: *click near point 1 shown in Figure 5.16 for the upper left corner of the viewport*

Specify opposite corner: *click near point 2 for the lower right corner of the viewport*

A second viewport is added to the drawing as shown in Figure 5.19. It shows the entire subdivision drawing, zoomed so that all of the drawing limits fit inside the viewport.

Figure 5.19

Making a Viewport Active

When you are in paper space, double-clicking inside a viewport will make the viewport active and switch to model space. Only one viewport can be active at a time. When a viewport is active, its border becomes highlighted and the crosshairs appear completely inside it. Next you will switch to model space and make the new smaller viewport active.

*Double-click: **inside the smaller viewport***

The smaller viewport border appears highlighted as shown in Figure 5.20. The crosshairs should be inside the viewport. If you move past the viewport border, the crosshairs change to a pointer.

Figure 5.20

Tip: *To avoid inadvertently changing the zoom scale for the viewport, you can lock the viewport scale. Doing so will manage zooming so that the zoom XP factor does not change.*

Once you are already in model space, to make a different viewport active, move the arrow cursor into that viewport and click.

Next, you will use the Zoom Window command to enlarge an area inside the smaller viewport you created.

Click: *Zoom Window button*

Specify first corner: *click to set the first corner*

Specify opposite corner: *click to create a window around lot 1*

The area inside the window you selected is enlarged inside the viewport, as shown in Figure 5.21.

Tip: *If you have trouble picking a viewport to make it active, press [Ctrl]-R to select it.*

On your own, use **Pan Realtime** if needed to position the objects inside the viewport. Don't forget to press [Esc] to exit the Pan command.

Tip: *You cannot edit a viewport when its layer is turned off. You can still edit the contents of the viewport, that is, the objects that are in model space. If at some time you are trying to change or erase a viewport while in paper space and you cannot get it to work, check to see if the layer where the viewport border was created is turned off, locked, or frozen. Making the layer non-plotting allows you to still see the layer so it is always available for editing but it will not plot. You can also use non-plotting layers to add notes to your drawing, such as reminders, that you do not want to print.*

Figure 5.21

Attributes and Fields

Attributes are a way of attaching data to items in your drawing. The ANSI C Title Block from which you started your drawing uses attributes to store information such as the revision and sheet number. In addition the title block uses fields to store information such as the file name and date. *Fields* are used to display data that can be read from information which may change, such as the date. You probably noticed that the date and your drawing name were already displayed in the title block. You will learn more about defining attributes in Tutorial 13. Some of the attributes have default values set for them in this title block that appear as number signs (###). This helps you notice them and provide the information.

On your own, switch to paper space.

Double-click: **on an attribute item (###)** *to show the Enhanced Attribute Editor as shown in Figure 5.22.*

Figure 5.22

On your own, resize the Enhanced Attribute Editor by dragging its corners so that you can see more of the attributes that are associated with the title block as shown in Figure 5.22.

Click: **SHEET** *from the list of attributes so that it appears highlighted*

The value area at the bottom of the dialog box displays the default value of #### - #### or the attribute named SHEET.

On your own, replace the current value with SUBD-4321.

Presently, the text for the attributes is on the same layer as the lines of the title block. They are all on layer, Titleblock.

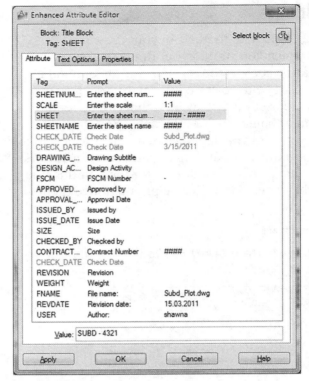

Figure 5.23

Click: ***Properties tab*** *from the dialog box*

Change the layer for the SHEET attribute to TEXT see Figure 5.24.

Figure 5.24

On your own, fill in the remaining values to complete the title block.

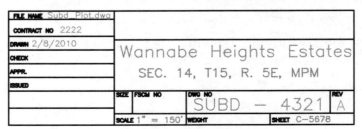

Figure 5.25

Next you will use the Circle command to draw a circle around the area shown in the second viewport, which is going to serve as a detail of lot 1. This circle will be drawn in paper space. Lines added to model space will show up in every viewport (unless you control the visibility of the viewport). Paper space represents a virtual sheet of paper on which you are laying out the drawing.

On your own, check that you are in paper space. You should see the paper space icon.

Click: **Zoom All button**

On your own, to the main drawing add a dashed circle in layer Titleblock. Fit it around the area that is zoomed in the detail. Use the circle's hot grips to stretch or move it as necessary so that it fits around the area in the main drawing that is zoomed up in the detail. Add text SEE DETAIL A below the circle. Below it, add text DETAIL A as shown in Figure 5.21.

Click: **Save button** *to save your drawing*

When you have finished these steps, your drawing should look like Figure 5.26.

Figure 5.26

Using Irregularly Shaped Viewports

Viewports do not have to display a rectangular shape. You can use the VPClip command to create irregularly shaped viewports from viewports you have already created. Using the Object option, you can convert an existing paper space object into a viewport. The Polygonal option allows you to select points to define an irregular boundary.

The boundary for a viewport must have at least three points and must be closed. The software locates a viewport object using the points you specify and then clips the content of the viewport to the specified boundary. You will try each of the viewport clipping methods next.

On your own, make the VIEWPORT layer current

*Select: **the small magenta rectangular viewport** so that its grips appear*

*Right-click: **in the drawing area** to show the short-cut menu*

*Click: **Viewport Clip***

Select clipping object or [Polygonal] <Polygonal>: ***[Enter]***

Specify start point: ***click a point near A in Figure 5.27***

Specify next point or [Arc/Close/Length/Undo]: ***click points B through L to form an irregular boundary inside the circle***

Specify next point or [Arc/Close/Length/Undo]: ***C [Enter]***

Figure 5.27

The contents of the viewport are clipped to the irregular polygon boundary as shown in Figure 5.23. Next you will use the option to clip the viewport to an object by drawing a circle in paper space and then clipping the viewport to that shape.

On your own, **draw a circle in paper space** in layer Titleblock to enclose the viewport you just clipped.

Command: ***VPClip [Enter]***

Select viewport to clip: ***click the irregular viewport boundary***

Select clipping object or [Polygonal/Delete] <Polygonal>: ***click the circle around the small viewport***

The contents of the viewport are clipped to the shape of the circle as shown in Figure 5.28.

Save your drawing on your own at this time.

Figure 5.28

Plotting from Paper Space

You set up your drawing in paper space and set a scaling factor for the number of units in model space that equal one unit in paper space. Because you used a template for a C-sized sheet, you will use 1=1 for the plot scale when choosing that sheet size. You will choose to plot the layout to show the title block.

Check that you are in **paper space.**

Click: Plot button

The Plot dialog box will appear on your screen as shown in Figure 5.29.

Figure 5.29

Tip: *If you do not have a plotter capable of using the C-sized sheet, you can plot a check print to a standard 8.5" X 11" printer or plotter. To do this, select this sheet and choose Fit to paper in the Plot scale area. The entire drawing border and contents will be scaled to fit on the smaller sheet size. Of course this means that the drawing scale of 1"=150' no longer applies. Make sure that the Save changes to layout box near the top of the Plot dialog box is not selected before you change your paper size.*

Tip: *If you do not have a printer or plotter that is capable of printing a C-sized sheet, try creating a PDF file of the drawing instead.*

*Choose: **Layout** for the Plot area*

*Choose: **ANSI C (22" X 17") paper size***

*Set: **1:1** as the Plot Scale*

Ensure that Save changes to layout box is not checked

*Click: **Preview***

*Click: **OK to plot** or Cancel to cancel plotting the drawing*

Sheet Sets

Large projects often have more than one drawing sheet associated with them. Sheet sets are a way to organize and publish drawing sets. Each sheet in a sheet set can show one layout at a time. Although it is possible to create multiple layout tabs for a single drawing, this is not useful when using the Sheet Set Manager.

The Sheet Set Manager is available from the ribbon View tab, Palettes panel, as well as the Quick Access toolbar.

Next you will create a sheet set that contains the layout for the subdivision drawing you just created along with other drawings.

Before creating a sheet set:

- Only one layout can function as a sheet within a sheet set. It is best to create your drawings with only one layout tab per drawing file. Using multiple layouts from a single drawing as separate sheets within a set makes it impossible for multiple users to access that sheet or layout at the same time. It also makes your sheet sets more complicated and harder to keep organized.

- Organize your drawing files. Generally you will want all of the drawings for a project to be in the same folder (or subfolders of one folder). The sheet set aids you in locating the files and publishing them but it will not overcome disorganized file storage habits.

- Think about which template file will be used to add new sheets to the set. You will specify this in the Sheet Set Properties dialog box.

- Consider the page setup file you will use to store page setups for plotting the entire set of sheets.

Figure 5.30

*Click: **Sheet Set Manager button** from the ribbon View, Palettes panel (as shown in Figure 5.30.)*

The Sheet Set Manager appears on your screen as shown in Figure 5.31.

Tip: *To learn more about the Sheet Set Manager, click Learn about Sheet Sets, from the Sheet Set Manager or pick Help, and type Sheet Set Manager into the search box.*

Figure 5.31

Click: **New Sheet Set** *from the pull-down list near the top of the dialog box as shown in the left Figure 5.31*

The Create Sheet Set wizard appears on your screen. You can begin a new sheet set from an example showing sheet organization or by adding your existing drawings.

Click: **Existing Drawings** *as shown in Figure 5.32*

Click: **Next**

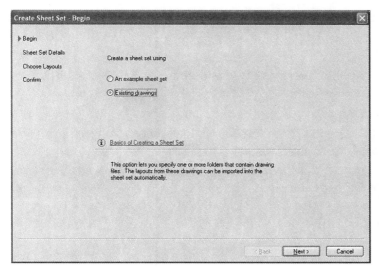

Figure 5.32

Using the Sheet Set Details page shown in Figure 5.33, you can specify the name for the sheet set, a description, and the path where the sheet set file (which uses the *.dst* extension) will be stored. You can also set additional properties by clicking on the Sheet Set Properties button.

*Type: **Wannabe Estates** for the name of the new sheet set and add a description as shown in Figure 5.33*

*Set: **c:\work** as the path in Store sheet set data file here*

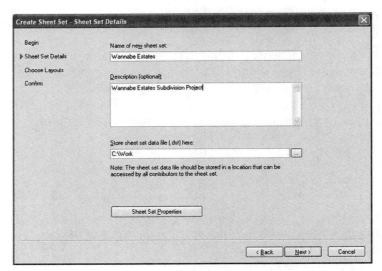

Figure 5.33

*Click: **Sheet Set Properties button***

Figure 5.34

To set the Sheet storage location to your *work* folder,

*Click: **the ellipsis button** that appears when you click in the Sheet*

Storage location input box

Navigate to c:\work.

Click: **Open**

Click: **OK** *to exit the Sheet Set Properties dialog box*

The Page Setup Overrides files area displays the path for the page setup file (containing the page size and other necessary printing information) that will override any different user settings when the sheet set is plotted as a batch.

Use your default location for your page setup files.

The Sheet Creation Template area displays the path for the template that will be used by default when a new sheet is added to the sheet set. This makes creating additional sheets that have the same sheet size and format quick and easy. Most drawing sets standardize on one sheet size and title block style for an organized appearance and ease of handling the printed sheets.

Use your default location (shown in the dialog box) and browse to select a C-sized color-dependent template.

Click: **Next**

The Choose Layouts page is used to select layouts from existing drawings to add as sheets in your organized sheet set.

Click: **Browse**

Select: **c:\work**

Click: **OK**

You should see a list of the drawings inside the folder *c:\work* that contain layouts that can be used as sheets as shown in Figure 5.35.

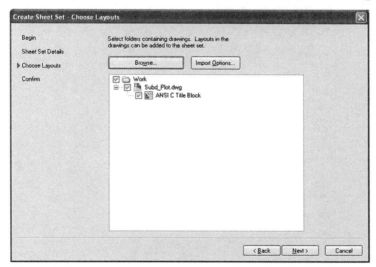

Figure 5.35

*Leave the **subd_plot.dwg** and its ANSI C Title Block sheet checked*

Click: **Next**

The Sheet Set Preview as shown in Figure 5.36 shows the drawings you have selected and the default paths you set for the sheet set to be defined.

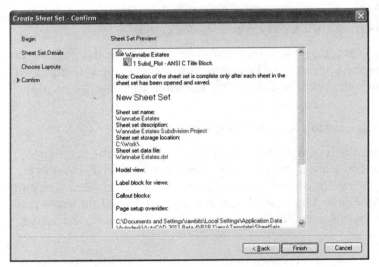

Figure 5.36

*Click: **Finish***

You return to the drawing editor where the Sheet Set Manager shows the drawing layouts you have selected listed. Figure 5.37 shows the appearance of the Sheet Set Manager.

Hover your mouse over the sheet name to show the sheet details

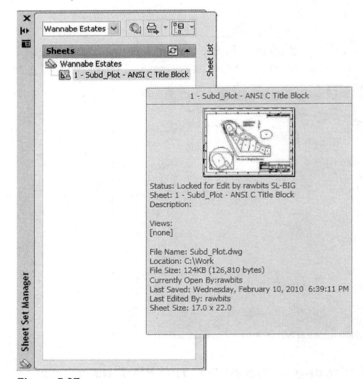

Figure 5.37

To open a sheet, you only need to double-click on its name in the Sheet Set Manager. To open a drawing from the sheet set you only need to double click on its file name.

Click: **Model Views tab**

Click: **the Add New Location button**

Browse to your **\work** folder and add it

You should see the drawings listed that are in your *c:\work* folder as shown in Figure 5.34.

Figure 5.38

Double-click: **plotplan.dwg**

The plot plan drawing opens in the drawing editor.

Right-click: **on Layout 2 tab if it appears and use the short-cut menu to delete it**

Switch to **Layout I** on your own to activate it.

Save and close plotplan.dwg on your own.

To add additional sheets to your sheet set, you can use the short-cut menu.

Click: **Sheet List Tab**

Right-click: **Wannabe Estates sheet set name**

The short-cut menu pops up on your screen as shown in Figure 5.39.

Figure 5.39

Notice that you can use this menu to create new sheets, new subsets or categories of sheets, and to publish a sheet set.

Sheet sets can be a very important productivity and organization tool when you are working on large projects. You can explore sheet sets more using Help.

You are finished with this portion of the tutorial.

Click: ***to close the Sheet Set Manager***

Click: ***to close any drawings that remain open***

Creating a Template Drawing

Next you will create a template drawing that you will use for most of the remaining tutorials in this book. The file you will create is also provided as a template named *proto.dwt* in the datafiles for this book (in case you do not complete this portion of the tutorial).

Click: **New button**

Click: **acad.dwt** *as the template to use*

You should be in the drawing editor with a blank drawing showing.

Click: **Save button**

The Save Drawing As dialog box appears. Located at the bottom of the dialog box is a Files of type: option as shown in Figure 5.37 used to save the drawing in various formats.

You will save your drawing as an AutoCAD template (*.dwt*) file. The only difference between a drawing file (*.dwg*) and a template file (*.dwt*) is the file extension. The default is Release 2010 (*.dwg*) format.

Figure 5.40

Click: ***AutoCAD Drawing Template (*.dwt)***

Type: ***MYTEMPLATE*** *as the File name*

Navigate to **c:\work**, if necessary.

Click: ***Save***

The main AutoCAD drawing editor appears on your display screen, with Mytemplate in the title bar.

You will set the limits, grid, snap, layers, text size, and text style in this drawing, as well as set up the paper space limits, viewport, and linetype scale. This approach will save time, make plotting and printing easier, and provide a system of layers to help you keep future drawings neatly organized.

Creating Default Layers

Using a template drawing helps you maintain a consistent standard for layer names. Using consistent and descriptive layer names allows more than one person to work on the same drawing without puzzling over the purpose of various layers. A template drawing is an easy way to standardize layer names and other basic settings, such as linetype.

Using different layers helps standardize the colors of groups of objects in the drawing, which in turn helps standardize plotting the drawing. Object color in the drawing helps you quickly recognize the type of information shown. Color can also be used to control line thickness on printers. The AutoCAD default is to set color by layer. You should use different colors for different types of objects in order to plot more than one color or line thickness effectively when using color dependent plot styles. Layers are also used to associate named plot styles with the objects on that layer.

Tip: *You can use the operating system to rename template files to drawing files and vice versa.*

The Layer Manager allows you to create groups and use filters to manage large numbers of layers efficiently.

Defining the Layers

Click: *Layer Properties button*

The Layer Properties Manager appears on the screen, as in Figure 5.39.

There are two panes in the Layer Properties Manager. The left one shows a tree-structured view of the layers. The right one shows the list view. You can use the New Property Filter and New Group Filter to display different groups of layers depending on layer properties or layer group membership. The Layer States Manager lets you save and restore various settings, such as on/off, frozen/thawed, color, linetype, lineweight, and the other layer properties.

From the keyboard, you will type in the new layer names followed by commas.

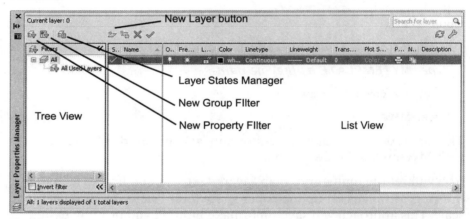

Figure 5.41

Click: *New Layer button near the top of the dialog box*

Type: *HIDDEN_LINES, TEXT, VISIBLE, THIN, CENTERLINE, CUTTING_PLANE, HATCH, PROJECTION, DIM, BORDER, VPORT [Enter]*

Each time you type a comma (,) a new "Layer1" pops up on the list of layer names. Then the name you type replaces the name Layer1.

Note that the layers you have created are turned on. The color for all the layers is white (or black depending on your system configuration). In addition to the color and linetype, you can also set a lineweight value in the default units of millimeters (mm) or inches. Lineweights in the drawing only show on the screen when paper space is enabled and when the LWT button on the status bar is turned on. You will set the lineweight for the HIDDEN_LINES layer to 0.30 mm, the standard for plotting or sketching hidden lines. Lineweights should be used only to control the plotted appearance, not to represent the actual thickness of an object. Next you will set the color, linetype, and then lineweight for the hidden line layer.

Click: **the color box in the Color column across from the HIDDEN_LINES layer**

Click: **Blue** *from the Standard Colors boxes*

Click: **OK**

Click: **Continuous** *in the Linetype area to the right of layer Hidden_Lines*

The Select Linetype dialog box appears on your screen.

Click: **Load**

Click: **HIDDEN**

Click: **OK** *to exit the Load or Reload Linetypes dialog box*

You will see the linetypes HIDDEN and CONTINUOUS.

Click: **HIDDEN**

Click: **OK** *to close the Select Linetype dialog box*

Now you should see that the linetype for layer HIDDEN_LINES is set to linetype HIDDEN. Its color should be set to blue.

Click: **HIDDEN_LINES** *from the layer name list if it is not already highlighted*

Click: **the thin line with the word Default** *from the Lineweight area across from the HIDDEN-LINE layer*

The Lineweight dialog box appears on your screen as shown in Figure 5.42.

Click: **0.30 mm**

Click: **OK**

Figure 5.42

The 0.30 lineweight is displayed as the setting for layer HIDDEN The list of layer names should now show layer HIDDEN_LINES having color blue, linetype HIDDEN, and a lineweight of 0.30.

Tip: *You can right-click on a heading in the Layer Properties Manager, and select Maximize Column Headings from the pop-up menu that appears.*

Tip: *If you selected dark lines on a light background when configuring your video display, white lines will be black on your monitor and color boxes indicating white will be black.*

Tip: *Many Windows programs identify typing shortcuts by use of an underlined letter. Note the underlined letter N on the tooltip for the New Layer icon. This indicates that you can quickly select this operation by typing the key combination [Alt]-N. Look for the quick key combinations in other dialog boxes.*

Tip: *If the list of layer names is long; you may need to use the scroll bars located on the right-hand side of the dialog box.*

Setting Up the Remaining Layers

Next, you will set the colors and linetypes for the remaining layers that you have created. You can select more than one Layer name at the same time by using the [Ctrl] or [Shift] keys in conjunction with the mouse (as you would to select multiple files in other Windows programs).

Use the arrow cursor to move to the desired layer name.

Click: **Thin**

Press: **[Ctrl]** *(keep it depressed) and then*

Click: **Hatch** *(keeping [Ctrl] depressed)*

Click: **Text** *(keeping [Ctrl] depressed)*

You should now have three layers selected.

Click: **the Color box across from one of the selected layers**

The Select Color dialog box, which you used earlier in this tutorial, pops up on the screen. Use the standard colors as before.

Click: **Red** *from the Standard Colors boxes*

Click: **OK**

Click: **the thin line with the word Default** *in the Lineweight area across from one of the selected layers*

Click: **0.30 mm**

Click: **OK**

Layers Thin, Hatch, and Text should now have their color set to red and lineweight set to 0.30 mm. Next, you will set the color, linetype, and lineweight for layer Centerline.

Select: **Centerline** *so that its name is highlighted*

Click: **the Color box** *across from the Centerline layer*

Click: **Green** *from the Standard Colors boxes*

Click: **OK**

Click: **Continuous** *from the Linetype column associated with layer Centerline*

The Select Linetype dialog box appears on your screen. You will need to load linetype CENTER before it can be used.

Click: **Load**

On your own use the Load or Reload Linetypes dialog box and select the line pattern CENTER to use for layer Centerlines.

Click: **the thin line with the word Default** *in the Lineweight area associated with layer Centerline*

Click: **0.30 mm**

Click: **OK**

When you have finished, the Centerline layer should be green, linetype

Tip: When you are selecting the color and linetype, be sure to highlight only the names of the layers you want to set.

Tip: You can click on the Name heading in the Layer Properties Manager to switch the list of layer names to reverse alphabetical order. Pick it again to restore it to A-Z order.

Tip: The variable Maxsort controls the number of layers that will be sorted in the Layer Control dialog box. It is set at 200 as the default. If you do not want your layer list to be sorted, you can type MAXSORT at the command prompt and then follow the prompts to set its value to 0.

CENTER, and lineweight 0.30 mm.

On your own, repeat these steps to set the colors and linetypes in the following table for the other layers that you have created. When you are setting the colors for the layers listed, remember that magenta is a purplish pink color (number 6 in the row of standard colors), and that the color white appears black if you have chosen to draw on a light background.

Layer	Color	Linetype	Lineweight
0	WHITE	CONTINUOUS	default
HIDDEN LINES	BLUE	HIDDEN	0.30 mm
TEXT	RED	CONTINUOUS	0.30 mm
VISIBLE	WHITE	CONTINUOUS	0.60 mm
THIN	RED	CONTINUOUS	0.30 mm
CENTERLINE	GREEN	CENTER	0.30 mm
PROJECTION	MAGENTA	CONTINUOUS	default
HATCH	RED	CONTINUOUS	0.30 mm
CUTTING_PLANE	WHITE	DASHED	0.60 mm
DIM	BLUE	CONTINUOUS	0.30 mm
BORDER	WHITE	CONTINUOUS	0.60 mm
VPORT	MAGENTA	CONTINUOUS	default

Before you exit the dialog box, you will set the current layer to VPORT.

Double-click: **Vport to set it as the current layer**—*it will show a green check mark*

Click: **the Plot button across from layer Vport** *so that the layer becomes non-plotting*

When you have finished creating the layers and setting the colors and linetypes, the dialog box should be similar to Figure 5.43.

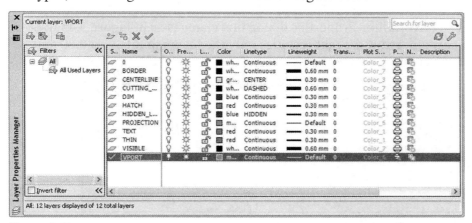

Figure 5.43

Remember that lineweights do not display unless the LWT button on the status bar is selected and paper space has been enabled. You will see the effect of the lineweight later in this tutorial.

Using layers to control the color and linetype of new objects that you create will work only if BYLAYER is active as the method for establishing object color, object linetype, and lineweight. It is the default, so you should not have to change anything. To check,

Examine the Color Control, Linetype Control, and the Lineweight Control on the

Properties panel. All three should be set to BYLAYER.

You have now created a basic set of layers for use in future drawings. Next you will explore the New Property Filter and New Group Filter.

Click: New Property Filter button from the dialog box upper left

The Layer Filter Properties dialog box appears as in Figure 5.44.

Figure 5.44

Type: Thick Lines in the Filter Name area at the upper left of the dialog box

Click: in the Lineweight area of the top part of the dialog box

Click: the ellipsis box that appears

Click: 0.60 mm from the Lineweight dialog box that appears

Click: OK

The Layer Filter Properties dialog box changes as in Figure 5.45 to show a preview list that includes only the layers that have a 0.60 mm lineweight.

Figure 5.45

Click: OK

You return to the Layer Properties Manager with the Thick Lines properties filter showing in the tree view as shown in Figure 5.46.

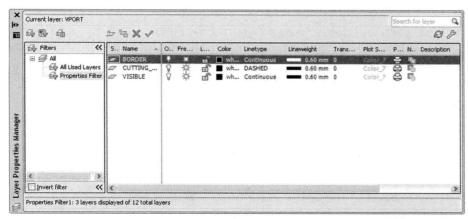

Figure 5.46

The only layers that appear in the list view are 0.60 mm lineweight. To see all of the layers,

*Click: **All** from the top of the tree list*

All of the layers display in the list area now. You can select the Thick Lines filter whenever you want to display just the 0.60 mm lines.

*Click: **New Group Filter***

Group Filter1 is added as a group to the tree list as shown in Figure 5.47. It is highlighted so that you can overtype it with a descriptive name.

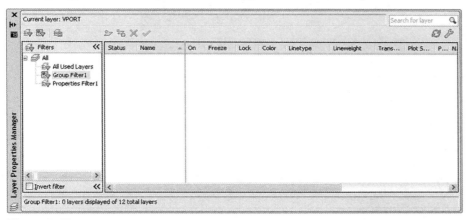

Figure 5.47

*Type: **SECTION LAYERS** as the Group name*

The group Section Layers appears in the tree view. Currently no layers are a member of this group, so nothing is displayed in the list view. Next you will display all of the layers and then drag the Hatch and Cutting_Plane layers onto the Section Layers group so that they will become its members.

*Click: **All** from the top of the tree view*

*Click: **Cutting_Plane and then press [Ctrl] and click Hatch** so that they both become highlighted*

*Click: **and drag the highlighted layers onto the Section Layers group** in the tree view as in Figure 5.46*

To see the layers that are a member of the group,

Click: **Section Layers group** *from the tree list*

The list view now displays only Hatch and Cutting_Plane.

Click: **All**

All of the layers now return to the list view.

Click: **to Freeze layers 0 and Projection**

Click: **Layer States Manager button**

Click: **New**

Type: **Frozen** *in the Layer State to Save dialog box*

Click: **OK** *to return to the Layer States Manager*

Figure 5.48

Click: **Save**

Click: **Close**

You return to the Layer Properties Manager.

On your own, thaw the frozen layers and set layer 0 current.

Click: **Layer States Manager button**

The layer state you created named Frozen should already be high-lighted as the selection. If it is not, select it.

Click: **Restore**

Click: **[X]** *to close the Layer States Manager*

You return to the Layer Properties Manager.

The thawed layers return to the frozen state. The current layer returns to Vport. Now you will close the Layer Properties Manager and continue setting up your template file.

On your own, **thaw** the frozen layers.

Click: [X] to close the Layer Properties Manager

Save your drawing before continuing.

Using the Drafting Settings Dialog Box

Next you will select the Drafting Settings dialog box and use it to set the Snap and Grid.

*Right-click: **on the Grid button** to show the short-cut menu*

*Click: **Settings***

The Snap and Grid tab should be active.

*Click: **to highlight the text in the input box next to Snap X spacing***

*Type: **.25 [Tab]***

The Snap Y spacing box automatically changes to match the Snap X spacing when you tab to (or click in) the Y box. If you press [Enter], the dialog box automatically closes. If you want unequal spacing for X and Y, you can change the Snap Y spacing separately.

Leave the Grid set to **0.5**.

Use the check boxes to **turn on Snap and Grid**.

When you have finished, the Drafting Settings dialog box should appear as shown in Figure 5.49.

Figure 5.49

*Click: **OK** to exit the dialog box*

You should see the grid on your screen. You will use Zoom All to show your drawing limits (12" X 9") on in the drawing area. When you start a drawing from your template, you will set the drawing limits at that time to a value large enough for the particular part you will draw. Then you can use the Zoom command to view the new drawing limits. For now,

Click: **Zoom All button**

Selecting the Default Text Font

The software offers various fonts for different uses. One of the best fonts that ships with the software for lettering engineering drawings is called *romans*, for Roman Simplex. The *.shx* fonts are provided, so all other AutoCAD users will also have this font. True Type fonts and other system fonts may look great in your drawing, but may not be available on someone else's system, causing them to have to substitute another font which may make the lettering not fit correctly in the drawing.

Click: **Text Style button** *from the Home tab, Annotation panel*

The Text Style dialog box, which you used in Tutorial 1, appears, showing the Style name, Font, and Effects choices.

Click: **New**

Type: **MYTEXT**

Click: **OK (or press [Enter])**

Click: **romans.shx** *from the Font Name pull-down*

You will use the defaults in all other areas of the dialog box. Remember, accepting the defaults now means you will be prompted for these values when you create the text; this method offers you a lot of flexibility when drawing. Do not become confused between style names and font names. A font is a set of characters with a particular shape. When you create a *style*, you can assign it any name you want, but you must specify the name of a font that already exists for the style to use. Your dialog box should look like Figure 5.50.

Figure 5.50

Click: **Apply**

Click: **Close**

Setting the Viewres Default

The *Viewres* command controls the number of line segments used to draw a circle on your monitor. It does not affect the way that circles are plotted—just how they appear on the screen. Have you noticed that when you use Zoom Window to enlarge a portion of the drawing, circles may appear as octagons? The reason is that Viewres is set to a low number. The default setting is low to save time when you draw circles on the screen. With faster processors and high-resolution graphics, you can use a larger value. You will type VIEWRES at the command prompt.

Command: *VIEWRES [Enter]*

Do you want fast zooms? [Yes/No] <Y>: *[Enter]*

Enter circle zoom percent (1-20000)<1000>: *5000 [Enter]*

*Click: **Save button** to save your template thus far*

Switching to a Paper Space Layout

Next you will create a drawing layout to use for plotting.

*Click: **Layout1 tab***

Figure 5.51 shows the paper space layout as it appears on your screen.

Figure 5.51

*Right-click: **Layout2 tab***

*Click: **Delete** from the short-cut menu*

At the message "The selected layouts will be permanently deleted ...",

*Click: **OK***

Layout 2 is deleted. Keep in mind that multiple layouts in a single drawing are not recommended for use with the Sheet Set Manager.

Tip: *If you are using a slower computer system, you may notice that performance on your computer slows down. It may be because of this setting. If you need to, you can reset Viewres to a lower number. Type REGEN at the command prompt to regenerate circles that do not appear round.*

The magenta box around the drawing view is the AutoCAD paper space viewport. You can think of it as a hole or window that you can use to look through the paper and see your model space drawing. Figure 5.52 shows another illustration of the concept of model space and paper space. The viewport border is a drawing object in paper space that defines the shape of the window to model space. The zoom factor determines the size at which the model space objects appear in the paper space viewport.

Figure 5.52

Adding a Title Block and Text to Paper Space

You can easily add a title block to your drawing using lines and text in paper space. The advantage of adding the title block, notes, and border to paper space is that the measurements there are the same as you would make them on a regular sheet of paper.

You will draw the border on a separate layer so that you can turn on the display of lineweights to their effect in paper space.

Select layer **BORDER** as the current layer

Click: **Show/Hide Lineweight button** from the status bar **to show lineweights**

Draw the lines for the border of the drawing shown in Figure 5.53.

Click: **Line button**

Specify first point: *.5,.25 [Enter]*

Specify next point or [Undo]: 1*0,.25 [Enter]*

Specify next point or [Undo]: *10,7.75 [Enter]*

Specify next point or [Close/Undo]: *.5,7.75 [Enter]*

Specify next point or [Close/Undo]: *C [Enter]*

Now you will use the Offset command to offset a line across the bottom of the viewport.

Click: **Offset button**

Specify offset distance or [Through/Erase/Layer] <Through>: *.375 [Enter]*

Select object to offset or [Exit/Undo] <Exit>: *click the bottom border line*

Specify point on side to offset or [Exit/Multiple/Undo] <Exit>: *click above the bottom border line*

Select object to offset or [Exit/Undo] <Exit>: *[Enter]*

The border lines and title strip should appear in your drawing as shown in Figure 5.53.

Figure 5.53

*Click: **Zoom Window button***

Enlarge the lower left corner of the drawing as in Figure 5.54 so that you can see the lineweight used to represent the border.

Figure 5.54

*Click: **Zoom Previous button***

Your view returns to show the entire drawing area.

Using Divide

The *Divide* command places points along the object that you select, dividing it into the number of segments you specify. You can also choose to have a block of grouped objects placed in the drawing instead of points. You will use the Divide command to place points along the line that you created using Offset, dividing it into three equal segments.

Click: **Divide button** *from the Home tab, Draw panel*

Select object to divide: ***click the line above the bottom border line***

Enter the number of segments or [Block]: *3 [Enter]*

Because the Point Style is set at just a dot, you probably won't be able to see the points that mark the equal segment lengths. You will use the Point Style dialog box to change the display of points in the drawing to a larger style so you can see them easily.

Click: ***Point Style button from the Home tab, Utilities panel***

Figure 5.55

The Point Style dialog box shown in Figure 5.55 appears. On your own, select one of the point styles that has a circle or target around the point so that it is easily seen. To exit the dialog box,

Click: OK

The points appear larger on the screen now, similar to Figure 5.56.

Figure 5.56

Tip: *The Measure command is similar to the Divide command. However, instead of specifying the number of segments into which you want to have an object divided, with Measure you specify the length of the segment you would like to have. Like Divide, Measure puts points or groups of objects called blocks (which you will learn about in Tutorial 10) at specified distances along the line.*

Tip: *When the points are sized relative to the screen, they may appear large when you zoom in. To recalculate the display file for your drawing in order to resize them, use the Regen command on the View menu.*

You can use the Node object snap to find point objects in your drawing. To draw lines dividing the title area exactly into thirds,

Right-click: **Object Snap button** *to show the short-cut menu*

Click: **Settings**

Click: **to turn on the Node and Perpendicular snap modes**

Click: **OK**

Click: **Object Snap button** *from the status bar to turn it on*

Click: **Line button**

Specify first point: **target one of the points with AutoSnap Node**

Draw a line straight down from the point by using the **Perpendicular** object snap.

Specify next point or [Undo]: **click the bottom line of the border when the Perpendicular marker appears**

Now repeat this process on your own to draw another line at the other point.

Click: **Point Style button**

On your own, use the Point Style dialog box to **change the point style** to a mode that does not display anything. Exit the Point Style dialog box when you are finished.

Adding the Titles

Next you will use the Text command to add titles to the drawing. The standard size for text on 8.5" X 11" drawings is 1/8". As the text you will add here is in paper space, you can just set its height as you want it to print.

Set **TEXT** as the current layer.

Make sure you are in **paper space**.

Click: **Single line text** *from the Annotation panel*

Specify start point of text or [Justify/Style]: **C [Enter]**

Specify center point of text: **5.25, .375 [Enter]**

Specify height <0.2000>: **.125 [Enter]**

Specify rotation angle of text: **0 [Enter]**

Type: **DRAWING TITLE [Enter] [Enter]**

The words DRAWING TITLE appear, centered on the point you selected. The centering is horizontal only; otherwise the letters would appear above the point selected for the center. If you want both horizontal and vertical centering, choose the Justify option and then Middle.

Now, repeat this process using the Justify, BL (Bottom Left) option of the Dtext command to position the words DRAWN BY: YOUR NAME in the left part of the title block. You are prompted for the bottom left starting point for the text that you will enter. Use the Justify, BR (Bottom Right) option to right justify the words Scale: 1=1 in the area to the right. The Justify BR option prompts you for the lowest, rightmost point

Tip: *The default justification for Dtext is Bottom Left, so you do not need to specifically select that option. If you want text to be justified bottom left, just select the start point and no other justification options.*

Tip: *A field storing information can be inserted into any text area except for tolerances. Fields store information that will update automatically, such as the date or sheet number. Pick Insert, Field from the pull-down menu and use the dialog box that appears to select the type of information to insert. From there follow the prompts similar to inserting text.*

for the text that you will enter.

Now you have completed a simple title block for your template drawing.

On your own, set the current layer to **VISIBLE**.

Command: *MS [Enter]*

Command: *Z [Enter]*

Specify corner of window, enter a scale factor (nX or nXP), or [All/Center/ Dynamic/Extents/Previous/Scale/Window/Object] <real time>: *1XP [Enter]*

You will save this drawing in floating model space so that you can see the paper space border, but still create your new drawing objects in model space. You will leave the drawing zoomed to a scale of 1=1 and with VISIBLE set as the current layer. Then, when you begin a new drawing from this template, you will be ready to start drawing on the layer for VISIBLE lines.

Your drawing should look like Figure 5.57.

Figure 5.57

Now save your drawing to the file name *mytemplate.dwt*.

Click: **Save button**

Click: **Application icon, Close**

Now you have completed *mytemplate.dwt*. Be sure to keep a copy of the drawing on your own disk. You also should keep a second copy of your drawings on a backup disk, in case the first copy becomes damaged.

You can easily edit the text by double-clicking on it to make changes to the standard information you provide in the title block. Refer to Tutorial 1 if you need to review the Edit Text (Ddedit) command.

Beginning a New Drawing from a Template Drawing

You can use any AutoCAD drawing as a starting point for a new drawing. The settings that you have made in drawing *mytemplate.dwt* will be used to start future drawings. An identical template drawing, called *proto.dwt*, is in your datafiles. If you want to use the template you just created, substitute *mytemplate.dwt* whenever you are asked to use *proto.dwt*. Next, you will start a new drawing from your template.

Click: **New**

Use the dialog box shown in Figure 5.58 to select the correct drive and directory and select *mytemplate.dwt*. (If you have not created the template in the previous steps, you may substitute the datafile *proto.dwt*.)

Figure 5.58

When you have finished making this selection, click Open to return to the drawing editor. Now when you choose Save and are prompted for a new drawing name, the original template file will remain untouched.

Click: **Save button**

Type: **TRY1** *for File Name*

Click: **Save**

Now you can work in the new drawing which is a copy of *mytemplate. dwt*. The drawing *mytemplate.dwt* remains unchanged so that you can use it to start other drawings. Your current drawing name is *try1.dwg*. For future drawings in this book, use *proto.dwt* or *mytemplate.dwt* as a template drawing unless you are directed to do otherwise.

Changing the Title Block Text

You created the border, text, and lines of the title block in paper space. To make a change to any of them, you must first return to paper space. Then, you will double-click on the text or use the Edit Text selection (Ddedit command) to change the title block text so that it is correct for the new drawing that you are starting.

Tip: *If you have access to several different printers or work with different sheet sizes, having several different template drawings is very useful. Or use a standard AutoCAD template and modify it for your uses. Then save it with a new template name.*

Tip: *You can rename a layout tab by right-clicking on it and picking Rename from the short cut menu.*

Tip: *You can change the style of text that has already been added to your drawing using the Text Style selection. Select a text object. Use the Text Style pull down to view the list of available styles and make a new selection. Remember that you must create styles with the Style command before you can use them. You can also use the Properties palette to change the style, height, width factor, rotation, and location of the text entry.*

Command: *PS [Enter] or double-click outside the viewports*

Double-click: on the text Drawing Title

The Edit Text box appears in place containing the text you selected.

Use the [Backspace] and/or [Delete] keys to remove the words "Drawing Title." Change the entry to "Try1."

When you have finished editing the text,

Select an annotation object or [Undo]: *[Enter] to end the command*

When using a template, remember to make sure that you are in model space before creating drawing objects. Only items like the border, titleblock, and general notes and keys should be placed in paper space.

Exit the AutoCAD program and discard the changes to drawing try1.dwg.

Key Terms

aspect ratio	paper space	template drawing
floating viewports	paper space layouts	text style
model space	pin-registry	tiled viewports

Key Commands

Divide	Measure	Pan Realtime	Tile
Insert Block	Model Space	Paper Space	Viewport Clip
Layer	Mview	Regen	Viewres

Exercises

Draw the following objects. The letter M after an exercise number means that the given dimensions are in millimeters (metric units).

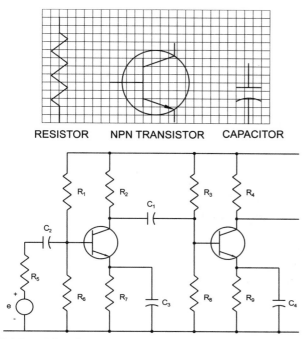

5.1 Amplifier Circuit

Draw the amplifier circuit. Use the grid at the top to determine the sizes of the components.
Each square = 0.0625.

5.2 Support

5.3 Vee Block

5.4M Grab Link

5.5M Tee Handle

5.6 Idler Pulley Bracket

Create the front view for the object shown.

*ALL UNSPECIFIED RADII = R.25

5.7 Hanger

Draw the object shown. Set Limits to (–4, –4) and (8, 5). Set Snap to 0.25 and Grid to 0.5. The origin (0, 0) is to be the center of the left circle. Do not include the dimensions.

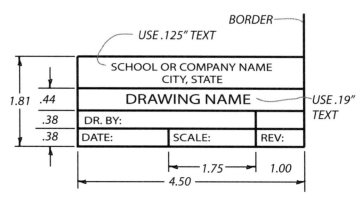

5.8 Title Block

Create this title block as a model space drawing. Explore using fields or attributes for the date, scale, and other changeable information. Use the Insert command to add this title block in paper space to other drawings.

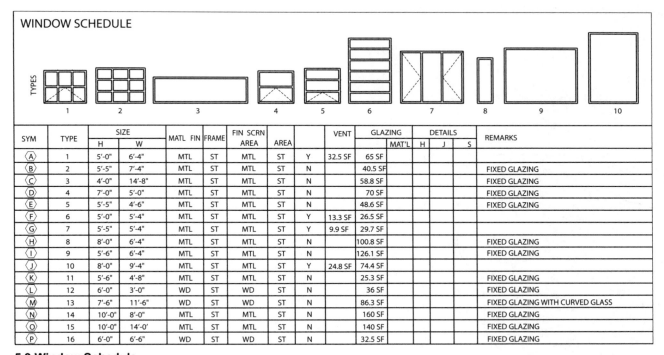

SYM	TYPE	SIZE H	SIZE W	MATL FIN	FRAME	FIN SCRN AREA	AREA		VENT	GLAZING	MAT'L	H	J	S	REMARKS
A	1	5'-0"	6'-4"	MTL	ST	MTL	ST	Y	32.5 SF	65 SF					
B	2	5'-5"	7'-4"	MTL	ST	MTL	ST	N		40.5 SF					FIXED GLAZING
C	3	4'-0"	14'-8"	MTL	ST	MTL	ST	N		58.8 SF					FIXED GLAZING
D	4	7'-0"	5'-0"	MTL	ST	MTL	ST	N		70 SF					FIXED GLAZING
E	5	5'-5"	4'-6"	MTL	ST	MTL	ST	N		48.6 SF					FIXED GLAZING
F	6	5'-0"	5'-4"	MTL	ST	MTL	ST	Y	13.3 SF	26.5 SF					
G	7	5'-5"	5'-4"	MTL	ST	MTL	ST	Y	9.9 SF	29.7 SF					
H	8	8'-0"	6'-4"	MTL	ST	MTL	ST	N		100.8 SF					FIXED GLAZING
I	9	5'-6"	6'-4"	MTL	ST	MTL	ST	N		126.1 SF					FIXED GLAZING
J	10	8'-0"	9'-4"	MTL	ST	MTL	ST	Y	24.8 SF	74.4 SF					
K	11	5'-6"	4'-8"	MTL	ST	MTL	ST	N		25.3 SF					FIXED GLAZING
L	12	6'-0"	3'-0"	WD	ST	WD	ST	N		36 SF					FIXED GLAZING
M	13	7'-6"	11'-6"	WD	ST	WD	ST	N		86.3 SF					FIXED GLAZING WITH CURVED GLASS
N	14	10'-0"	8'-0"	MTL	ST	MTL	ST	N		160 SF					FIXED GLAZING
O	15	10'-0"	14'-0'	MTL	ST	MTL	ST	N		140 SF					FIXED GLAZING
P	16	6'-0"	6'-6"	WD	ST	WD	ST	N		32.5 SF					FIXED GLAZING

5.9 Window Schedule

Redraw the window schedule shown below. Experiment with different fonts.

5.10 Saw Blade

Draw the saw blade shown below. Use Array and Polyline. Do not include dimensions. Use the Arc option of the Polyline command to create the thick arc. Add the arrow to the arc by making a Polyline with a beginning width of 0 and a thicker ending width to show the blade's rotation

FIVE—LOBE KNOB

5.11 Five Lobe Knob

2D ORTHOGRAPHIC DRAWINGS

Introduction

In this tutorial you will apply many of the commands that you have learned to create orthographic views. *Orthographic views* are two-dimensional (2D) drawings that you use to depict accurately the shape of three-dimensional (3D) objects. You will draw a set of 2D drawing views that define a 3D object. In Tutorial 11 you will learn to create a 3D solid model of an object.

The Front, Top, and Right-Side Orthographic Views

Technical drawings usually require front, top, and right-side orthographic views to define the shape of an object. Some objects require fewer views and others require more. All the objects in this tutorial require three views. Each orthographic view is a 2D drawing showing only two of the three dimensions (height, width, and depth). Thus no individual view contains sufficient information to define completely the shape of the object. You must look at all three views together to comprehend the shape being represented. For this reason it is important that the views be shown in the correct relationship to each other.

Figure 6.1 left shows a pictorial drawing of a part. At the right are the front, top, and right-side orthographic views of the part.

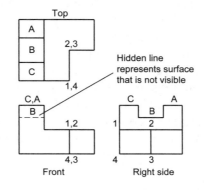

Figure 6.1

Three rectangular surfaces, labeled A, B, and C, are located on the left side of the top view. Which surface is the highest? The top view alone is not sufficient to answer this question. You must locate the three surfaces in the other views to determine the relationships between them. The right-side view (often just referred to as the side or profile view) shows that surfaces A and C are the same height and that surface B is lower.

Objectives

When you have completed this tutorial, you will be able to

1. Create 2D orthographic drawings.

2. Use Ortho for horizontal and vertical lines.

3. Create construction lines.

4. Draw hidden, projection, center, and miter lines.

5. Set the global linetype scaling factor.

6. Add correctly drawn centermarks to circular shapes.

The side view shows the relative locations of surfaces A, B, and C, but the surfaces appear as straight lines. You need all three views to determine the shape of the surfaces.

All surfaces should be drawn in all views or the view should be clearly labeled as a partial view. Surface B is shown in the front view of Figure 6.2 with a hidden line. A *hidden line* represents a surface not directly visible, that is, hidden from view by some other surface on the object.

View Location

The locations of the front, top, and side views on a drawing are critical. The top view must be located directly above the front view. The side view should be located directly to the right of the front view. An alternative position for the side view is to rotate it 90° and align it with the top view. By aligning the views precisely with each other, you can interpret them together to understand the 3D object they represent. Because views are shown in alignment, you can project information from one view to another. Refer to Figure 6.2.

Figure 6.2

Surfaces A, B, and C appear as three straight lines in the front view. Which line represents which surface? Because the front and side views are aligned, you can draw horizontal lines from the *vertices* of the surfaces in the front view to locate them in the side view. These lines are called projection lines and each surface is located between its projection lines in both views. You can locate surfaces between the front and top views by using vertical projection lines. Without exact view alignment, you couldn't relate the lines and surfaces of one view to those of another view, making it difficult or impossible to interpret the object shown in the drawing.

Starting

Before you begin, **launch AutoCAD® 2012.**

You will begin this tutorial by drawing an orthographic view for the adapter in Figure 6.6. The file *proto.dwt* has been provided with the datafiles so that you can be sure you are using the same settings as are used in the tutorial.

To start a drawing from a template as you did at the end of Tutorial 5,

Click: **New button**

Use the dialog box that appears on your screen to select the file ***proto.dwt*** from the datafiles that accompany this text **in the Datafile2012** folder.

Click: *Save button*

Type: *ADAPTORT for the file name and c:\work for the directory*

Click: *Save*

The main AutoCAD drawing editor should reappear on your screen with Adaptort in the title bar as shown in Figure 6.3.

Tip: *You can substitute your drawing mytemplate.dwt if you have finished it correctly.*

Figure 6.3

On your own, check that the grid is set to **0.5** spacing and the snap to **0.25** and that grid and snap are turned on. You should be in floating **model space**. Make sure that **VISIBLE** is the current layer. Check that the **Polar Tracking, Object Snap, Object Snap Tracking, Show/Hide Lineweight**, and **Dynamic Input** buttons on your status bar are turned **off**.

Figure 6.6 shows the adapter that you will create. All dimensions are in decimal inches.

Figure 6.4

Switching to Model Space

You can view and edit model space from a layout in the area inside a viewport (floating model space) as you see on your screen. You can also choose to work in model space alone. You will work in model space during this tutorial and then switch back to the layout for plotting.

   Click: **Model tab** *labeled in Figure 6.3*

The border and text should disappear from your screen leaving only model space, as shown in Figure 6.5. Notice that the model tab is highlighted and the model/paper space shows model.

Figure 6.5

Deciding the Model Space Limits

Use the Limits command in model space to set the limits of the area that you will use to create your real-world model of the object. The limits set in paper space and in model space do not have to be the same. Set the limits in model space to the value necessary to fit the views of the object that you are creating. You can change the limits at any time during a drawing session by using the Limits command.

Examine the size of the part and the amount of space the views will require. Then set the model space limits to allow a big enough area to create the views. The adapter is 3 inches wide, 1.5 inches high, and 1.5 inches deep. The slot in the top of the adapter is 0.5 inch deep. The default limits for model space are 12 X 9 units. The adapter that you will draw does not require much space, so 12 X 9 units is sufficient. You will not need to reset the limits at this time.

Viewing the Model Space Limits

Zoom to show the drawing limits or extents (of the drawing objects), whichever is larger.

Double-click the middle mouse button

Move the cursor around inside the drawing area. You should see that the coordinates and grid match the limits of the drawing.

Using Ortho

You can use the Ortho command to restrict Line and other commands to operate only horizontally and vertically. This feature is very handy when you are drawing orthographic views and projecting information between the views. You toggle the Ortho mode on and off by clicking the Ortho Mode button on the status bar or by pressing the [F8] function key to easily activate it when you are in a different command.

 Click: **Ortho Mode button**

The Ortho Mode button on the status bar should now be highlighted to show that it is active.

Next, you will draw the horizontal and vertical construction lines, as shown in Figure 6.7. These lines will represent the leftmost and bottommost margins of your orthogonal views. The coordinates are given for the lines you will create to ensure that your results will be the same as in the tutorial. In general, you can create the construction lines at any location and then move the views if necessary. Don't worry if the views are not perfectly centered when you begin your drawing. You will center the views after you've drawn them and seen how much room is needed.

Drawing Construction Lines

Construction lines extend infinitely. The default method for drawing a construction line is to specify two points through which it passes. When you use the Horizontal option, the line is drawn parallel to the X-axis through the point you select. The Vertical option is the same, but creates a line parallel to the Y-axis. Using the Angle option, you can specify the construction line by entering the angle and a point through which the line passes. The Bisect option lets you define an angle by three points and create a construction line that bisects it. Finally, the Offset option allows you to specify the offset distance or through point, as when you use the Offset command, to create an infinite construction line.

 Click: **Construction Line button** *from the Home tab, Draw panel*

Specify a point or [Hor/Ver/Ang/Bisect/Offset]: *2,1.5 [Enter]*

Specify through point: *click to the right to define a horizontal line*

Specify through point: *click above to define a vertical line*

Specify through point: *[Enter]*

Two infinite construction lines appear in your drawing similar to Figure 6.8: One is vertical through point (2,1.5), and the other is horizontal through the same point. They are on layer VISIBLE. You should have the Show/Hide Lineweight button turned off, which often makes it easier to work on the drawing. If the grid makes it hard to see your lines, turn it off.

(2,1.5)

Figure 6.6

Next, you will offset a series of parallel horizontal and vertical lines to define the overall dimensions of each view, as shown in Figure 6.9. Then, you will trim the lines to remove the excess portions. If you need to, review the Offset command in Tutorial 3.

For the first horizontal line,

 Click: ***Offset button***

> Specify offset distance or [Through/Erase/Layer] <Through>: *1.5 [Enter]*

> Select object to offset or [Exit/Undo] <Exit>: *click the horizontal line*

> Specify point on side to offset? *click any point above the horizontal line*

A new line is created, parallel to the bottom line and exactly 1.5 units away. You will end the command with the [Enter] key because the next line will be a different distance away.

> Select object to offset or [Exit/Undo] <Exit>: *[Enter]*

You will restart the Offset command by pressing [Enter] so that you are prompted again for the offset distance.

> Command: *[Enter]*

> Specify offset distance or [Through/Erase/Layer] <1.5000>: *1 [Enter]*

> Select object to offset or [Exit/Undo] <Exit>: *click the newly offset line*

> Specify point on side to offset? *click any point above the line*

A line appears 1.00 unit away from the line you selected.

> Select object to offset or [Exit/Undo] <Exit>: *[Enter]*

Now repeat this process on your own until you have created all the horizontal and vertical construction lines according to the dimensions shown in Figure 6.9. The lines are parallel to the bottom horizontal line at distances of 1.5 (the given height of the object), 2.5 (the 1.5-inch height and an arbitrary 1-inch spacing between the front and top views), and 4 (the 1.5-inch height plus 1 plus the 1.5-inch depth of the object).

Your drawing should look like Figure 6.7.

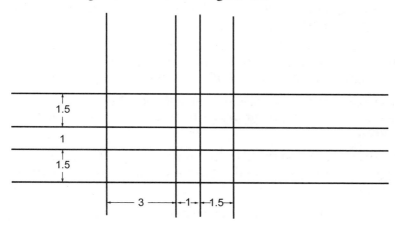

Figure 6.7

Trim to remove excess lines to define the areas for the front, top, and side views. Remember, the Trim button is on the Modify panel. Press [Enter] to select all the lines as cutting edges. When construction lines have one end trimmed, they become rays. When rays are trimmed, they become lines. Refer to Figure 6.8.

Create a crossing box to select the items to trim

Figure 6.8

 Click: Trim button

Select cutting edges

Select objects or <select all>: *[Enter]*

Select object to trim or shift-select to extend or [Fence/Crossing/Project/Edge/eRase/Undo]: *click to the right of the lines to create a crossing box as shown in Figure 6.8*

Select object to trim or shift-select to extend or [Fence/Crossing/Project/Edge/eRase/Undo]: *create a crossing box to trim the vertical lines where they extend above the upper horizontal line*

Select object to trim or shift-select to extend or [Fence/Crossing/Project/Edge/eRase/Undo]: ***create a crossing box to trim the vertical lines*** *where they extend below the lower horizontal line*

Select object to trim or shift-select to extend or [Fence/Crossing/Project/Edge/eRase/Undo]: ***create a crossing box to trim the horizontal lines*** *where they extend to the left of the leftmost vertical line*

Select object to trim or shift-select to extend or [Fence/Crossing/Project/Edge/eRase/Undo]: ***use crossing boxes to trim the lines between the view areas***

Next use the Erase option of the Trim command to remove the lines in the upper right as shown in Figure 6.9. You should still have the Trim command active.

Select object to trim or shift-select to extend or [Fence/Crossing/Project/Edge/eRase/Undo]: ***R [Enter]***

Select objects to erase or <exit>: ***use a crossing box to select the upper right lines*** *to erase as shown in Figure 6.9 [Enter]*

Create a crossing box to use with the eRase option of the Trim command

Figure 6.9

On your own, **zoom** to enlarge the drawing so that it fills the screen.

Your drawing should be similar to Figure 6.10. The overall dimensions of the views are established and aligned correctly.

Figure 6.10

Next, draw the slot in the front view. Use the following points or create the lines on your own by looking at the dimensions specified on the object in Figure 6.4.

Click: **Line button**

Specify first point: *3,3 [Enter]*

Specify next point or [Undo]: *3,2.5 [Enter]*

Specify next point or [Close/Undo]: *4,2.5 [Enter]*

Specify next point or [Close/Undo]: *4,3 [Enter]*

Specify next point or [Close/Undo]: *[Enter]*

On your own, use the **Trim** command and remove the center portion of the top horizontal line.

Your drawing should look like Figure 6.11.

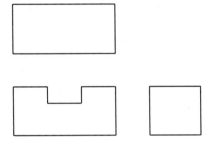

Figure 6.11

Hidden Lines

You will use hidden lines to represent the lines that are not visible in the side view. Remember, each view is a view of the entire object drawn from that line of sight. All surfaces are shown in every view. A hidden line in the drawing represents one of three things:

1. An intersection of two surfaces that is behind another surface and therefore not visible;

2. The edge view of a hidden surface; or

3. The hidden outer limit of a curved surface, also called the limiting element of a contour.

You should follow at least three general practices when drawing hidden lines to help prevent confusion and to make the drawing easier to read. See Figure 6.12.

*   Clearly show intersections, using intersecting line segments.

*   Clearly show corners, using intersecting line segments.

*   Leave a noticeable gap (about 1/16") between colinear continuous lines and hidden lines.

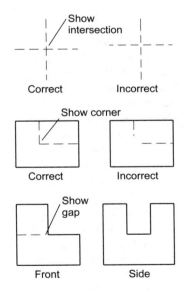

Figure 6.12

Traditional hidden line practices are sometimes difficult to implement using CAD. If you change one hidden line using the global linetype scale command, so that it looks better, all the other hidden lines take on the same characteristics and may be adversely affected. As you saw in Tutorial 4, you can change individual lines to have different linetype scales than the general pattern. However, hidden line practices are not followed as strictly as they once were, partly because with CAD drawings plotted on a good-quality plotter, the thick visible lines can easily be distinguished from the thinner hidden lines. The results of a reasonable attempt to conform to the standard are considered acceptable in most drawing practices.

Hidden lines are usually drawn in a different color than the one used for the continuous object lines on the AutoCAD drawing screen. This practice helps distinguish the different types of lines on the screen and makes them easier to interpret. Also, you often control printers and plotters by using different colors in the drawing to represent different thicknesses or patterns of lines on the plot. You can use any color, but be consistent. The best approach is to set the color and linetype by layer and draw the hidden lines on that separate layer with the correct properties. That's why BYLAYER is the AutoCAD default choice for color, lineweight, and linetype. A separate layer for hidden lines already exists in the *proto.dwt* template drawing from which you started *adaptort.dwg*.

Drawing Hidden Lines

Now you will create a hidden line in the side view of your drawing to represent the bottom surface of the slot. You will use the Layer Control to set the current layer.

Click: **HIDDEN_LINES** *to make it current using the Layer Control*

Next you will add a horizontal line from the bottom edge of the slot in the front view into the side view. This line will be used to *project* the depth of the slot to the side view. Verify that the ORTHO button on the status bar is highlighted. For drawing the following lines, the running object snap Intersection will be quite helpful.

Right-click: **Object Snap button**

Click: **Settings**

Click: **Clear All** *(from the Object Snap tab of the dialog box)*

Click: **Intersection**

Click: **OK** *to exit the dialog box*

Click: **Object Snap button** *to turn it on*

Click: **Line button**

Specify first point: *click the lower right corner (A) of the slot in the front view then the object snap Intersection marker appears*

Specify next point or [Undo]: *click any point to the right of the side view*

Specify next point or [Undo]: *[Enter]*

Tip: *To improve the appearance of hidden lines, you can use the Linetype Control on to set the linetype scale for individual graphical objects. Another way to improve their appearance is by drawing polylines. For hidden lines drawn with a polyline, you can set the Plinegen variable to 1 to make the linetype a continuous pattern over the length of the polyline. When you set this variable to 0, each segment of the polyline begins and ends with a dash. Use the Pedit, Ltypegen command option to set this variable. This method can improve the appearance of intersecting hidden lines.*

Your drawing should look like Figure 6.13.

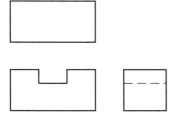

Figure 6.13

> On your own, **trim** the projection line so that only the portion within the side view remains.

Your drawing should look like Figure 6.14.

Figure 6.14

Next, you project the width of the slot from the front view into the top view using vertical lines on layer VISIBLE. Use the running object snap Perpendicular.

> *Click: **VISIBLE** to set it current using the Layer Control*
>
> *Right-click: **Object Snap button***
>
> *Click: **Settings***
>
> *Click: **Perpendicular** from the Object Snap tab of the dialog box*
>
> *Click: **OK** to exit the dialog box*
>
> On your own, make sure that **Ortho** is **on**, so that your projection lines will be straight. Now you are ready to draw the lines for the slot.
>
> *Click: **Line button***
>
> Specify first point: ***click the upper left corner of the slot** in the front view, labeled 1 in Figure 6.15[Enter]*
>
> Specify next point or [Undo]: ***target the upper line of the top view, labeled 2,** using snap to Perpendicular*
>
> Specify next point or [Undo]: *[Enter]*
>
> Command: *[Enter] to restart the Line command*
>
> Specify first point: ***click the upper right corner labeled 3** of the slot in the front view*
>
> Specify next point or [Undo]: ***target the upper line of the top view, labeled 2, using snap to Perpendicular***
>
> Specify next point or [Undo]: *[Enter]*
>
> On your own, use the **Trim** command to remove the excess lines.

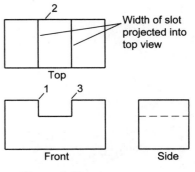

Figure 6.15

Your drawing should be similar to Figure 6.16.

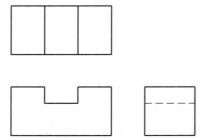

Figure 6.16

Save *adaptort.dwg* before you continue.

Line Precedence

Different types of lines often align with each other within the same view, as illustrated in Figure 6.17.

Figure 6.17

Which line should you draw when two overlap? The rule is:

- visible lines take *precedence* over hidden lines
- hidden lines take precedence over centerlines.

Note that in the side view of Figure 6.17, the short end segments of the covered-up centerline show beyond the edge of the object. This practice has sometimes been used to show the centerline underlying the hidden line. It is best to leave off the less important line. If you must show the short end segments where a centerline would extend, leave a gap so that the centerline does not touch the other line, as that makes interpreting the lines difficult.

The AutoCAD software doesn't determine line precedence for you. You must decide which lines to show in your 2D orthographic views. If you draw a line on top of another line, both lines will be in your AutoCAD drawing. Both lines will print, which may not show correctly. On your screen you may not notice that there are two lines because one line will be exactly over the other.

Delete Duplicate Objects
(OVERKILL)

Tip: *You can use the new command named OVERKILL to delete duplicate objects. This is particularly useful for making a perfectly closed boundary needed for 3D modeling and hatch boundaries.*

Slanted Surfaces

Orthographic views can only distinguish *inclined surfaces* (surfaces that are tipped away from one of the viewing planes) from normal surfaces (surfaces that are parallel to the viewing plane) if the surfaces are shown in profile. Inclined surfaces are perpendicular to one of the principal viewing planes and tipped away, or foreshortened, in the other views. As illustrated in Figure 6.18, you can't tell by looking at the top and side views which surfaces are inclined and which are normal.

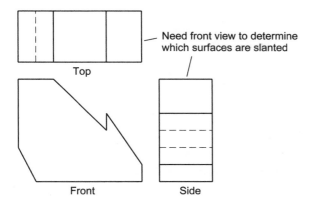

Figure 6.18

The front view is required, along with the other two views, to define the object's size and shape completely. In the next steps you will add a slanted surface to the adapter as shown in Figure 6.19.

Figure 6.19

You will add the slanted surface to the side view using relative coordinates. The surface will appear as a slanted line starting 0.5 inch to the left of the top right corner of the right-side view and angled at 45-degrees.

Click: **Line button**

Specify first point: **7,3 [Enter]**

Specify next point or [Undo]: **@3<225 [Enter]**

Specify next point or [Undo]: **[Enter]**

The distance 3 was chosen because the exact distance is not known and 3 is obviously longer than needed, as the entire object is only 1.5 inches high. Your screen should look like Figure 6.20.

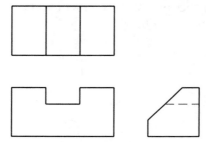

Figure 6.20

On your own, use the **Trim** command to remove the lines above the slanted surface. When you have finished, your drawing should look like Figure 6.21.

Figure 6.21

Top-View to Side-View Projection

You can *project* locations from the top view to the side view and vice versa by using a 45-degree *miter line*. The miter line can be anywhere above the side view and to the right of the top view, but it is often drawn from the top right corner of the front view as shown in the example in Figure 6.22.

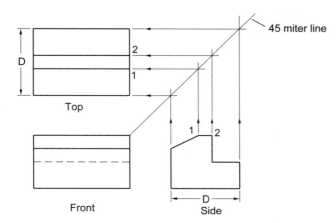

Figure 6.22

To project information from the side view to the top view, draw vertical projection lines from the points in the side view so that they intersect the miter line. From the miter line, project horizontal lines where the vertical lines intersect it, across to the top view. In Figure 6.22, points 1 and 2 are projected.

Use layer PROJECTION for your miter line.

*Click: **PROJECTION** as the current layer using the Layer Control*

Drawing the Miter Line

You will draw a 45-degree line, starting where the front edge of the top view and the front edge of the side view would intersect. So that you can draw angled lines,

On your own, turn **Ortho** mode **off**

Using Object Snap Tracking

Object Snap Tracking constrains your selections to line up with the X-, Y-, or Z-coordinates of an acquired tracking point. Object Snap Tracking also works with other commands such as Move and Copy.

You can use the Tracking object snap to start a line from any point on the screen, based on reference points. This method helps you find an intersection where two objects would meet if extended. You will use it to find the point where the bottom edge of the top view and the left edge of the side view would intersect.

To acquire an Object Snap Tracking point, move the cursor over the object location temporarily. Do not click with the mouse, just hover the mouse over the object until you see the Object Snap marker or a small plus sign (+) appear.

Tip: *To clear an Object Snap Tracking point once it has been acquired, move the cursor back over the point until the plus sign (1) marker is gone. Starting a new command will also clear the Object Snap Tracking points, as will toggling the Object Snap Tracking button on the status bar.*

Refer to Figure 6.23 for the objects you will use to acquire tracking points. Once the tracking points are acquired you will start to draw the line.

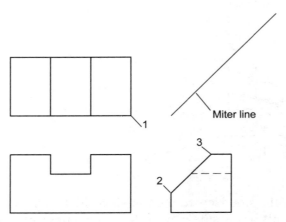

Figure 6.23

On your own, make sure that **Object Snap Intersection** is turned on.

*Click: **Object Snap Tracking** button from status bar to turn it on*

*Click: **Line button***

Specify first point: ***move the cursor over intersection 1 until it is acquired as an Object Snap Tracking point, then move the cursor over point 2 until it is acquired***

You should see the tracking points acquired as in Figure 6.24.

Figure 6.24

Specify next point or [Undo]: ***click where the tracking lines intersect, as shown in Figure 6.25, to begin drawing the miter line***

Specify next point or [Undo]: ***@3<45 [Enter]***

Specify next point or [Undo]: *[Enter]*

Click: ***Object Snap Tracking*** *button to turn it off*

The line that you will use for the miter line is added to the drawing, as shown in Figure 6.25.

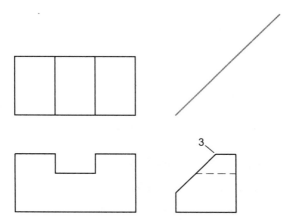

Figure 6.25

Next, you will project the corner point of the slanted surface from the side view to the miter line by drawing a vertical ray from the intersection. The Ray command is on the Draw panel.

Click: ***Ortho mode button*** *to turn it on before you click any points*

Click: ***Ray button***

Specify start point: ***click point 3*** *using Object Snap Intersection*

Specify through point: ***click anywhere above point 3***

Specify through point: *[Enter]*

The ray is added to your drawing, extending up from point 3. Next, project a ray from the intersection of the vertical ray with the miter line.

Click: ***Ray button*** *or press [Enter] to restart the Ray command*

Specify start point: ***click where the vertical ray meets the miter line***

Specify through point: ***click a point to the left of the miter line***

Specify through point: *[Enter]*

Your drawing should look like Figure 6.26.

Figure 6.26

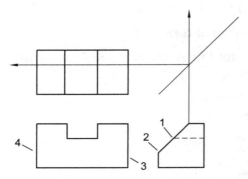

Figure 6.27

On your own, **project point 1** to the top view using the same method as you used for the previous projection lines.

Next you project point 2, shown in Figure 6.27, into the front view.

Make sure that **Object Snap** is **on** with **Perpendicular** selected.

Make sure that **SNAP** and **Ortho mode** are toggled **off**, and **Object Snap Tracking** is on.

Click: Line button

Specify first point: acquire tracking point 2 and click on line 3 *using the AutoSnap Intersection marker to start the line*

Specify next point or [Undo]: click on line 4 *using the AutoSnap Perpendicular marker*

Specify next point or [Undo]: [Enter]

The front view should now have a solid line representing the lower part of the block's sloping surface. Now you only have to trim the Rays used in projecting the surface depths to the top view. Remember, when rays are trimmed they become regular lines.

On your own, **trim** the lines so that your screen looks like Figure 6.28.

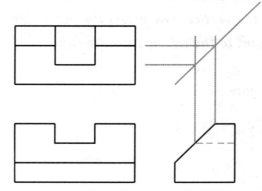

Figure 6.28

Now, you will change the new lines in the top and front views to the layer VISIBLE. Then you will set layer VISIBLE as the current layer and freeze layer PROJECTION. Leaving the projection lines frozen in the drawing is useful because, if you need to change something, you can just thaw the layer instead of having to re-create the projection lines.

Tip: *For a quick pop-up menu of Object Snaps, you can press the Shift key in combination with the right mouse button.*

On your own, select the new lines in top and front views so the grips appear

Select layer VISIBLE from the Layer Control to change the lines to that layer

Press: *[Esc]* to remove the hot grips

Click: *VISIBLE* to set it current using the Layer Control

Click: *to Freeze layer PROJECTION* using the Layer Control

The selected lines change to reside on layer VISIBLE. The magenta projection lines disappear from your screen.

Sizing and Positioning the Drawing

Next you will switch to the paper space layout and verify the scaling factor for the drawing view, as you learned in Tutorial 5. When you used Zoom All in model space, the entire drawing or the limits area is fit on the screen, which does not give you any particular scale for the end drawing. You will check the viewing scale to make sure that the drawing will print so that 1 unit in paper space is equal to 1 unit in model space.

Click: *Layout1 tab*

Double-click: *inside the viewport to ensure that you are in floating model space inside the viewport*

Check that the Viewport Scale is still set to 1:1 as shown in Figure 6.29.

Figure 6.29

Next, use pan to position the views you drew inside the viewport.

Press and hold the mouse scroll wheel to use pan to position the views so that they appear centered in the viewport.

When you have finished, your screen should look like Figure 6.30.

Tip: *If your paper space layout does not fill the screen, switch to paper space and then use Zoom All. Make sure to return to model space.*

Tip: *It is good practice to frequently save your drawings on your disk. If your system experiences a power failure and you lose the drawing in memory, you can always retrieve a recent version from your disk.*

Locking the Viewport Scale

You can lock the scaling for the viewport so that zooming inside the floating viewport does not change the scale relationship between paper space and model space.

Click: ***Lock/Unlock Viewport button*** *so that it appears locked*

Now that the viewport display is locked, when you zoom in or pan, it will not change the relationship between the model space drawing and its position or scale inside the viewport.

Make sure you are in **model space** inside the viewport.

On your own, try using Zoom and Pan.

Did you notice that your view enlarges with the viewport staying at the same size relationship? And when you pan, the entire drawing moves on the screen? When the display is locked, the AutoCAD software zooms and pans by switching to paper space and performing the zoom or pan and then switching back to model space.

Figure 6.30

Click: ***Object Snap*** *on the status bar to turn it off*

Click: ***Object Snap Tracking*** *to turn it off*

Click: ***Save***

Drawing Holes

Figure 6.31 shows an object with two holes and the ways in which they are represented in front and top views. The *diameter symbol* (Ø) indicates a diameter value. If no depth is specified for a hole, the assumption is that the hole goes completely through the object. As no depth is specified for these holes, the hidden lines in the front view go from the top surface to the bottom surface.

Figure 6.31

You will add a hole to the orthographic views that you have drawn to represent the adapter, as shown in Figure 6.32.

Figure 6.32

A centermark and four lines extending beyond the four quadrant points are used to define the center point of a hole in its *circular view* (the view in which the hole appears as a circle). A single centerline, parallel to the two hidden lines, is used in the other views, called *rectangular views* because the hole appears as a rectangle. Centerlines should extend beyond the edge of the symmetrical feature by a distance of about 3/16" on the plotted drawing.

First you will switch back so that you are working in model space.

Click: **Model tab**

The layout disappears from your screen as you are showing only model space. Next you will draw the 0.375 diameter circle for the top view of the hole. The hole's center is 0.5 from the left surface of the view and 0.25 from the back surface.

Click: **to turn Snap on**

Click: **Circle button**

Specify center point for circle or [3P/2P/Ttr (tan tan radius)]: **2.5,5.25 [Enter]** *or pick using snap*

Specify radius of circle or [Diameter]: **D [Enter]**

Diameter: **.375 [Enter]**

Drawing Centerlines and Centermarks

Next, you will draw the centerlines for the circle. Engineering drawings involve the use of two different thicknesses of lines:

- thick lines are used for visible lines, cutting plane lines, and short break lines

- thin lines are used for hidden lines, centerlines, dimension lines, section lines, long break lines, and phantom lines.

Tip: *You can also use the Properties button to change the linetype for your centermarks to Continuous.*

Because centerlines in the circular view should be thin, you will draw them on layer THIN. You could also use layer CENTERLINE, but it has a CENTER linetype. The Center Mark command automatically creates the dashes at the center of the circle by drawing short lines. These centermarks usually look better if they are not drawn with a linetype that already contains a dash (e.g., the centerline linetype). This is why you will use layer THIN, which has a continuous linetype.

*Click: **THIN** as the current layer*

The Dimcen variable controls the size and appearance of the centermark. The absolute value of the Dimcen variable determines the size of the centermark. The sign (positive or negative) determines the style of the centermark. Figure 6.34 shows the different styles of centermarks that you can create by setting Dimcen to a positive or negative value. Setting Dimcen to zero will cause no centermark to be drawn. (This lack of a centermark is useful when using dimensioning commands such as Radial, which automatically add a centermark.)

DIMCEN = +.125   DIMCEN = −.125

Figure 6.33

You will learn more about dimensioning and adding centermarks in Tutorial 7. Usually the cross at the center should be about 1/8" wide, but as this hole is relatively small, so use the value −.05.

Command: **DIMCEN [Enter]**

Enter new value for DIMCEN <0.0900>: **−.05 [Enter]**

*Click: **to expand the Dimension panel** from the Annotation tab*

*Click: **the pin icon** from the lower left of the toolbar to keep the Dimension panel expanded as shown in Figure 6.34*

Figure 6.34

*Click: **to turn Snap off** to make selection easier*

 *Click: **Center Mark button***

Select arc or circle: click on the outer edge of the circle

The circular view centerlines appear as shown in Figure 6.35.

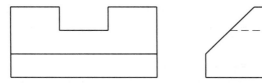

Figure 6.35

Next, project the hole into the front view.

> *On your own, set **HIDDEN_LINES** as the current layer. Turn on **Object Snap** and check that **Intersection** is on. Turn on **Ortho** mode.*

*Click: **Line button***

Specify first point: ***click the intersection of the circle's horizontal centerline with the left edge of the circle identified as point 1***

Specify next point or [Undo]: ***click Snap to Perpendicular button***

Per to: ***click on the bottom line in the front view***

Specify next point or [Undo]: ***[Enter]***

> On your own, repeat this procedure to draw the projection line for the right side of the hole (point 2) and for the centerline (point 3). Save your drawing

Next change the layer for the middle line to layer CENTERLINE.

*Select: **the middle hidden line** so that its grips appear*

*Click: **CENTERLINE** from the Layer Control*

The line changes to reside on layer CENTERLINE (Figure 6.36.)

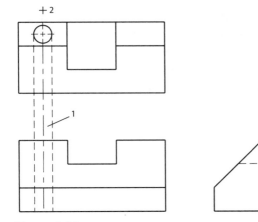

Figure 6.36

Tip: *Use Zoom Window if you need to make targeting the objects and intersections easier.*

Tip: *Use Zoom Previous or Zoom All, if necessary, to return your screen to full size.*

Breaking the Centerline

You will break the middle vertical line so that you can use it as a centerline by selecting the Break button on the Modify panel. Centerlines should extend about 0.1875" past the edge of the cylindrical feature when the drawing is plotted. You will extend the centerline 0.25" past the bottom of the front view to meet this criterion.

When you break the centerline, the first point of the break will end up as the top of the centerline. The second point is past the end, where the line extends into the top view, which will cause all of the centerline extending into the top view to be broken off.

Click: **Break button**

Select object: ***select the middle vertical line near point 1*** *(Figure 6.36)*

Specify second break point or [First point]: ***select point 2, past the top end of the line***

On your own, use hot grips with the **Stretch** command to stretch the centerline down 0.5" past the bottom of the front view. Refer to Tutorial 4 if you need to review using hot grips and Stretch.

Trim the two hidden lines where they extend past the front view of the object.

Your drawing should look like Figure 6.37.

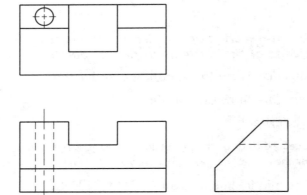

Figure 6.37

Next, project the location for the hole into the side view.

Click: **to thaw layer PROJECTION and make it current.**

On your own, draw a projection line from the top view where the vertical centerline intersects the circle to a point past the miter line. Refer to Figure 6.38. Use the Object Snap (Intersection) mode and Ortho to help you.

Now project that line from the miter line into the side view, creating a vertical projection line locating the center of the hole in the side view.

Tip: *Be sure that Snap is on and that Object Snap is off to make selecting easier.*

Tip: *If you click on the end of the line, you may not get a location past the end of the line for the second point of the break; instead, short segments of the line may remain and look like random points in your drawing.*

Tip: *You can use grips and stretch a line to lengthen it. You can also use the Lengthen command and select the DElta option to lengthen a line by a specified amount.*

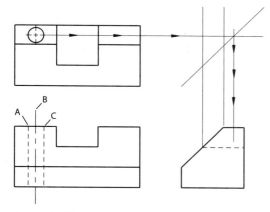

Figure 6.38

Because holes are symmetrical, the side view of the hole appears the same as the front view, except for the location. You will use hot grips with the Move, Copy option to copy the two hidden lines and the centerline from the front view to the side view. You will also change the Basepoint to the intersection of the centerline with the top line.

Check that you have Object Snap active, with Intersection selected.

Select: ***the hidden lines and centerline*** *(A, B, and C in Figure 6.38)*

Click: ***any grip as the base grip***

Specify stretch point or [Base point/Copy/Undo/eXit]: ***right-click*** *to show the menu and click* ***Move***

Specify move point or [Base point/Copy/Undo/eXit]: ***right-click*** *to show the menu and click* ***Copy***

Specify move point or [Base point/Copy/Undo/eXit]: ***right-click*** *to show the menu and click* ***Base point***

Specify base point: ***click the intersection of the centerline and top line of the front view*** *identified as Basepoint in Figure 6.39*

Specify move point or [Base point/Copy/Undo/eXit]: ***click the intersection of the top line and the projection line*** *(D in Figure 6.39)*

Figure 6.39

You see faint lines attached to your cursor as they are copied to this location. To exit the command,

Specify move point or [Base point/Copy/Undo/eXit]: *[Enter]*

Press: [Esc] twice to remove the grips from the screen

On your own set **VISIBLE** as the current layer. Freeze layer **PROJECTION**.

Your drawing will look like Figure 6.40.

Figure 6.40

Setting the Global Linetype Scaling Factor

You can change the linetype scale factor for all linetypes at once by setting the global linetype scaling factor. Each linetype is defined by the distance that each dash, gap, and dot is to be drawn. Because linetypes are defined by specific distances, you may need to adjust the lengths of the dashes and gaps for use in your drawing. The LTscale command lets you adjust all the linetype lengths by the scaling factor you specify.

Since you will be plotting from a paper space layout, that is the best place to adjust the appearance of the line patterns, first using the LTscale command and then adjusting individual lines as needed.

You will switch to paper space to adjust your lines with LTscale to make the CENTER linetype dashes show and the HIDDEN linetype have shorter dashes.

On your own, switch to **Paper space.** You should see the paper space icon.

Command: **LTSCALE [Enter]**

Enter new linetype scale factor <1.0000>: **.65 [Enter]**

Regenerating Layout

Your drawing should look like Figure 6.41.

On your own, turn on the **Show/Hide Lineweight** button on the status bar.

Save and close drawing *adaptort.dwg*.

You have completed this orthographic drawing.

Tip: *The variable PSLTscale controls whether the Ltscale command in paper space controls the appearance of the linetypes over the same command in model space. By default PSLTscale is set to 1, so that the paper space LTscale has control.*

Tip: *Especially when you are working in metric units, the linetypes may not always appear correctly. Using a standard AutoCAD template for a metric drawing can help provide the proper settings. Sometimes a line may appear to be the correct color for the layer but not the correct pattern. The reason is that the lengths defined in the linetype file are defined in terms of inches. Incorrectly shown metric lines may have changed pattern, but the spacing is so small that you can't see it. Use LTscale to adjust the spacing. For metric units, try a value of 25.4 when in model space. Figure 6.42*

Figure 6.41

Projecting Slanted Surfaces on Cylinders

Next, you will start a drawing from the datafile *cyl1.dwt* and use it to practice projecting slanted surfaces on cylinders.

> On your own, begin a new drawing called ***cyl1orth.dwg*** from the datafile template drawing ***cyl1.dwt***.
>
> *Double-click:* mouse scroll wheel *to zoom to the drawing extents*

Your screen should be similar to Figure 6.42.

Figure 6.42

Tip: *If possible, install your datafiles on the hard drive. If you are opening a file from a USB drive, pick New and then use the file you want to open as a template. You should specify the new drawing file name so that it is created on the hard drive. These actions will prevent many problems and the likelihood of corrupted drawing files. Copy the completed files to your USB drive. Make sure to close the software before removing your drive.*

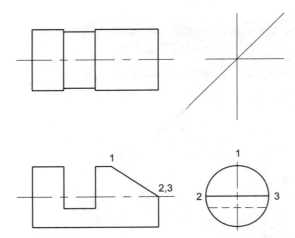

Figure 6.43

On your own, add a slanted surface to the front view and on edge in the side view, as shown in Figure 6.43.

The top of the slanted surface is located 1.5 inches from the right end of the cylinder, and the bottom of the surface is at the horizontal centerline. The top point of the slanted surface (the intersection of the vertical centerline and the edge of the cylinder in the side view) is labeled 1 in Figure 6.43. The bottom edge of the slanted surface is labeled 2, 3 and is located directly on the horizontal centerline in the side view.

On your own, remove all excess lines left from the shallow surface in the front view.

Remove the same surface from the top and side views; you will be creating a different surface in its place.

Your drawing should look like Figure 6.43.

What is the shape of the slanted surface in the top view? The front view of the surface appears as a straight slanted line. The side view of the surface is a semicircle. In the top view the slanted surface is a portion of an ellipse, as shown in Figure 6.45.

Since the locations of points 1, 2, and 3 on the ellipse are known, you can use the Ellipse command to draw the shape in the top view. Use Help or refer to Tutorial 2 to review Ellipse if necessary.

You will first project point 1 into the top view, as shown in Figure 6.44.

On your own, make layer **PROJECTION** current.

Use Object Snap Intersection and the **Line** command to draw a vertical line from point 1 in the front view extending into the top view past the center.

Change the current layer back to layer **VISIBLE**.

Click: Ellipse button

Specify axis endpoint of ellipse or [Arc/Center]: *C [Enter]*

Specify center of ellipse: *click the intersection marked C*

Specify endpoint of axis: *click on point 1 in the top view, where your projection line crosses the centerline*

Specify distance to other axis or [Rotation]: *click on point 2 in the top view*

Your ellipse should look like the one shown in Figure 6.44.

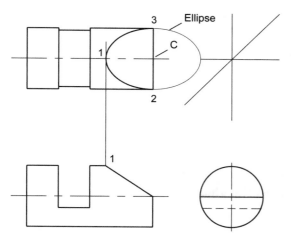

Figure 6.44

On your own, use the **Trim** command to remove the unnecessary portion of the ellipse.

Freeze layer **PROJECTION**.

The remaining curve represents the top view of the slanted surface. Your drawing should be similar to Figure 6.45.

Figure 6.45

Circular shapes appear as ellipses when tipped away from the direction of sight. Not all curved surfaces are uniform shapes like circles and ellipses; some are irregular. You can create irregularly curved surfaces by using the Polyline command and the Spline option that you learned in Tutorial 3. To project an irregularly curved surface to the adjacent view, identify a number of points along the curve and project each point. Use the Polyline command to connect the points. Then use the Pedit, Spline option to create a smooth curve through the points.

You have now completed Tutorial 6.

Save the drawing as *cyl1orth.dwg* and **print** the drawing from the paper space layout. Turn off any extra toolbars that you may have open, leaving only the Draw and Modify toolbars on the screen. Exit the AutoCAD software.

Key Terms

circular view	inclined surface	orthographic views	rectangular view
diameter symbol	limiting element	precedence	Ø sign
edge view	miter line	project	
hidden line	normal surface	projection lines	

Key Commands

Center Mark	Ellipse	Object Snap Tracking
Dimcen	Ortho	Ray

Exercises

Draw front, top, and right-side orthographic views of the following objects. The letter M after an exercise number means that the problem's dimensional values are in millimeters (metric units). If no letter follows the exercise number, the dimensions are in inches.

6.1 Base Block

6.2 Piston Guide

6.3M Shaft Guide

6.4M Lock Catch
The orthographic views are started for you. Add the missing lines and the top view.

6.5 Bearing Box

R22.5

82.5

ø4

6

15

30

45

15

ø15 THRU
ø30 SFACE
3 DEEP

6.6M Bushing Holder

5

¼ R*

*

2¼

2¾

2¼

7

4

3

LIFT GUIDE
C I

6.7 Lift Guide

38 DIA

32R

41

32

41

38

20

96

12

20

STOP PLATE
C R S

SI

6.8M Stop Plate

25 R

F & R = R6

45 R

90

K

50

25 R

20 DIA
2 HOLES

13

20

25

32

70

140

CLAMP
CAST IRON

SI

6.9M Clamp

ALL INTERNAL
RADII R2

44

Ø13

BRASS
I REQD

95

29

51

22

30°

6

10

110

22

METRIC

13

143

21

19

30

22

2X R7

Ø8

STOCK
3 THICK

R3 ALL BENDS

6.10M Holder Clip

2X Ø11

32

19

25

2X Ø13

19

25

45°

13

R35

10

13

16

13

113

35

46

64

87

13

39

FAO

BRASS
2 REQD

17

6.11M Rod Support

ø2.25

ø1.00 THRU
⌴ ø1.60 ⯊ .44

2 X ø.50

.48

.48

1.60

2.25

.48

1.95

38

R.52 TYP

6.12 Shaft Support

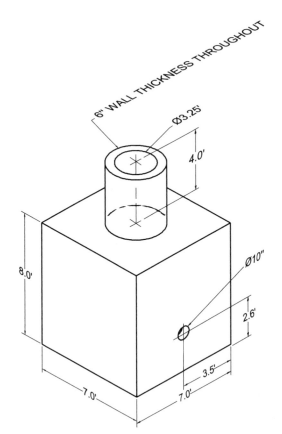

6" WALL THICKNESS THROUGHOUT

Ø3.25'

4.0'

8.0'

Ø10"

2.6'

3.5'

7.0'

7.0'

6.13 Manhole Junction
Draw standard orthographic views. Wall thickness is 6 inches throughout. The 10-inch hole is through the entire manhole junction (exits
opposite side).

DIMENSIONING

Introduction

In the preceding tutorials you learned how to use the AutoCAD® program to define the shape of an object. Dimensioning is used to show the size of the object in your drawing. The *dimensions* you specify will be used in the *manufacture* and *inspection* of the object. Figure 7.1 shows a dimensioned drawing.

For the purpose of inspecting the object, a *tolerance* must be stated to define to what extent the actual part may vary from the given dimensions and still be acceptable. In this tutorial you will use a general tolerance note to give the allowable variation for all dimensions. Later, in Tutorial 8, you will learn how to specify tolerances for specific dimensions and geometric tolerances.

Figure 7.1

Terminology and Conventions

Dimensions are used to accurately describe the details of a part or object so that it can be manufactured. In engineering drawings, dimensions are placed outside the object outline, unless placing the dimension on the object would result in a drawing that is easier to interpret.

Extension lines relate the dimension to the feature on the part. On the plotted drawing, there should be a gap between the feature and the beginning of the extension line, called the *extension line offset*, as shown in Figure 7.1.

Centerlines can be extended across the object outline and used as extension lines without leaving a gap where they cross object lines.

Dimension lines are drawn between extension lines and have arrowheads at each end to indicate how the dimension relates to the feature on the object.

Objectives

When you have completed this tutorial, you will be able to

1. Understand dimensioning nomenclature and conventions.

2. Control the appearance of dimensions.

3. Set the dimension scaling factor.

4. Locate dimensions on drawings.

5. Set the precision for dimension values.

6. Dimension a shape.

7. Use baseline and continued dimensions.

8. Use quick dimension.

9. Save a dimension style and add it to the template drawing.

10. Use associative dimensioning to create dimensions that can update.

11. Use associative styles.

Keep these general rules in mind when you are dimensioning:

- Dimensions should be grouped around a view and evenly spaced to give the drawing a neat appearance.

- The *dimension values* should never touch the outline of the object.

- Dimension values are usually placed near the midpoint of the dimension line, except when it is necessary to stagger the numbers from one dimension line to the next so that all the values do not line up in a row. Staggering the numbers makes the drawing easier to read.

- Because dimension lines should not cross extension lines or other dimension lines, begin by placing the shortest dimensions closest to the object outline. Place the longest dimensions farthest out. In this way, you avoid dimension lines that cross extension and other dimension lines.

- It is perfectly acceptable for extension lines to cross other extension lines.

- When you are selecting and placing dimensions, think about the operations used to manufacture the part. When possible, provide *overall dimensions* that show the largest measurements for each dimension of the object. Doing so tells the manufacturer the starting size of the material to be used to make the part.

- The manufacturer should not have to add shorter dimensions or make calculations to arrive at the sizes needed for anything in the drawing.

- All necessary dimensions should be specified in your drawing. However, no dimensions should be duplicated, as this may lead to confusion, especially when an inspector is determining whether a part meets the specified tolerance.

Semiautomatic Dimensioning

The AutoCAD semiautomatic dimensioning feature does much of the work for you. You can create the extension lines, arrowheads, dimension lines, and dimension values automatically. To get the most benefit from the dimensioning feature, use *associative dimensioning*. Associative dimensions are linked to their locations in the drawing by information stored on the DEFPOINTS layers that the program creates. As a result, associative dimensions automatically update when you modify the drawing. Although you can also use non-associative dimensions, it isn't good practice because these dimensions are created from separate line, polyline, and text objects and do not update when the drawing changes.

Associative dimensioning is the default. This allows for trans-spatial dimensioning, which makes it possible to add dimensions in paper space for an object that is in model space. When dimensions are associative, if the model space object is moved, the paper space dimension will update to the new location.

Starting

Start by launching the AutoCAD 2012 program.

*Click: **New button***

Use the file ***proto.dwt*** located in the datafiles as a template.

*Click: **Application icon, SaveAs***

Save your drawing as ***obj-dim.dwg***.

You return to the drawing editor with the border and settings you created in the template drawing on your screen.

Dimensioning a Shape

Review the object in Figure 7.2. You will draw this shape and then dimension it.

Figure 7.2

Tip: *If your paper doesn't fill the drawing window, switch to paper space and use Zoom All to enlarge the paper area to fill the view. Then make sure to switch back to model space to create the drawing.*

Layer **VISIBLE** should be the current layer in the drawing. If it is not, set layer VISIBLE as the current layer. Set **Grid** to **0.25** and **Snap** to **0.25**. Be sure that both are turned on.

Make sure that you are drawing in **model space**.

On your own, use the commands that you learned in the preceding tutorials to **draw the object** according to the specified dimensions.

You don't have to draw the centerlines now. Create the drawing geometry exactly, in order to derive the most benefit from the AutoCAD software's semiautomatic dimensioning capabilities. When you have finished, your drawing should look like Figure 7.3.

Figure 7.3

Using the DIM Layer

In order to produce a clear drawing of a subject, the outline and visible lines of the object are drawn with a thick-width pen when printing or plotting. The dimension, hidden, center, and hatch lines are plotted or printed with a thin-width pen. This way your eye is drawn first to the bold shape of the object and then to the details of its size and other features. The color of the object or a lineweight setting (usually set by layer) can be used to set a thin width for the dimension lines when plotting.

Also, you will frequently want to turn off all of the dimensions in the drawing. Having dimensions on a separate layer makes plotting and turning off dimensions an easy task.

*Click: **DIM** as the current layer*

Dimension Standards

There are standards and rules of good practice that specify how dimension lines, extension lines, arrowheads, text size, and various aspects of dimensioning should appear in the finished drawing. Mechanical, electrical, civil, architectural, and weldment drawings, among others, each have their own standards. Professional societies and standards organizations publish drawing standards for various disciplines. The American Society of Mechanical Engineers (ASME/ANSI) publishes a widely used standard for mechanical drawings to help you create clear drawings that others can easily interpret.

Typical spacings for an 8.5" X 11" drawing are:

- A .0625" space is used between the extension lines and the feature from which they are extended.

- Extension lines should extend .125" past the last dimension line.

- Arrowheads and text should be approximately .125" tall. Titles should be .20" tall.

- The dimension line closest to the object outline should be at least .375" from the object outline on your plotted drawing.

- Each succeeding dimension line should be at least .25" from the previous dimension line.

Associating Dimensions

Dimensions in the AutoCAD program are fully associated with the drawing objects. Versions of the program prior to Release 2004 created points in the non-printing layer, DEFPOINTS, with which to associate the dimension. The defpoints that were created coincided with the locations on the object that you selected for the dimension endpoints. Updating dimensions was accomplished by changing the location of these defpoints if they were selected when the object was moved or scaled, which did not fully associate the dimension. Now the dimensions are associated with the object geometry, but still use layer defpoints.

When adding dimensions to your drawing, it is important to have already determined the scale at which you will plot your drawing on the sheet of paper and established the zoom scaling factor. That way you can place the dimensions where they will show clearly on the layout for the final plot. If you are going to plot using a layout (paper space), you should set the scaling factor for the view before you dimension your drawing. Setting the scaling factor first allows you to place the dimensions around the drawing views where they will show clearly. If you change the scale, you will generally have to spend some time cleaning up the dimension placement. For this drawing the scale is already set to 1=1, as you started your drawing from *proto.dwt*, which had that setting. You should check it using the Viewports Scaling button on the status bar, or by showing the viewport properties and checking that the standard scaling option is set to 1=1.

Annotation Scaling

Annotation is the general term for any type of notes and labels that are added to a drawing. For example, a parts list, dimensions, notes, callouts, and other items.

The text information needs to be visible in the drawing. Consider the subdivision plot that you created in Tutorials 2 and 3. The final drawing was planned to plot on a C-sized (17"X 22") sheet at a scale of 1"= 150'. What if you decided to plot it at a scale of 1"= 300'? This might make the text too small to read. One advantage of CAD is the ability to easily plot the drawing to a different scale, without having to redraw it. If the text is set to a specific size, plotting to a smaller scale, will result in smaller text; at some point too small to be legible.

AutoCAD provides a method to flexibly scale the text and other annotation items based on the viewport scale for the plotted drawing. Annotation items that use this special annotative scale feature are able to automatically update to a new size when the scale of the drawing changes. The types of objects that can have this annotative scale feature include:

- Text (single-line and multiline)
- Dimensions
- Leaders and multileaders
- Tolerances
- Hatches
- Tables
- Blocks
- Attributes

You will learn more about tolerances, hatches, tables, blocks and attributes in later tutorials.

Tip: *You can quickly display the Properties dialog box for an object by double-clicking on it or selecting it and then pressing [Ctrl]-1.*

Tip: *Dimensions take a lot of drawing space, especially between the views of a multi-view drawing. Often you may need to zoom your drawing to half-size (.5XP) (standard scale of 2:1) or some other smaller scale to have room for dimensions. Keep this possibility in mind for future drawings. Do not change your XP scale factor for this tutorial unless directed to do so.*

The Dimension Panel

You can quickly select the dimensioning commands from the Dimension panel on the ribbon Annotate tab.

> On your own, expand and pin the Dimension panel from the Annotate tab as shown in Figure 7.4.

Figure 7.4

Using Dimension Styles

Many features controlling the appearance of the dimensions are set by *dimension variables (dim vars)*, which you can set using the Dimension Style Manager. Dimension variables all have names, and you can set each one by typing its name at the command prompt. However, the dialog box allows you to set many dimension variables at the same time.

You start this dialog box from the ribbon Annotation tab, Dimension panel as shown in Figure 7.4, or by typing Dimstyle or DDIM at the command prompt.

> Click: *the small arrow in the lower right corner of the dimension panel to show the Dimension Style manager*

The Dimension Style Manager appears on your screen, as shown in Figure 7.5.

Figure 7.5

Creating a Named Dimension Style

You use the Dimension Style Manager to change the dimension variables that control the appearance of the dimensions. The current style name is STANDARD. It is displayed on the dimension panel. This basic set of features is provided as the default.

You can create your own *dimension style* with a name that you specify. This way you can save different sets of dimension features that will be useful for different types of drawings—such as mechanical or architectural. You will create a new dimension style named MECHANICAL.

   Click: **New** *from the right side of the dialog box*

The Create New Dimension Style dialog box appears on your screen. In the New Style Name area, highlight the existing text, Copy of Standard, and

   Type: **MECHANICAL**

Mechanical now appears as the new style name. See Figure 7.6. In the Start With area, Standard is listed as the style to use as the basis for the new Mechanical style.

   Leave the Annotative box unchecked. *You will learn more about this feature later in the tutorial.*

Near the bottom of the dialog box you will see the Use for area. This style will be used for all dimension types: linear, angular, radial, etc.

Figure 7.6

Click: **Continue**

The New Dimension Style dialog box now appears. It has tabs for Lines, Symbols and Arrows, Text, Fit, Primary Units, Alternate Units, and Tolerances. You will use it to set the appearance of dimensions that use the style MECHANICAL.

The Lines tab should be uppermost as shown in Figure 7.7.

Figure 7.7

Scaling Dimension Features

As you go through the next steps of setting up the sizes and appearance of the dimensions using the dialog box, keep in mind that there are at least three different ways to control the sizes of the dimensions as a group. These are accomplished using an important dimensioning variable called the *dimension scaling factor* (Dimscale). It can be set from the Fit tab.

You will see later that using Dimscale, you can rescale as a group all of the values that control dimension appearance; either by calculating a value to multiply times all the dimension size settings or to automatically determine that value based on the viewport scale factor. You can also use annotative styles to automatically scale annotation items like dimensions. (The use of annotative styles automatically sets Dimscale to 0.) You will learn more about these scaling methods later in the tutorial.

Lines tab

The lines tab of the New Dimension Style dialog box is used to set the appearances of the dimension lines and extension lines. You will set the sizes of dimension features to the size that should be plotted on a standard 8.5" X 11" mechanical drawing. You will use the Fit tab in a moment to tell the program that the sizes you have specified for dimensions are the sizes on the plotted layout, and not the size in model space. The settings that you will make are based on an 8.5" X 11" sheet size. Larger drawing sheets often use larger sizes.

Dimension Lines

Use the Dimension Lines area at the upper left of the dialog box, to control the appearance of the dimension lines. You can set the color, linetype, lineweight, and the distance for the baseline spacing. The value entered in the box to the right of baseline spacing controls the distance between successive dimensions added using *baseline dimensioning*. The default value, 0.38, will work for now. (The ANSI standard states that successive dimensions should be at least 1/4" (0.25") apart, so 0.38 will meet this criterion.) You can choose to suppress the first or second dimension line when the dimension value divides the dimension line into two parts by checking the boxes near the bottom of this area.

On your own make sure that none of the suppress dimension line boxes are checked. You will set the color, linetype, and lineweight for dimension lines so that they are controlled by the dimension's layer.

Click: **ByLayer** *from the pull-down adjacent to* **Color**

Click: **ByLayer** *from the* **Linetype** *pull-down*

Click: **ByLayer** *from the* **Lineweight** *pull-down*

Extension Lines

The Extension lines area lets you control the color, linetype and lineweight for extension lines. In addition, you can set the distance that extension lines extend beyond the dimension line drawn, and the distance from the selected dimension placement that the extension line will begin (offset from origin). You can also suppress either extension line. Make sure that neither box is checked to suppress the extension lines. You will use this area to control the color by layer, and then set the distance to extend beyond dimension lines to .125 (the ANSI standard for this size drawing).

Click: **ByLayer** *from the* **Color** *pull-down*

Click: **ByLayer** *from the* **Linetype ext line 1** *pull-down*

Click: **ByLayer** *from the* **Linetype ext line 2** *pull-down*

Click: **ByLayer** *from the* **Lineweight** *pull-down*

Select: **the text in the input box to the right of Extend beyond dim lines** *so that it appears highlighted*

Type: .125

When you have made the settings the dialog box should look like Figure 7.8.

Tip: *You can set the lineweight for extension and dimension lines so that it is controlled by layer or to a specified width using the Lineweight area of the Lines tab.*

Tip: *You can also use the downward arrow to set the value to .125.*

Figure 7.8

Symbols and Arrows tab

Use the Symbols and Arrows tab of the dialog box to set the arrow size, centermark size and style, arc length style, and jogged radius dimension angle.

Click: the Symbols and Arrows tab

Click: to pull down the list of available arrow styles adjacent to the First Arrowhead box as shown in Figure 7.9

Figure 7.9

SYMBOLS AND ARROWS TAB **289**

When you select an arrowhead style from the list, the arrows shown in the *image tile*, or active picture near the top right changes. Scroll through the available styles. Return the setting to Closed filled when you are finished. Notice that when you select a style for the first arrowhead, the second arrowhead box automatically changes to reflect that. You can select a different style for the second arrowhead by choosing it last. Next set the size for the arrowhead.

Click: **to highlight the value in the box below Arrow size**

Type: **0.125 to replace the value**

Centermark Size and Style

The Center Marks area controls the size and style of the centermark which is added when you create radius or diameter dimensions. Selecting Line draws a full set of centermarks. Selecting Mark draws just a tick at the center of the circle. Selecting None will cause no centermarks to be drawn.

Click: **the button to the left of Line in the Centermark area**

Set the size of the centermark using the box below the word Size. The value for Size sets the distance from the center to the end of one side of the center cross of the centermark. To make a smaller center cross, set it to a smaller value; for a larger center cross, set the size larger. Leave the value for your centermarks set to the default value, 0.09, for now. You can type Dimcen at the command prompt, as you did in Tutorial 6.

Notice the Arc length symbol and Radial dimension jog areas at the right of the dialog box. These are used to set the placement for the arc length symbol used for arc length dimensions and for specifying the angle used for jogged radial dimension lines. For now, leave these areas set at the defaults. When you have finished selecting, the Symbols and Arrows tab should look like Figure 7.10.

Tip: *If the value for the centermark size is too large, full centermarks will not be drawn even when the style is set to Line; instead, just the mark will appear in the center of the circle.*

Figure 7.10

Tip: *Using a text style with the text height set to 0 for dimensioning allows the dimension settings to control the text appearance.*

Text tab

The Text tab allows you to control the text style, height, color, background fill, and the gap between the end of the dimension line and the start of the dimension text.

*Click: **the Text tab** so that it appears uppermost*

The Text Alignment area (bottom right) controls whether text always reads horizontally (i.e., is unidirectional text) or whether it will be aligned with the dimension line. The image tile changes to display the appearance for the selected setting.

> On your own, choose Aligned with dimension line. Then choose ISO Standard. When you have finished experimenting, return the settings to **Horizontal** alignment.

The Text Placement area has a control for horizontal or vertical text placement. Use the pull-down menu adjacent to Horizontal to center text, place it near the first or second extension line, or place it over the first or second extension line. Usually, the default choice, Centered, is used for mechanical drawings.

> On your own, try each setting and notice the effect of the selection on the image tile. When you are finished, return the setting to the default choice, **Centered**.

The pull-down menu adjacent to Vertical sets the placement of text relative to the dimension line. The options for vertical justification are Centered, Above, Outside, and JIS (Japanese Industrial Standard). For ANSI standard mechanical drawings, select Centered to create dimension values that are centered vertically, breaking the dimension line. The ISO (International Standards Organization) standard usually uses the options for text above or outside the dimension line. The JIS option orients the text parallel to the dimension line and to its left. The Above selection is often used on architectural drawings.

> When you are finished examining this portion of the dialog box, return its setting to **Centered** on your own.

The Text style selection is used to select text styles you have predefined in the drawing with the Style command. Style MYTEXT was previously created in the template drawing you started from. MYTEXT was created with a text height of 0 (zero) which allows you to set the text height at the time the text is placed. This is important for correct looking dimension text. Clicking the ellipsis (...) next to the style name, opens the Text Style dialog box, so that you can create new styles if needed.

*Click: **MYTEXT** from the pull-down for Text Style*

Next you will set the text height to 0.125, the standard height for 8.5" X 11" drawings.

Replace the Text height value with .125

Now you will set the color for the dimension text to BYLAYER.

*Click: **ByLayer** from the pull-down adjacent to Color*

On your own, try a color from the Fill color selection and then return it to **None**. Notice the image tile shows the fill color shading behind the dimension value.

The Text tab should now appear as shown in Figure 7.11.

Figure 7.11

Fit Tab

The Fit tab lets you set the options for how the dimensions will be placed in the drawing. These settings are especially helpful when there is not enough room to place both the dimension value and dimension lines and arrowheads inside the extension lines.

Click: **the Fit tab**

The setting "Either text or arrows (best fit)", places both the text and arrows inside the extension lines, if possible. If that is not possible, either the text or the arrows will be placed inside the extension lines. If neither will fit, both the arrows and text are placed outside the extension lines. Generally, these are all accepted practices, as long as the dimension can be correctly interpreted. You can also set which will be moved outside first: the text, the arrows, or both text and arrows; or to always keep the text between the extension lines. You can also specify to suppress the arrows if they don't fit inside the extension lines.

On your own, choose **Either text or arrows (best fit)**.

The Text placement area of this dialog box allows you to control how text is placed when it is not in the default location (between the extension lines). You can select to place it beside the dimension line, or over the dimension line, either with or without a leader.

The Fine Tuning area in the lower right of the dialog box lets you select either to place text manually or to force a line to be drawn between the extension lines, even when text and arrows are placed outside the

Tip: *To make radial dimensions that look like those shown in the exercises, choose the Place text manually selection in the Fine Tuning area of the Fit tab. Then you can drag the radial and diameter dimension value to place it around the outside of the object.*

extension lines. If you select Place text manually, when you click or type the location for the dimension line, the dimension value will appear at that position. This can be important for creating radial and diameter dimensions that are placed outside the drawing outline. You will learn more about specific "child" dimension styles to do this in Tutorial 8 on advanced dimensioning.

The Dimension Scaling Factor

There are essentially three ways to scale the dimension features:

1. use an overall scale factor (usually relative to model space)
2. scale dimensions to the layout (paper space)
3. use an annotation style to manage scaling the dimensions to the layout

Think about a drawing that is to be plotted to a scale of 1 plotted inch in paper space to 2 model units. If you want your arrowheads and text to be .125" on the plotted sheet, then at this scale the arrows need to be .25" high in model space so that when reduced by half they will be .125". You could double all the settings that control sizes of the dimension elements, such as arrowhead size, but there are many of them, so this method would be time-consuming. Instead, you can automatically scale all the size features by setting the overall scale.

Overall scale sets a scaling factor to use for all of the dimension variables that control the sizes of dimension elements. Its value appears in the box to the right of "Use overall scale of:." Setting the overall scale to 2 doubles the size of all the dimension elements in the drawing so that, when plotted half-size, your arrowheads, text, and other elements will maintain the correct proportions on the final plot. (You can also type Dimscale at the command prompt and enter the value by which the dimension elements are multiplied.)

Clicking Scale dimensions to layout uses the viewport scale (zoom XP) factor to set the scaling for dimension elements so that the values you enter in the dialog box are the sizes on the drawing when paper space is plotted at a scale of 1=1.

For this portion of the tutorial,

Click: **Scale dimensions to layout button**

Leave the Annotative box unchecked

Your Fit tab should appear as shown in Figure 7.12.

Figure 7.12

Primary Units

You use the Primary Units tab to set up the number of decimal places, the prefix, and the suffix for dimensions. When dimensioning a drawing, you must consider the precision of the values to be used in the dimensions. Specifying a dimension to four decimal places, which is the AutoCAD default, implies that accuracies of 1/10,000th of an inch are appropriate tolerances for this part. Standard practice is to specify decimal inch dimensions to two decimal places (an accuracy of 1/100th of an inch) unless the function of the part makes a tighter tolerance desirable.

You can select the type of units and set the number of decimal places displayed for linear and angular dimension values. For this tutorial you will leave the linear dimension units set to Decimal.

> Click: **Primary Units tab** *so that it appears uppermost*

Set the precision for the dimension values using the pull-down as shown in Figure 7.13.

> Click: **0.00** *from the pull-down the choices for* **Precision**

Figure 7.13

Measurement Scale

The Measurement Scale area is used to specify a scaling factor by which all the actual dimension values are multiplied. This factor is different from the overall scaling factor because the dimension value is affected, not the size of the dimension elements.

Leave the value to the right of **Scale factor** set to **1.0000**.

You can use this area to scale only layout (paper space) dimensions by clicking the check box.

Zero Suppression for Linear Dimensions

The Zero Suppression area allows you to suppress leading or trailing zeros in the dimension value. You can also suppress dimensions of 0 feet or 0 inches. In decimal dimensioning, common practice is to show leading zeros in metric dimensions and to suppress them in inch dimensions when dimensions are less than 1 unit. Zero Suppression is available for both linear dimensions and angular dimensions, in four categories: leading zeros, trailing zeros, 0 feet, and 0 inches. Selecting the box to the left of any of these items suppresses those zeros; a check appears in the box when you select it. In the Linear Dimensions area under Zero Suppression,

Click: to suppress Leading zeros

Angular Dimensions

The type of units used to dimension angles can be set using the Angular Dimensions area of the Primary Units tab. To select, pull down the list and choose from the types of units shown. (You can further control the appearance of angular dimensions by selecting the Angular in the Dimension Styles dialog box.)

Zero Suppression for Angular Dimensions

You will suppress the leading zeros for angular dimensions as you did for linear dimensions. In the Angular Dimensions area under Zero Suppression,

Click: to suppress Leading zeros

When you have finished setting this tab of the dialog box, it should appear as shown in Figure 7.14.

Figure 7.14

Alternate Units

Alternate units are useful when you want to dimension a drawing with more than one system of measurement. For example, dimensioning drawings with both metric and inch values is fairly common. When you use alternate units, the AutoCAD program automatically converts your drawing units to the alternate units, using the scaling factor you provide. You can enable alternate units by clicking the box to the left of "Display alternate units" in the upper left of the Alternate Units tab. Until you select the box to display the alternate units, the remaining selections are grayed out.

Next you will look at the settings that can be controlled using the Alternate Units tab.

   *Click: **Alternate Units tab***

   *Click: **Display alternate units** so that it is checked*

The Alternate Units tab appears on your screen as shown in Figure 7.15.

Figure 7.15

To set the scale for the alternate units, you set a Multiplier, using the up/down arrows or typing in a scaling factor. The value you set will be multiplied times the primary units to arrive at a value for the alternate unit. You can also type a prefix and suffix for the alternate units in the appropriate boxes. The prefix you enter appears in front of the dimension value; the suffix appears after the dimension value.

You can control the appearance of the alternate units by clicking the button to place them After primary value or Below primary value. The default places the alternate units inside square brackets following the normal units. For this drawing you will not use alternate units so,

> Click: *to unselect Display alternate units so that it is not checked*

Tolerances

You can use the Tolerances tab to specify limit or variance tolerances with the dimension value. You can set the tolerance method to Symmetrical, Deviation, Limits, Basic, or None. You will learn more about setting tolerances in Tutorial 8.

> Click: *Tolerances tab*

> Click: *Deviation from the pull-down for Method*

The image tile shown in Figure 7.16 reflects the choices you have made thus far in setting up the Dimension style. Notice that now the tolerance is shown after the dimension values.

Figure 7.16

On your own, click on the other tolerance methods to view the effect of these settings in the image tile.

Click: **None** *from the pull-down for Method so that tolerances are not used*

Now you have set up your basic style for the dimensions.

Click: **OK**

You are returned to the Dimension Style Manager dialog box.

Setting the Current Style

In order to apply your dimension style MECHANICAL so that new dimensions use this style, click the Set Current button near the top of the Dimension Style Manager.

Click: **Set Current**

The selections you have made apply to dimension style MECHANICAL only. As you dimension your drawing, you can return to this dialog box and create a new style if you need to create dimensions with a different appearance.

When you change a style and click OK, the changes are applied to all existing dimensions in the drawing that you created with that style. If you want to make changes to a style and not have them take effect on existing dimensions, you can click the Override button to allow changes to take effect on newly created dimensions, but not on existing dimensions having that style. The Compare button lets you compare two different styles to view their differences.

Click: **Close** *to exit the Dimension Style Manager*

Notice that the name MECHANICAL now appears in the Dimension panel as the current style as shown in Figure 7.17.

Figure 7.17

Checking Your Dimension Settings

As you have seen, you can change many settings to affect the appearance of the dimensions you add to your drawings. You can set these variables either through the Dimension Styles dialog box or by setting each individual dimension variable at the command line. Most commands that use dialog boxes to select settings can be run at the command prompt by typing a hyphen (-) in front of the command name.

You can use the -Dimstyle command to list and set dimension styles and variables at the command line. If any dimension variable overrides are set, they will be listed after the name of the dimension style. There should not be any overrides set for style MECHANICAL because you have saved your settings to the parent style.

Command: *-DIMSTYLE [Enter]*

Current dimension style: Mechanical

Enter a dimension style option [Save/Restore/STatus/Variables/Apply/?]<Restore>: *ST [Enter]*

The dimension variables and their current settings are listed in the text window on your screen as shown in Figure 7.18. On your own, use the scroll bars to scroll up and down to see all the entries.

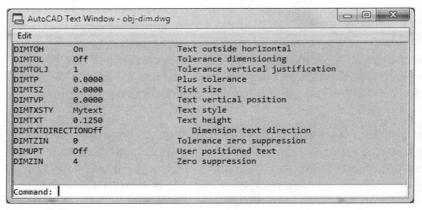

Figure 7.18

*Click: **the Windows Close button [X]** to exit the Text window*

Associative Dimensioning

The Dimassoc variable controls whether associative dimensioning is turned on or off. Associative dimensioning inserts each dimension as a block or group of drawing objects relative to the points selected in the drawing. If the drawing is scaled or stretched, the dimension values automatically update. Dimassoc was a new variable starting in the AutoCAD 2004 release, replacing the old Dimaso variable from prior releases. The Dimassoc variable has three settings for the associativity between dimensions and drawing objects. A setting of 2 causes dimensions to automatically adjust their locations, orientations, and measurement values when the geometric objects associated with them are modified. A setting of 1 causes dimensions to be nonassociative. This means that the dimension does not change when the geometric object it measures is modified. Finally, a setting of 0 causes the dimension to be a collection of separate objects (exploded) rather than a single dimension object. Dimensions created with Dimassoc set to 0 cannot be updated, but their individual parts, such as arrowheads or extension lines, can be erased or moved.

Dimensions created with Dimassoc set to 0 also do not automatically update when you change their dimension styles. When Dimassoc is set to 2 or 1, the entire dimension acts as one object in the drawing.

Make sure that Dimassoc is set to the default value of 2,

Command: **DIMASSOC [Enter]**

Enter new value for DIMASSOC <2>: **2 [Enter]**

Now you are ready to start adding dimensions to your drawing. Look at the status bar. You will see that the coordinates still display the cursor position with four decimal places of accuracy, even though you selected to display only two decimal places in your dimensions. The AutoCAD software can keep track of your drawing and the settings you have made in the drawing database to a precision of at least fourteen decimal places. However, the dimensions will be shown only to two decimal places, as set in the current style. The display of decimal places on the status bar is set independently of the dimension precision (using the Units command you learned in Tutorial 1). This feature is useful because you can still create and display an accurate drawing database while working on the design, yet dimension according to the often lower precision required to manufacture acceptable parts.

Adding Dimensions to the Layout or the Model

Dimensions can be added in model space, where your geometric objects reside, or to the paper space layout, which is the virtual sheet of paper where notes, borders, and other such information are placed. Many factors influence the decision whether to add the dimensions to model space or to paper space. Adding the dimensions to the layout is not common, but can be useful for layout dimensions or showing a dimension between two separate viewports. Generally, you will add the dimensions for most shapes in model space.

Note: *Prior to Release 2005, this was not preferred because dimensions added to the layout were not associated to the objects in a way that let them move as the model was panned inside the viewport.*

Tip: *Dimensioning in Model Space is also perfectly acceptable. For this tutorial, add the dimensions to paper space. For future drawings, decide whether you prefer dimensions in model or paper space.*

Tip: *If you see two grids that don't align with one another, check to see that you have the grid turned off in model space before you turn the grid on in paper space.*

All in all it depends on your particular drawing application, company practices, and downstream uses for the drawing which one you should ultimately choose. You will try each method in this tutorial. For this drawing you will add the dimensions to paper space.

Grid and Snap can be set differently for model space and for paper space. It can look confusing when both grids are turned on at the same time.

On your own, turn the model space **Grid off**.

Switch to **paper space** by clicking on the Model/Paper button so that it shows Paper.

Set the paper space **Snap** to **.25** but wait to turn it on.

Turn the paper space **Grid on**.

Notice that turning on the grid in paper space shows a grid that extends outside the viewport boundary to the edges of the layout sheet.

You will use the paper space grid to help you visually locate the dimensions 0.5 unit away from the object outline (thus meeting the criterion that a dimension must be at least 3/8", or 0.375, from the object outline).

Adding Linear Dimensions

The Linear Dimension command measures and annotates a feature with a horizontal or vertical dimension line. The value inserted into the dimension line is the perpendicular distance between the extension lines. If you use the Linear Dimension command and dimension a line drawn at an angle on the screen, the value returned is just the X- or Y-axis component of the length. The dimension is adjusted to horizontal or vertical, depending on the points selected.

You will use the intersection and quadrant modes to select the exact intersections in the drawing for the extension lines so that the dimensions will be drawn accurately. You will dimension the horizontal distance from the end of the block to the center of the upper hole. Refer to Figure 7.19 for your selections.

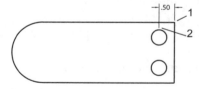

Figure 7.19

On your own, turn the **Intersection** and **Quadrant** running mode object snaps on and all other object snaps and tracking off.

Click: *Linear Dimension button*

Specify first extension line origin or <select object>: *click point 1 at the top right-hand corner*

Specify second extension line origin: *click on the upper small hole, using snap to Quadrant to locate point 2*

Tip: When dimensioning a full circle of 360 degrees (as opposed to an arc), use the diameter command rather than the radius. This is important because equipment used to manufacture and inspect holes and cylinders is designed to measure diameter, not radius.

The machinist making the part should never have to calculate any dimensions, including not having to double the radius to arrive at the diameter. Measuring the radius of a hole is difficult because the center has already been drilled out.

Specify dimension line location or [Mtext/Text/Angle/Horizontal/Vertical/Rotated]: ***Press [F9] to toggle Snap to on and click a point two snap increments above the top line of the object***

Dimension text = 0.50

The dimension should appear in your drawing, as shown in Figure 7.19. Next you will add the diameter dimensions for the two small holes.

Creating a Diameter Dimension

The Diameter Dimension selection adds the centermarks and draws the *leader line* from the point you select on the circle to the location you select for the dimension value. The leader line produced is a radial line, which, if extended, would pass through the center of the circle. Keep in mind that you can make changes to these appearances by setting the dimension style.

You will click the Diameter Dimension button from the flyout on the Dimension panel. After you have entered the dimension, you will use the Text option of the Diameter Dimension command to add an additional line of text below the dimension value. Refer to Figure 7.17 for the placement of the dimension.

 Click: **Diameter Dimension button**

Select arc or circle: ***click on the lower of the two small circles***

Specify dimension line location or [Mtext/Text/Angle]: ***M [Enter]***

The Text Editor similar to Figure 7.20 appears on your screen. You will use the dialog box to add the text 2 X in front of the dimension value.

On your own, position the cursor in front of the .50 value.

Type: **2 X**

Click: **X Close Text Editor**

Figure 7.20

Specify dimension line location or [Mtext/Text/Angle]: ***click a point below and to the left of the circle at about 7 o'clock, about .5 outside the object outline*** *see Figure 7.21*

Tip: *Be sure that Snap and Ortho are off to make selecting the circles and drawing angled leader lines easier.*

Tip: *Take care that the text is not highlighted; you want to insert text, not replace the dimension value.*

Tip: *You can replace the default value for the dimension with a different value. If you do so, however, your dimension values won't automatically update when you change your drawing. A better practice is to create your drawing geometry accurately and accept the default value provided.*

Tip: *Use the grid as a visual reference to help you position the dimension text 0.5 unit away from the object outline.*

Figure 7.21

Next, you will add a centermark for the upper of the two small holes.

 Click: ***Center Mark button***

Select arc or circle: ***click on the edge of the top circle***

The centermark is added to the drawing, as shown in Figure 7.22.

Figure 7.22

Next add a radius dimension and centermarks for the rounded end. You will use the Radius Dimension button on the flyout from the Dimension panel to select the command.

 Click: ***Radius Dimension button***

Select circle or arc: ***click on the rounded end***

Specify dimension line location or [Mtext/Text/Angle]: ***click a point above and to the left of the circle at about 10 o'clock, about .5 outside the object outline***

The radial dimension and centermark for the arc are added. Your drawing should look like that in Figure 7.23.

Figure 7.23

Next, you will add a linear dimension for the vertical distance from the upper edge of the part to the center of the top hole.

Click: **Linear Dimension button**

Specify first extension line origin or <select>: **click intersection 1 at the top right-hand corner** *(refer to Figure 7.23)*

Specify second extension line origin: **target quadrant point 2**

Specify dimension line location or [Mtext/Text/Angle/Horizontal/Vertical/Rotated]: **click a point three snap units to the right of the object**

The dimension added to your drawing should look like that in Figure 7.24.

Figure 7.24

When you use the best fit method for placing text, the AutoCAD software automatically places the text value outside in instances where there is not enough space to fit the text cleanly. You can click on a dimension and use its grips to fine tune the placement if needed. If the dimension value is not inside the extension lines, turn Snap off to make it easier to position the value.

> On your own, turn Snap and Object Snap off. Click on the linear dimension. Use the grips that appear and click the grip centered in the dimension value to make it active. Use it to drag the text inside the extension lines.

Next, you will use baseline dimensioning to add the horizontal dimension between the edge of the part and the rounded end.

Baseline Dimensioning

Baseline and *chained dimensioning* are two different methods of relating one dimension to the next. In baseline dimensioning, as the name suggests, each succeeding dimension is measured from one extension line or baseline. In chained or *continued dimensioning*, each succeeding dimension is measured from the last extension line of the previous dimension. Baseline dimensioning can be the more accurate method because the tolerance allowance is not added to the tolerance allowance of the preceding dimension, as it is in chained dimensioning. However, chained dimensioning often may be preferred because the greater the tolerances allowed, the cheaper the part should be to manufacture. The more difficult the tolerance is to achieve, the more parts will not pass inspection. Figure 7.25 depicts the two different dimensioning methods. Note that, if a tolerance of ±.01 is allowed, the baseline dimensioned portion can be as large as 4.26 or as small as 4.24. However, with chained dimensions, an acceptable part could be as large as 4.27 or as small as 4.23.

Tip: *To add the linear dimension for the location of the hole and have the centermark appear correctly, pick the quadrant point of the circle, not the center. If you select the center, the extension line will extend into the circle and obscure the centermark.*

Turn *Snap on and off as need to make selecting easier.*

Figure 7.25

Adding dimensions with Baseline or Continue is preferable because adding a second dimension with the Linear Dimension command will draw the extension line a second time, which may give a poor appearance to your drawing when it is printed or plotted.

Figure 7.26

Use the Baseline Dimension command to create the next dimension. Refer to Figure 7.26 as you make selections.

You will use the Select option to specify the dimension you want to use as the base dimension. As you have added several dimensions since determining the horizontal location for the upper small hole, you will need to specify that it is the base dimension before you can create the baseline dimension. If you were continuing from the previous dimension, you would not need to do this.

Click: **Baseline Dimension button from the flyout**

Specify a second extension line origin or [Undo/Select] <Select>: *[Enter]*

Select base dimension: **click A for the base dimension**

Specify a second extension line origin or [Undo/Select] <Select>: **click intersection B**

Specify a second extension line origin or [Undo/Select] <Select>: *[Enter]*

Select base dimension: *[Enter]*

The new dimension appears, as in Figure 7.27. Note that the program located the dimensions automatically based on your dimension style settings.

Figure 7.27

Next you will add baseline dimensions for the vertical location of the lower hole and for the overall height. Refer to Figure 7.27 for the points to select.

Click: **Baseline Dimension button**

Specify a second extension line origin or [Undo/Select] <Select>: *[Enter]*

Select base dimension: **click 1 for the base dimension**

Specify a second extension line origin or [Undo/Select] <Select>: **click the centerline endpoint 2**

Specify a second extension line origin or [Undo/Select] <Select>: **click intersection 3**

Specify a second extension line origin or [Undo/Select] <Select>: *[Enter]*

Select base dimension: *[Enter]*

Save your drawing now.

Your drawing should now look like that in Figure 7.28.

Figure 7.28

Using Xplode

The Xplode command lets you change dimensions, blocks, polylines, and other grouped objects back to their individual components; at the same time, you can control the color, layer, and linetype of the components. You will use Xplode to erase just the single right line of the centermark for the rounded end. You will select the Layer option of the Xplode command and the default layer, DIM, for the exploded object's layer.

The Xplode command has suboptions that allow you to control the color, layer, linetype and other options as the object is changed back into its original components. Explode and Xplode are different commands. Refer to on-line help to investigate the differences between these two commands further.

Note: *There is also a command named Explode that
doesn't have any options.
Explode simply changes
the grouped objects back to
individual objects, regardless
of the X-, Y-, and Z-scaling
factors. (In early AutoCAD
releases, the X-, Y-, and Z-
scaling factors of a block had to
be the same or it could not be
exploded.)*

Because the rounded end is an arc, not a full circle, its centermark
should extend only for the half-circle shown. Because associative
dimensions are created as blocks, they are all one object: No part can be
erased singly. To eliminate the extra portion of the centermark on the
rounded end, you will type the Xplode command.

Command: **XPLODE [Enter]**

Select objects to XPlode.

Select objects: **click on the dimension for the rounded end**

Select objects: **[Enter]**

[All/Color/LAyer/LType/LWeight/Inherit from parent block/Explode]
<Explode>: **LA [Enter]**

Enter new layer name for exploded objects <DIM>: **[Enter]**

The message "Object exploded onto layer DIM" appears. The drawing
doesn't look any different, but now the dimension is made up of individual pieces that you can select.

> On your own, **erase** the extra line from the centermark for the rounded end and
> **save** your drawing at this time.

Adding Text with Special Characters

When you are using AutoCAD shape fonts (e.g., Roman Simplex),
you can type in special characters during any text command and when
entering the dimension text.

One way to add special text characters is by inserting the code %%
(double percent signs) before special characters. The most common special characters have been given letters to make them easy to remember.
You can also specify any special character by typing its ASCII number.
(Most word processor documentation includes a list of ASCII values for
symbols in an appendix.) You can also use the Symbol selection for the
Text Editing ribbon to quickly click the special symbols from the list.

The most common special characters and their codes are listed below.

Code	Character	Symbol
%%C	Diameter symbol	Ø
%%D	Degree symbol	°
%%P	Plus/minus sign	±
%%O	Toggles on and off the overscore mode	On
%%U	Toggles on and off the underscore mode	On
%%%	Draws a single percent sign	%
%%N	Draws special character number n	n

Next use MultilineText to add a block of notes.

On your own, make layer **TEXT** current.

Start the **Multiline Text** command and define an area near the lower right of the drawing to add the notes. Notes in engineering drawings are often in uppercase letter, so you may want to use Caps Lock.

Add the note "ALL TOLERANCES ± .01 UNLESS OTHERWISE NOTED." Use the Symbol selection from the Text editor to enter %%P to make the ± sign as shown in Figure 7.29.

Below the tolerance note add notes indicating the material from which the part is to be made, such as "MATERIAL: SAE 1020" and a note stating "ALL MEASURE-MENTS IN INCHES."

Use the Edit Text command to change the text in your title block, noting the name of the part, your name, and the scale, to complete the drawing.

Save your drawing.

Figure 7.29

Tip: *You can double-click on text to edit it in place.*

Using Quick Dimension

Next you will erase the dimensions that you added and try using the Quick Dimension command to add them.

On your own, **erase** the dimensions that you added.

Switch to **Model** space inside the viewport by toggling the Model/Paper button to Model.

Make layer **DIM** current

 Click: *Quick Dimension button from the Annotate tab, Dimension panel*

Select geometry to dimension: *use Window to select all of the drawing lines and press [Enter]*

Specify dimension line position, or [Continuous/Staggered/Baseline/Ordinate/ Radius/Diameter/datumPoint/Edit/seTtings]: ***click two snap increments above the object***

Two dimensions are added to the drawing as shown in Figure 7.30.

Figure 7.30

Next you will restart the Quick Dimension command and add the dimension for the rounded end.

Command: ***[Enter]***

Associative dimension priority = Endpoint

Select geometry to dimension: ***Click on the rounded end***

Select geometry to dimension: ***[Enter]***

Specify dimension line position, or [Continuous/Staggered/Baseline/Ordinate/Ra-dius/Diameter/datumPoint/Edit/seTtings] <Radius>: ***click to the left of the rounded end***

The dimension for the rounded end appears in your drawing as a radial dimension.

> On your own, click on the dimension for the rounded end and use its grips to position it so that the leader to the value is at an angle.

Saving As a Template

Any drawing that you have created can be used as a template from which to start new drawings. You will use Save As and save your *obj-dim.dwg* with a new name and file type so that you can use it as a template to start other drawings.

> On your own, **erase** the object and all dimensions and set layer **VISIBLE** as the current layer.

> Use **Save As** to save this drawing as *dimtemplate.dwt* (by changing the file type to a Drawing Template *.dwt).

> In the Template Description, describe this template as a dimensioning template and leave measurement with English units.

> **Close** the file when you have finished saving it.

Dimensioning the Adapter

Next, you will add dimensions to a drawing similar to the adapter you created in Tutorial 6. Here, the hole has not been added and the views have been moved apart to make room for dimensions. You will be adding the dimensions to model space for this drawing.

> On your own, use the **New** button to start a drawing from the datafile template, *adapter1.dwt* **Save** your drawing as *adapt-dim.dwg*.

> Check that **Intersection** running object snap mode is turned on.

> Check the Layer Control to be sure that you are on layer **DIM**.

Next, set the dimension style using the Annotate tab, Dimension panel.

> *Click: **on the dimension style name STANDARD** to show the pull down list as shown in Figure 7.31*

> *Select: **MECHANICAL** from the pull-down list*

Tip: *You can use the AutoCAD DesignCenterTM to import dimension styles from an existing drawing into your current drawing. You will learn more about the DesignCenter in Tutorial 10.*

Tip: *Drawings started from dimtemplate.dwt will have the dimension styles that you created earlier in this tutorial available for use.*

Figure 7.31

Dimensions are placed between views when possible, except for the overall dimensions, which are often placed around the outside.

Next you will add the horizontal dimension that shows the width of the left portion of the block. The shape of this feature shows clearly in the front view, so add the dimension to the front view between the views. You will use the Select object option, which allows you to click an object instead of specifying the two extension line locations. The software will automatically locate the extension lines at the extreme ends of the object you select.

Click: ***Linear Dimension button***

Specify first extension line origin or <Select object>: *[Enter]*

Select object to dimension: ***click the top left-hand line in the front view***

Specify dimension line location or [Mtext/Text/Angle/Horizontal/Vertical /Rotated]: ***click 0.5 unit above the object outline***

Your drawing should be similar to Figure 7.32.

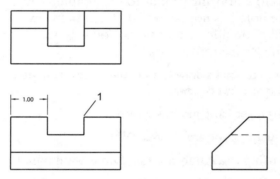

Figure 7.32

Using Continue Dimension

Now use the Continue Dimension command to add a chained dimension for the size of the slot. You will use the Select option again to choose which dimension is to be continued. (The Baseline Dimension command has a similar option.) When using this feature, click near the extension line that you want to have continued. Refer to Figure 7.32.

Click: ***Continue Dimension button***

Select continued dimension: ***click the right extension line*** *of the dimension you just added*

Specify a second extension line origin or [Undo/Select]<Select>: ***click point 1 using AutoSnap Intersection***

Specify a second extension line origin or [Undo/Select] <Select>: *[Enter]*

Select continued dimension: *[Enter]*

The chained dimension should appear in your drawing, as shown in Figure 7.33.

Tip: *When using the Continue Dimension command, you can press [Enter] to select a different dimension to continue from.*

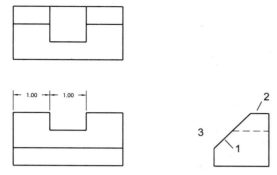

Figure 7.33

Angular Dimensions

The Angular Dimension command lets you add an angular dimension by selecting two angled lines and then clicking the location for the angle dimension. Depending on where you select, you will define the major angle or the minor angle between the lines. You also have the option during the command of pressing [Enter] instead of selecting the first line. If you do so, you will be prompted for three points to define the angle. You do not have to use the %%D special character to make the degree sign; it is inserted automatically unless you override the default text.

Next, add the angular dimension for the angled surface to the side view,

> **Click: Angular Dimension button**
>
> Select arc, circle, line or <specify vertex>: *click line 1*
>
> Select second line: *click line 2*
>
> Specify dimension arc line location or [Mtext/Text/Angle/Quadrant]: *click near point 3*

The angular dimension is added to the side view, as in Figure 7.34. Notice that since the precision for angular dimensions was set to zero (0) decimal places in the MECHANICAL style, the angle value is shown to a whole number of degrees.

Figure 7.34

Tip: *You can right-click on a dimension and use the pop-up menu to pick Flip arrows and quickly change whether the arrows are inside or outside the extension lines.*

Tip: *Use the [X] in its upper right corner to close the Navigation Bar if it is in the way.*

Tip: *Note that you do not need dimensions for the short vertical line in the side view. Its length is already defined by the overall dimension for the height of the part, the 0.50 distance across the top surface, and the 45° angle. To include this dimension would be overdimensioning. If you want to give this dimension, include the value in brackets, or followed by the word REF, to indicate that it is a reference dimension only.*

Next, add the dimension for the depth of the top surface in the side view.

Figure 7.35

> *Click:* **Linear Dimension button**

Specify first extension line origin or <select object>: *[Enter]*

Select object to dimension: *click the short horizontal line labeled A in Figure 7.35*

Specify dimension line location or [Mtext/Text/Angle/Horizontal/Vertical/Rotated]: *click 0.5 unit above the top line of the side view*

Now add the dimension for the height of the slot in the front view. Refer to Figure 7.31.

> *Click:* **Linear Dimension button**

Specify first extension line origin or <select object>: *click the intersection labeled 1*

Specify second extension line origin: click the right-hand bottom corner of the slot, labeled 2

Specify dimension line location or [Mtext/Text/Angle/Horizontal/Vertical/Rotated]: *click 0.5 unit away from the right side of the front view*

The dimension for the slot should appear in your drawing, as shown in Figure 7.36.

> On your own, **add the overall dimensions** to the outsides of the views so that your drawing looks like Figure 7.36.

Figure 7.36

Centering the Views

Now you will use the Pan command to center the dimensioned drawing views inside the border. To do this you will use the Pan command in model space.

Check that you are in **model space**. and that the viewport is **unlocked**.

Press and hold the mouse scroll wheel and use the **Pan** function to position the view upward to center the dimensioned views inside the border.

Dimensions that are located in paper space sometimes do not pan with the drawing objects even with fully associated dimensions. You can use the Dimension Update button to help if that is the case. Generally, it is often better to locate the dimensions in model space.

Adding the Tolerance Note

Next you will add a notes and titles in paper space.

Click: *Model/Paper button so that it displays Paper*

Click: *TEXT as the current layer*

Click: *Multiline Text button*

Use the Mtext command on your own to add 0.125" text stating ALL TOLERANCES ARE ± .01 UNLESS OTHERWISE NOTED.

MATERIAL: SAE 1020.

ALL MEASUREMENTS ARE IN INCHES.

On your own, change the drawing title to **DIMENSIONED ADAPTER** and the YOUR NAME text to your actual name.

If you want, plot your drawing from paper space using the drawing limits at the scale of 1=1.

Save your drawing *adapt-dm.dwg* before you continue.

Your finished drawing should be similar to Figure 7.37.

Figure 7.37

Updating Associative Dimensions

Dimensions created using associative dimensioning are AutoCAD block objects. Blocks are a group of objects that behave as a single object. If you try to erase an associative dimension, the entire dimension is erased, including the extension lines and arrowheads. Because these dimensions have the special properties of a block, you can also cause them to be updated automatically.

As the geometric objects that you are going to change are in model space, you must return to model space in order to change them.

Click: **Model/Paper button so that it displays Model**

Using Stretch

The Stretch command is used to stretch and relocate objects. It is similar to stretching with hot grips, which you did in Tutorial 4. You must use implied Crossing, Crossing, or Crossing Polygon methods to select the objects for use with the Stretch command. As you select, objects entirely enclosed in the crossing window specified will be moved to the new location rather than stretched. Keep this in mind and draw the crossing box only around the portion of the object you want to stretch, leaving the other portion unselected to act as an anchor.

Next, make the front and top views of the adapter wider. The starting width of the front view is currently 3.00. Refer to Figure 7.38.

Figure 7.38

Click: **Stretch button** *(from the Modify panel)*

Select objects to stretch by crossing-window or crossing-polygon

Select objects: **use Crossing and select point A**

Tip: *When a Crossing selection box is being drawn, it appears green or with a dashed outline depending on your settings. When a Window selection box is being drawn, it appears blue or has a solid outline. Use this visual cue. Crossing boxes are drawn from right to left.*

Specify opposite corner: **select point B**

Select objects: **[Enter]**

Specify base point or [Displacement] <Displacement>: **target the lower right-hand corner of the front view**

Specify second point or <use first point as displacement>: **move the cursor .5 units to the right and click**

Note that the overall dimension now reads 3.50 and that it has updated automatically. The result is shown in Figure 7.39.

Figure 7.39

Modifying Dimensions

You can modify individual dimensions and override their dimension styles using the Properties palette. To edit a dimension's properties, you must be in the same space (model/paper space) where that dimension resides.

*Click: **on the vertical dimension labeled A** to select it (grips show)*

*Right-click: **to show the shortcut menu***

*Click: **Properties** to show the Properties palette*

As with other objects, you can modify the dimension's layer, color, linetype, lineweight, linetype scale. Near the bottom of the palette are selections for Misc, Lines & Arrows, Text, Fit, Primary Units, Alternate Units, and Tolerances (like in the Modify Dimension Style dialog box). You can click on the arrows (v) to the right of the name to expand the list for the related feature.

You will change the text orientation to be parallel to the dimension line.

*Click: **to expand Text selections (using the down arrow)***

The Text area should appear expanded as shown in Figure 7.40.

*Click: **the text box to the right of Text inside align to expand it***

*Click: **On** to align the dimension text inside the extension lines with the dimension line*

*Click: **Windows Close button** to close the Properties palette*

*Press: **[Esc]** to remove the grips from vertical dimension*

Tip: *If you have trouble stretching, double-check to be sure that you are in model space. Also, the Stretch command works only when you use the Crossing option. If you type the command, you must be sure to select Crossing or type C and press [Enter] afterward, or use implied Crossing (by drawing the window box from right to left), as you did in the previous step.*

Tip: *You can trim and extend linear and ordinate dimensions with the Trim and Extend commands. When trimmed or extended, the dimension acts as though there were a line between the endpoints of the extension line origins. Trimming and extending takes effect on the dimension at that location.*

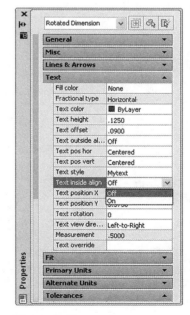

Figure 7.40

The 0.50 dimension value changes to be parallel to the dimension line, as shown in Figure 7.41. The dimension style for MECHANICAL has not changed; only that single dimension was overridden to produce a new appearance.

Figure 7.41

Updating a Dimension Style

Tip: *If you are not sure what dimension style and overrides you may have used when creating a particular dimension, use the List command and pick on the dimension. You will see a list of the dimension style and any overrides that were used for the dimension.*

When you change a dimension style, all the dimensions using that style automatically take on the new appearance (when using associative dimensioning.) Next you will use the Dimension Styles Manager to update the arrow style used for the dimensions in your drawing.

Click: to Show the Dimension Style Manager

Make sure that MECHANICAL is the style name highlighted.

Click: Modify

Click: Symbols and Arrows tab as shown in Figure 7.42

Click: Right Angle for the First and Second Arrowhead

Click: OK

Click: Close to exit the Dimension Style Manager

Figure 7.42

The dimensions in the drawing update automatically to reflect this change. The arrows are now right-angled arrows instead of filled arrows. Your drawing should be similar to Figure 7.43.

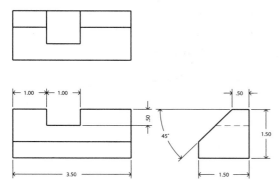

Figure 7.43

Changing the Drawing Scale

You have been working in the drawing with the drawing zoomed so that the viewport scale is at 1:1. Since the paper units are inches and the drawing units are inches, this drawing is full scale. If you plot the drawing from paper space at a scale of 1=1, you should be able to measure the lines and have them be equal to the dimension value.

Next you will change the drawing viewport scale.

On your own, make sure you are in **Model** space.

If locked, use the status bar button to **Unlock the viewport scale**.

At the command prompt, you will type the alias for the Zoom command,

Command: *Z [Enter]*

Specify corner of window, enter a scale factor (nX or nXP), or [All/Center/Dynamic/Extents/Previous/Scale/Window/Object] <real time>: *.5XP [Enter]*

The zoom factor changes as shown in Figure 7.44. Now the viewport shows the drawing with each .5 model space unit equals 1 paper space unit. In other words, half size. The viewport scaling displays 6"=1'

Figure 7.44

Tip: *If you find the magenta colored viewport border distracting, you can freeze its layer so that it doesn't appear.*

By switching to paperspace, you can click and drag the viewport grips to the size of the outer border.

Notice the appearance of the dimensions. They are almost too small to read. The size set for the height of the dimension value text is too small at this scale.

The Fit tab of the Dimension Style Manager is used to manage the scaling of the dimensions for the entire style as a group.

Click: **to Show the Dimension Style Manager**

Make sure that MECHANICAL is the style name highlighted.

Click: **Modify**

Click: **Fit tab** *as shown in Figure 7.45*

Figure 7.45

The Scale for dimension features area is currently set to Use overall scale of 1.000. So the text height of .125", now that the drawing is zoomed to half scale, will only appear half that size (.0625") which is too small to read comfortably.

There are three ways to set the scale for the dimension features as a group (by setting the dimension variable named Dimscale):

1. **Use overall scale** of lets you specify a value to multiply times the dimension size settings to adjust the size based dimension features for the entire style at once.

2. **Scale dimensions to layout** automatically multiplies the size dimension features based on the viewport scale factor.

3. **Annotative** uses the annotative styles to automatically scale annotation items like dimensions. (The use of annotative styles automatically sets Dimscale to 0.)

Click: **Scale Dimensions to layout**

Click: **OK**

Click: **Close**

Figure 7.46

The drawing automatically updates to show the dimensions with the dimension features sizes scaled to the layout. Now the height of the dimension values, arrow sizes, etc. are .125".

The Annotation Property

The scale at which you plot your drawing directly affects the size and placement required for drawing notes and dimensions. You can see in Figure 7.46 that the dimension values need to be repositioned now that the scale of the drawing has changed.

In the past, CAD designers had to create copies of dimensions and local notes on multiple layers, which they would turn on and off for different plot scales. This was time consuming to set up and hard to maintain as note changes had to be made in multiple places. In addition, errors could creep in, when a copy was neglected.

Now annotation scale is an object property that certain types of objects like text, dimensions, and hatching have. The annotation property is similar to the other object properties like color, linetype, and layer, except that it is used to scale the object. The annotation property for each object can set its size, placement, and appearance based on the scale set for the viewport.

At the right-hand of the status bar there are special annotation tools. Figure 7.47 shows the right side of the status bar with the buttons labeled. You can also find similar selections on the Annotation Scaling panel of the Annotate tab.

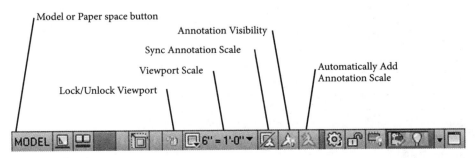

Figure 7.47

Annotative objects support one annotation scale: the one that is current when you create the object. So, you want to set the annotation scale and then create the objects. Existing annotative objects can be updated if necessary to allow additional annotation scales.

This is another reason why it is a good practice to create your model, then determine the sheet size and scale, and finally add the notes and dimensions. You will spend less time revising the text, if it is added when you are pretty clear on what scale or scales you will use.

Synch the Annotative and Viewport Scales

In drawing *adapt-dim.dwg* the viewport scale and the annotation scale may now not be the same. In order for the annotative property to work well, you need these two scales to be the same.

Check that your viewport and annotation styles are synchronized using the button on the status bar. If it is grayed out, they are in synch, if not you will see the message "Annotation scale is not equal to viewport scale: Click to synchronize," when your cursor is over the Sync Annotation Scale button as shown in Figure 7.48.

Click: *to synchronize the viewport and annotation scales*

Figure 7.48

Your viewport zoom factor changes as the scales synchronize. The dimensions now appear too large, as shown in Figure 7.49. This is because when they were created, the zoom factor was different. Remember, the dimension style did not use annotative text. It did have Scale to paper space layout selected from the Dimension Style Manager's Fit tab.

Figure 7.49

If your viewport scale is not set to **1:1**, set to that on your own at this time.

To update the dimension appearance,

> *Click:* **Dimension Update button**
>
> Select objects: **ALL [Enter]**
>
> Select objects: **[Enter]**

The dimensions update as shown in Figure 7.50.

Figure 7.50

Creating an Annotative Text Style

Next, create a new annotative text style,

> *Click:* **to show the Text Style Manager**
>
> *Click:* **New**

The New Text Style dialog box appears on your screen.

> *Type:* **AnnText** *for the new style name*
>
> *Click:* **OK**
>
> **Select the Annotative check box** *from the Size area, so it appears checked as shown in Figure 7.51*
>
> **Set Paper Text Height to .125**
>
> *Click:* **Apply**
>
> *Click:* **Set Current** *to set AnnText as the current text style*
>
> *Click:* **Close**

Figure 7.51

Notice AnnText has the special annotative icon next to it where it shows as the current style in the Text panel. See Figure 7.52.

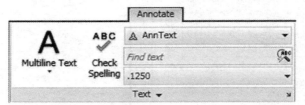

Figure 7.52

Next add some local notes to model space.

On your own, add the text "PAINT THIS SURFACE" to the top view, as shown in Figure 7.53.

Figure 7.53

On your own, use the status bar to change the viewport scale to **6" = 1'**.

The view is resized. Now the new note does not show up. To add the new annotation scale to the annotative objects,

Click: **Add Current Scale** from the Annotation Scale panel

The text updates to the annotative size. It may not be positioned on the surface correctly. See Figure 7.54.

Figure 7.54

On your own, select the "PAINT THIS SURFACE" text and use the grips to position the text off of the surface, if it is not positioned correctly.

Click: **Sync Scale Positions button** from the Annotation Scale panel

Use the status bar to reset the Viewport scale to 1:1. Notice the text resizes automatically. Reset the Viewport Scale to 6" = 1'-0". Now the text resizes and repositions to fit at that scale.

There are several variables that control the tools for annotative objects. Learn more about using annotative styles by reading the AutoCAD Help files.

Save the drawing when you have finished.

Exit the AutoCAD program.

You have completed Tutorial 7.

Key Terms

associative dimensioning	dimension style	extension line	manufacture
baseline dimensioning	dimension value	extension line offset	overall dimensions
chained (continued) dimensioning	dimension variables (dim vars)	image tile	tolerance
		inspection	
dimension line	dimensions	leader line	

Key Commands

Angular Dimension	Dimassoc	Radius Dimension	Annotation Property
Baseline Dimension	Dimension Status	Stretch	
Continue Dimension	Dimension Style	Xplode	
Diameter Dimension	Linear Dimension	Annotation Scale	

Exercises

Draw and dimension the following shapes. The letter M after an exercise number means that the units are metric. Add a note to the drawing saying, "METRIC: All dimensions are in millimeters for metric drawings." Specify a general tolerance for the drawing.

7.1M Stop Plate

ALL FILLETS R6

7.2M Hub

EXERCISES 325

7.3 Guide Block

ALL FILLETS R.06

7.4 Interchange

Draw and dimension this intersection, then mirror the circular interchange for all lanes.

Hint: *To make radial dimensions with placements as shown, you may need to use the Dimension Style, Fit tab and then select Place text manually in the Fine Tuning area of the dialog box.*

7.5 Angle Bracket

7.6 Bearing Box
Draw and dimension the orthographics views for the bearing box.

7.7 Plot Plan
Draw and dimension using the civil engineering dimensioning style shown. Find the missing dimensions.

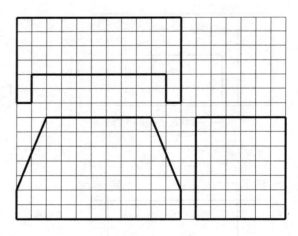

7.8 Hub
Draw and dimension the drawings above. Use 1 grid unit = .0125 " for a decimal inch drawing or 25 mm for a metric drawing.

7.9 Support

7.10 Index Feed

HEAT TREAT
10-250

CRS
1 REQD

7.11M Socket Bearing

METRIC

3X Ø9

3X R14

C1-1 REQD

FILLETS &
ROUNDS R2

Draw dimensioned orthographic views of the parts shown above. Show only the necessary views.

7.12 Floor Plan

Use architectural units to draw and dimension the floor plan shown, making good use of layers.

ADVANCED DIMENSIONING

Tolerance

No part can be manufactured to exact dimensions. There is always some amount of variation between the size of the actual object when it is measured and an exact dimension specified in the drawing. To take this variation into consideration, tolerances are specified along with dimensions. A *tolerance* is the amount of variation that an acceptable part is allowed to have from the specified dimension.

Dimensions given in the drawing are used to make and inspect the part. In order to determine whether a part is acceptable, the measurements of the actual part are compared to the toleranced dimensions specified in the drawing. If the part feature falls within the tolerance range specified, it is acceptable.

To better understand the role that tolerances play in dimensioning, consider Figure 8.1. Surface A on the actual object is longest when the 5.00 overall dimension shown for surface B is at its largest acceptable value and when the 2.00 dimension shown for surface C is at its shortest acceptable value.

$$A_{max} = 5.04 - 1.95 = 3.09$$

Surface A is shortest when surface B is at its smallest acceptable value and surface C is at its largest acceptable value. Thus

$$A_{min} = 4.96 - 2.05 = 2.91$$

In other words, the given dimensions with the added tolerances permit surface A to vary between 3.09 and 2.91 units.

Figure 8.1

Objectives

When you have completed this tutorial, you will be able to

1. Use tolerances in a drawing.

2. Set up the dimension variables to use limit tolerances and variance (plus/minus) tolerances.

3. Add geometric tolerances to your drawing.

4. Use dimension overrides.

Limit tolerance

Deviation tolerance

Geometric tolerance

Tolerance Formats

In Tutorial 7, you learned how to add a general tolerance note to your drawing to specify this allowable variation. The AutoCAD program provides three ways to add a tolerance to the dimension for a feature: limit tolerances, variance tolerances, and geometric tolerances.

Limit tolerances specify the upper and lower allowable measurements for the part. A part measuring between the two limits is acceptable.

Deviation (variance) tolerances or *plus/minus tolerances* specify the *nominal dimension* and the allowable range that is added to it. From this information you can determine the upper and lower limits. Add the plus tolerance to the nominal size to get the upper limit; subtract the minus tolerance from the nominal size to get the lower limit. (Or you can think of it as always adding the tolerance, but when the sign of the tolerance is negative, it has the effect of subtracting the value.) The plus and minus values do not always have to be the same. There are two types of variance tolerances: bilateral and unilateral. *Bilateral tolerances* specify a nominal size and both a plus and minus tolerance. *Unilateral tolerances* are a special case where either the plus or the minus value specified for the tolerance is zero. You can create both bilateral and unilateral tolerances.

Geometric tolerances use special symbols inside feature control frames that describe *tolerance zones* that relate to the type of feature being controlled. The Tolerance command allows you to create feature control frames quickly and select geometric tolerance symbols for them. You will learn to create these frames later in this tutorial.

Figure 8.2 shows the drawing from Tutorial 7 with tolerances added to the dimensions. Tolerances A, B, F, and G are examples of bilateral tolerances. Tolerances C, D, and E are limit tolerances.

Figure 8.2

Starting

Start the AutoCAD program.

On your own, use the datafile **obj-dim.dwt** as the template for a new drawing.

Name your new drawing **tolernc.dwg**.

Your screen should be similar to Figure 8.3. Be sure that layer DIM is set as the current layer. Next, set up the dimension variables to use tolerances.

Tip: *There are some setting differences between the datafile and the similar file you created in Tutorial 7, so make sure to use the datafile.*

Figure 8.3

Tip: *If the full drawing does not show on your screen, switch to paperspace and zoom out to the drawing extents. Then switch back to model space.*

Automatic Bilateral Tolerances

You can have the program automatically add bilateral tolerances by setting the dimensioning variables with the Dimension Styles dialog box. The small arrow in the lower right corner of the ribbon Annotate tab, Dimension panel launches the Dimension Style Manager (Figure 8.4).

Click on the small trtiangle to launch
the Dimension Style Manager

Figure 8.4

Click: ***to show the Dimension Style Manager***

The Dimension Style Manager appears on your screen, as shown in Figure 8.5. You will use it to set up the appearance of the tolerances to be added to the dimensions. The dimension style MECHANICAL is current. It is like the style you created in Tutorial 7. You will make changes to it so that the dimensions in the drawing created with that style will show a variance, or deviation tolerance.

Figure 8.5

In Tutorial 7 you used the New button to create a new dimension style. This time you will change style MECHANICAL to include deviation tolerances. When you are done making the following changes to the dimension style, the dimensions in the drawing will automatically reflect the changes to the style used for them.

Click: **Modify**

The Modify Dimension Style dialog box appears on your screen.

Click: **Tolerances tab**

The Tolerances tab appears uppermost.

*Click: **to pull down the Method list** in the Tolerance Format area as shown in Figure 8.6*

Figure 8.6

The choices of tolerance methods are None, Symmetrical, Deviation, Limits, and Basic.

- *None* uses just the dimension and does not add a tolerance, as your current dimensions reflect.

- *Symmetrical tolerances* are lateral tolerances with the same upper and lower values; these tolerances generally specify the dimension plus or minus a single value.

- *Deviation tolerances* are lateral tolerances that have a different upper and lower deviation.

- *Limit tolerances* show the maximum value for the dimension and the minimum value for the dimension.

- *Basic dimension* is a term used in geometric dimensioning and tolerancing to specify a theoretically exact dimension without a tolerance. Basic dimensions appear in your drawing with a box drawn around them.

If you choose any of the tolerance methods, you can preview what your dimensions will look like in the image tile.

Click: **Deviation**

Note the image tile at the right of the dialog box; it shows a dimension with a deviation style tolerance added.

Click: **Limits (as the tolerance Method)**

Notice the change to the image tile. Continue clicking the tolerance methods on your own until you cycle through all the options and return to Deviation tolerance, as shown in Figure 8.7.

Figure 8.7

Setting the Tolerance Precision

The tolerance values can have a different precision from the dimension values. You control the precision by using the Precision pull-down near the top left of the dialog box.

*Click: **to show the Precision list** as shown in Figure 8.8.*

*Click: **0.00***

Figure 8.8

Specifying Tolerance Values

The text boxes for setting tolerance values were formerly grayed. Now that you have selected a tolerance method, they are available for input. You will use them to specify the upper and lower values that you want to use with the dimension to specify the allowable deviation. Both values will be positive. The upper value will be added to the dimension value; the lower value will be subtracted from the dimension value. The program will automatically add the plus or minus sign in front of the value when showing the tolerance.

*Type: **.05** for the Upper Value*

*Type: **.03** for the Lower Value*

Note that you can also control the vertical position of the tolerance. For now you will leave it set to Middle, the default.

Setting the Tolerance Text Height Scaling

The default setting of 1.0000 appears in the Scaling for height input box in the Tolerance Format area. This value is a scaling factor. A setting of 1.0000 makes the tolerance values the same height as the standard dimension text. For this tutorial you will set tolerance height to 0.8 (so

Tip: *You can press [Tab] to move to the next text entry box. Doing so will also highlight the text in that box.*

that the height of the tolerance values will be 8/10 the height of the dimension values).

Type: .8 in the Scaling for height input box

The same text style used for the dimension text, MYTEXT, will also be used for the tolerance text. You can control the text style and the dimension text height, color, and gap using the Text tab of the dialog box. You will leave these features set as they are. The Tolerances tab should now appear as shown in Figure 8.9.

*Click: **OK** to exit the Modify Dimension Style dialog box*

*Click: **Close** to exit the Dimension Style Manager*

Figure 8.9

You return to your drawing. The dimensions created with style ME-CHANICAL automatically update to show the deviation tolerance. Your drawing should look like that in Figure 8.10.

Figure 8.10

On your own, use the grip to edit the dimensions and move the dimension values so that the text is not crossing drawing lines as shown in Figure 8.11.

Figure 8.11

You can find information about the dimension using the List command.

Command: **LIST [Enter]**

Select objects: ***click the radial dimension at the left end of the object [Enter]***

The List command displays the information in a Text window as shown in Figure 8.12.

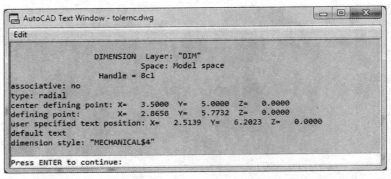

Figure 8.12

Note that the style name for this dimension is MECHANICAL$4. When you list a dimension, the $# code tells you that the dimension uses a substyle different from the main style. Here, it tells you that the dimension was created with a substyle that has different settings than the parent style, MECHANICAL. The codes for the substyles are:

$0   Linear

$2   Angular

$3   Diameter

$4   Radial

$6   Ordinate

$7   Leader (also used for tolerance objects)

Using Dimension Overrides

Dimension overrides let you change the dimension variables controlling a dimension and leave its style as is. A good approach is to change the general appearance of the dimensions by changing the dimension style and to change individual dimensions that need to vary from the overall group of dimensions (to suppress an extension line, for instance) by using overrides.

You can change dimension variables by typing DIMOVERRIDE at the command prompt. Dimoverride has the alias Dimover. When you use Dimoverride at the command prompt, the program prompts you for the exact name of the dimension variable you want to control and its new value. Then you select the dimensions to which you will apply the override. The Clear option of the Dimoverride command lets you remove overrides from the dimensions you select. You can also use the Dimension Style command, and select the Override button from the Dimension Style Manager.

You can also use the Properties palette to do the same thing.

Click: **the radial dimension for the rounded end** *to select it*

Right-click: **to show the short-cut menu**

Click: **Properties** *to show the Properties palette*

The Properties palette appears on your screen. You will use it to override the dimension style for the radial dimension. Because the 2.00 vertical dimension at the right side of the part controls the part's height, providing the radial dimension is an example of overdimensioning. When you want to call attention to the full rounded end, which is tangent to the horizontal surfaces at the top and bottom of the object, you can show the 1.00 radius value as a *reference dimension.* Or you can simply identify it with the letter R, indicating the radius but leaving its value to be determined by the other surfaces. You will turn off the tolerance and add REF to the end of the radial dimension value to indicate that it is provided as a reference dimension only. You can also note reference dimensions by including the dimension value in parentheses ( ).

Click: **to expand the Tolerances area**

Click: **None** *as the selection in the Tolerance display area*

Click: **to expand the Primary Units area**

Type: **REF** *in the Dim suffix text box*

When you have finished making these selections, your palette should look like Figure 8.12.

Click: **to Close the Properties palette**

Press: **[Esc] twice** *to unselect the radial dimension*

You can also use the Properties palette to override the dimension text by clicking to expand the Text area and using the Text override input box that appears to change the text. After you have overridden the text, your dimension values no longer update if you stretch or change the object. As usual with the Properties palette, you can change the layer, color, linetype, lineweight, and linetype scale. Your drawing should look like the one in Figure 8.13.

Figure 8.13

Next, use List again to list the radial dimension.

Command: **LIST [Enter]**

Select objects: *click the radial dimension [Enter]*

A Text window appears, as shown in Figure 8.14, listing the information about the radial dimension. Note that overrides for the dimension variables Dimgap, Dimlim, Dimpost, and Dimtol are now listed. Dimpost displays the dimension suffix, which is set to REF. Dimlim is set to Off, so that no deviation tolerance is applied to the dimension.

When dimensioning, keep your dimension styles organized by creating new dimension styles and controlling the substyles as needed. Use dimension overrides when certain dimensions need a different appearance than the general case for that type of dimension.

Press [Enter] if needed to show additional text in the text window.

You can now close the Text window.

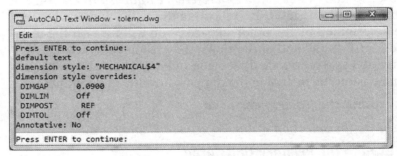

Figure 8.14

Using Limit Tolerances

Next you will create a new style for dimensions using limit tolerances, and then you will change the object's overall dimension to use that style.

Click: **to show the Dimension Style Manager**

The Dimension Style Manager appears; you will create a new style.

Click: **New**

The Create New Dimension Style dialog box appears. For the New Style Name,

> Type: **LIMITTOL**

> Check that the Start With selection says MECHANICAL, and the Use for area says All dimensions.

> Click: **Continue**

> Click: **Tolerances tab**

> Click: **Limits as the tolerance method**

The dialog box should now look like Figure 8.15.

Figure 8.15

You can leave the upper and lower values and text height set as you did for deviation tolerances.

> Click: **OK** to exit the dialog box

> Click: **Close** to exit the Dimension Style Manager

Next, you will change the overall dimension of the object to use the new style, LIMITTOL. To do so, you will use the Styles toolbar.

> Select: **the 4.25 overall dimension** so that its grips appear

To change the dimension to style LIMITTOL,

> Click: **to expand the dimension styles** as shown in Figure 8.16

> Click: **LIMITTOL** from the list of dimension styles

> Press: **[Esc]** to release the grips

Tip: *You can also use the Properties palette to change the selected dimension. Expand the MISC heading and select the desired style.*

Figure 8.16

The limit tolerance appears, as shown in Figure 8.17

Figure 8.17

Creating Feature Control Frames

Geometric tolerancing (GD&T) allows you to define the shapes of tolerance zones in order to control accurately the manufacture and inspection of parts. Figure 8.18 shows two holes. The location for the center of hole A can vary within a square zone 0.1 unit wide, as defined by the location dimensions 1 and 2 and the ± 0.05 tolerance.

Figure 8.18

This tolerance zone is not the same length in all directions from the true center of the hole. The stated tolerances allow the location for the center of the actual hole to be off by a larger amount diagonally. Figure 8.19 shows hole A and the square zone where the location of its center may still pass inspection according to the dimensions given. Its size is exaggerated in the picture.

.10 Square

.142 Diagonal
tolerance allowed
by square
tolerance zone

Enlarged view of hole A

Figure 8.19

The realization that this method did not sufficiently meet the need for specifying tolerances, led to the development of specific tolerance symbols for controlling the geometric tolerance characteristics for position, flatness, straightness, circularity, concentricity, runout, total runout, angularity, parallelism, and perpendicularity.

Geometric tolerances allow you to define a *feature control frame* that specifies a tolerance zone shaped appropriately for the feature being controlled (sometimes this method is called feature-based tolerancing). A feature control frame is shown in Figure 8.20.

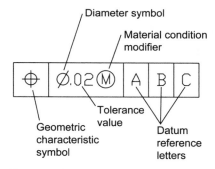

Diameter symbol

Material condition
modifier

Tolerance
value

Geometric
characteristic
symbol

Datum
reference
letters

Figure 8.20

The feature control frame begins with the *geometric characteristic symbol*, which tells the type of geometry being controlled. Figure 8.20 first shows a geometric characteristic symbol for positional tolerance. It next specifies the total allowable tolerance zone; in this case a diametral-shaped zone 0.02 wide around the perfect position for the feature. These two symbols are followed by any modifiers for material condition or projected tolerance zone. The circled M shown is the modifier for maximum material condition, meaning that at maximum material, in this case the smallest hole, the tolerance must apply, but when the hole is larger a greater tolerance zone may be calculated, based on the size of the actual hole measured. The remaining boxes indicate that the position is measured from datum surfaces A, B, and C. Not every geometric tolerance feature control frame requires a datum; for example, flatness can just point to the feature and control it, without respect to another surface. Features such as perpendicularity that are relationships between two different surfaces require a datum.

Among other things, proper application of geometric tolerancing symbols requires that you understand:

- design intent for the part
- shapes of the tolerance zones specified with particular geometric characteristic symbols
- selection and indication of datum surfaces on the object
- placement of feature control frames in the drawing

Next, you will use the Tolerance command to add a feature control frame specifying a geometric tolerance to the drawing. To understand the topic of geometric tolerancing fully, refer to your engineering design graphics textbook or a specific text on geometric tolerancing. Merely adding feature control frames to the drawing will not result in a drawing that clearly communicates your design intent for the part to the manufacturer.

Next you will create the feature control frame shown in Figure 8.20. To create a feature control frame, you will click the Tolerance button from the Dimension panel.

 Click: *Tolerance button*

The Geometric Tolerance dialog box shown in Figure 8.21 appears on your screen.

Figure 8.21

You will use it to create the geometric tolerance feature control frame by filling in tolerance values and selecting symbols.

Click: on the blank symbol area at the top left of the dialog box

The Symbol palette appears on your screen as shown in Figure 8.22.

Figure 8.22

Click: **the positional tolerance symbol** *from the upper left corner of the tolerance symbol palette*

The symbol you selected appears in the box you clicked. You will make selections so that the dialog box appears as shown in Figure 8.23. The positional tolerance symbol should already be shown at the left.

Figure 8.23

The box to the right of the positional tolerance symbol is a toggle.

Click: **in the empty box to turn on the diameter symbol**

When you click in the empty box, the symbol should appear.

Click: **in the empty input box and type 0.02.**

To add a modifier,

Click: **the blank symbol tile to the right of the value you typed**

The Material Condition dialog box appears as shown. To select the modifier for maximum material condition,

Click: **on the circled M**

You return to the Geometric Tolerance dialog box. The modifier appears for the feature control frame. Next, specify datum surfaces A, B, and C.

Click: **in the empty text box below Datum 1**

Type: **A**

Repeat this process for **datum B** and **datum C** on your own.

Note that datums can also have modifiers. If you wanted to, you could click on the empty symbol tile to add a modifier for the datum.

Now you are ready to add the feature control frame to your drawing.

Click: **OK** *to exit the Geometric Tolerance dialog box*

Locate the feature control frame below the 0.50 diameter dimension.

Enter tolerance location: **click below the diameter dimension for the holes as the location for the tolerance symbol**

Your drawing should look like that shown in Figure 8.24.

Figure 8.24

Using Leader with Tolerances

You can also use the Quick Leader (QLeader) command to add a leader with an attached geometric tolerance symbol to your drawing. You will create the next feature control frame by starting with the Quick Leader command.

Turn on running Object Snap for **Nearest**.

Command: **QLeader**

Specify first leader point, or [Settings] <Settings>: **[Enter]**

*Click: **Tolerance** from the Leader Settings dialog box, as shown in Figure 8.25*

*Click: **OK***

Figure 8.25

Specify first leader point, or [Settings] <Settings>: *click at about 2 o'clock on the upper hole, using AutoSnap Nearest*

Specify next point: *click above and to the right of the drawing*

Specify next point: *[Enter]*

The Geometric Tolerance dialog box appears; from there you can start creating the feature control frame.

On your own, **create another feature control frame like the first one.**

*After you've finished making selections in the Geometric Tolerance dialog box, click **OK**.*

The feature control frame is added to the end of the leader line, as shown in Figure 8.26.

Figure 8.26

Next, you will override the location dimensions for the holes so that they appear as basic dimensions. When you specify a positional toler-ance, the true position is usually located with basic dimensions, which are theoretically exact dimensions. The feature control frame for posi-tional tolerance controls the zone in which the true position can vary. To create basic dimensions by overriding the dimension style,

> *Click: **the 0.50 vertical dimension** at the upper right of the object to select it*
>
> *Right-click: to show the **short-cut menu***
>
> *Click: **Properties** to show the Properties palette*

The Properties palette appears on your screen.

> *Click: **to expand the Tolerances area***
>
> *Click: **Basic** as the tolerance display*

When you have finished

> *Press: **[Esc] twice** to unselect the dimension*

Figure 8.27 shows the drawing with the 0.50 basic dimension.

> On your own, override the dimension style for the 0.50 horizontal dimension below the object, and then for the 1.50 vertical dimension so they are basic dimensions.
>
> Double-click on the text "Ø.50 X 2 HOLES" dimension and change it to read, "2X Ø.50".
>
> *Click: **to Close the Properties palette***

When you have finished, save your drawing on your own.

Figure 8.27

Creating Datum Flags

Datum flags are boxed letters identifying the feature on the object that is being used as a datum. Often they are attached to the extension line that is parallel to the surface being identified as the datum surface. Next, you will add datum flags to identify datum surfaces A and B, from which the position feature can vary. To create a datum flag, you will use the Quick Leader command and then select to add the tolerance.

Command: *QLeader [Enter]*

Specify first leader point, or [Settings] <Settings>: *[Enter]*

*Check to see that **Tolerance** is still selected on the Annotation tab.*

Click: *Leader Line & Arrow tab*

Click: *Datum triangle filled for the arrowhead style as shown in Figure 8.28*

Click: *OK*

Tip: *If you have trouble making the straight leader segment for the datum flag, create the datum identifier separately using the Tolerance command. Use the leader command to draw the filled triangle and line or just use the Line command and add a filled triangle on your own.*

Figure 8.28

You will return to your drawing to select the location for the leader line that will attach the datum flag.

>   Turn on **ORTHO Mode** *from the status bar*

>   Specify first leader point, or [Settings] <Settings>: *click on the upper right extension line*

>   Specify next point: *click a point above the previous point*

>   Specify next point: *click a point to the right of the previous point*

The Geometric Tolerance dialog box appears on your screen. You will leave the selections blank, except for the datum identifier.

>   Click: *in the input box to the right of Datum Identifier*

>   Type: *A*

When you have finished, the dialog box should look like Figure 8.29.

Tip: *Datum plane C would be identified in another view if used.*

Figure 8.29

>   Click: *OK*

The datum flag appears in your drawing as shown in Figure 8.30.

>   **Add datum flag B** to the drawing on your own.

Figure 8.30

Creating an Annotative Dimension Style

In the previous chapter, you created an annotative text style. Dimensions, Multileaders, and hatches (which you will learn about in Tutorial 9) also can have annotative properties, so that their size is relative to the zoom scale. To create a new annotative dimension style:

Click: to show the Dimension Style Manager

Click: New

Type: AnnotDim for the New Style Name

Select: MECHANICAL as the style to Start With

Select: Annotative so it appears checked as shown in Figure 8.31

Figure 8.31

Click: Continue

On your own, navigate to the **Fit tab** which should look like Figure 8.32. Notice Annotative is selected for the scaling for dimension features method.

Figure 8.32

Click: OK

*Click: **Set Current** to set AnnotDim as the current dimension style*

*Click: **Close** to exit the dialog box*

Using an Annotative Dimension Style

To use an annotation style, check that it shows as the current style on the Dimension panel.

Once you have created a paper space layout and set the viewport to the proper plot scale, the annotation scale will affect the scale of the associated annotative objects and their visibility. Recall that you will want the viewport scale and annotation scales to be synchronized. With normal visibility set for the annotative objects, only those with the same annotation scale will be visible. Objects with other annotation scales will not show. ANNOALLVISIBLE is the variable which controls this visibility.

> Experiment on your own, with adding some dimensions to layouts at different scales.
>
> **Save** your drawing, and **exit** the AutoCAD program.

You have completed Tutorial 8.

Note: *If you see the alert prompting whether to discard the style overrides, click **OK** for this tutorial. In general, deciding whether to save the overrides to a style depends on whether you would save time in the future by reusing that set of dimension appearances as a style.*

Key Terms

annotative style	feature control frame	nominal dimension	tolerance zones
basic dimension	geometric characteristic symbol	plus/minus tolerances	unilateral tolerances
bilateral tolerances		reference dimension	variance tolerances
datum flags	geometric tolerances	symmetrical tolerances	
deviation tolerances	limit tolerances	tolerance	

Key Commands

Annoallvisible	Dimpost
Dimgap	Dimtol
Dimlim	QLeader
Dimoverride	Tolerance

Exercises

Draw the necessary 2D orthographic views and dimension the following shapes. Include tolerances if indicated.

8.1 Stop Base

8.2 Tolerance Problem
Calculate the maximum and minimum clearance between Parts A and B and Part C as shown.

8.3M Lathe Stop
Show bilateral tolerances of ±.02 for the Ø.75 hole and the 1.50 upper slot.

8.4M Mill Tool
Consider the symmetry of this part as you dimension the orthographic views.

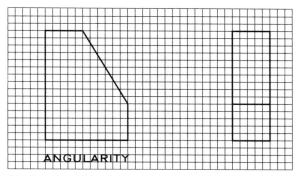

8.5 Angular Tolerance
Using a feature control frame and the necessary
dimensions, indicate that the allowable variation
from the true angle specified for the inclined plane
is 0.7 mm, using the bottom surface of the object
as the datum.

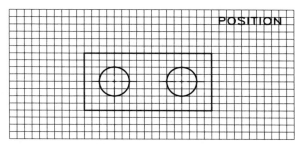

8.6 Positional Tolerance
Locate the two holes with an allowable size tolerance
of 0.05 inches and a position tolerance of Ø.02 inches.
Use the proper symbols and dimensions. Each square is .25 inches.

8.7 Hub
Create the drawing shown.

SECTION AND AUXILIARY VIEWS

9

Introduction

In this tutorial you will learn first how to draw section views and, in the second half of the tutorial, how to draw auxiliary views.

Section Views

A *section view* is a special view used to show the internal structure of an object. Essentially, it shows what you would see if a portion of the object were cut away and you were to look at the remaining part. Section views are often used when the normal orthographic views contain so many hidden lines that they are confusing and difficult to interpret. In this tutorial you will learn to use two-dimensional (2D) projection to create section views. In Tutorial 14 you will learn to use solid modeling to generate a section view directly from a solid model.

Section View Conventions

Figure 9.1 shows the front and side views of a cylindrical object. The side view contains many hidden lines and is hard to interpret. Figure 9.2 shows a *pictorial section* drawing of the same object.

Figure 9.1

Figure 9.2

Objectives

When you have completed this tutorial, you will be able to

1. Show the internal surfaces of an object, using 2D section views.

2. Locate and draw cutting plane lines and section lines on appropriate layers.

3. Hatch an area with a pattern.

4. Edit associative hatching.

5. Draw auxiliary views, using 2D projection.

6. Set up a UCS to help create a 2D auxiliary view.

7. Rotate the snap to help create a 2D auxiliary view.

8. Draw auxiliary views of curved surfaces.

In a section view, the portion of the object that has been cut is shown filled with a pattern to make the drawing easier to interpret. You can accomplish this *crosshatching* or pattern filling by using the AutoCAD Hatch command.

Figure 9.3 shows front and section views of the same circular object. A *cutting plane line*, A–A, defines the location of the sectional cut and shows arrows to indicate the viewing direction for the section view.

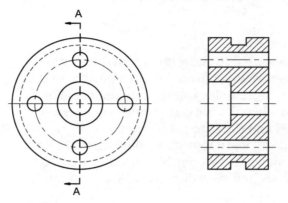

Figure 9.3

Compare the side view in Figure 9.1 with the section view in Figure 9.3 and the pictorial section view shown in Figure 9.2. The sectional views are easier to interpret than drawings that just show the front and side views.

Crosshatching

Crosshatching is used to show where material has been cut. Figure 9.4 shows a new object with a cutting plane line and the appropriate section view. Note that the surfaces labeled A and B are not crosshatched. Only material that has been cut by the cutting plane is crosshatched. Surfaces A and B are shown in section A–A because they would be visible if the part were cut on the cutting plane line. They are not hatched because they were not cut by the cutting plane.

Section A-A

Figure 9.4

A section view shows what you would see if the object were cut along the cutting plane line and you looked at the remaining portion of the object in the direction the arrows point. For the view shown in section, ignore the portion of the object that would be cut off. Draw the view to show the remaining portion. Some features that were previously hidden will be visible and should be shown. The hole labeled C in Figure 9.4 is in the remaining portion of the object, but is not visible in the section view, so it is not shown. The purpose of a section view is to show the internal structure without the confusion of hidden lines. You should use hidden lines only if the object would be misunderstood if the lines were not included. (To show hole C in the section view, you could use an *offset cutting plane* line—which bends 90° to pass through features that are not all in the same plane. Refer to any standard engineering graphics text to review conventions for cutting plane lines and types of section views.)

Starting

Start the AutoCAD 2012 program on your own.

Use the datafile *cast2.dwt* as a template file to begin a new drawing.

Save the drawing as *bossect.dwg*.

Creating 2D Section Views

The top, front, and side orthographic views of a casting are displayed on your screen. The horizontal centerlines have been erased in the top view. Your screen should look like Figure 9.5.

Figure 9.5

Often one or more of the orthographic views are replaced with section views. You will change the front orthographic view to be a front section view. You will change the side view to be a side section view.

Cutting Plane Lines

The cutting plane line uses one of two different linetypes: either long dashes (DASHED) or long lines with two short dashes followed by another long line (PHANTOM). You should use only one type of cutting plane line in any one drawing. You will make dashed cutting plane lines using the Cutting_Plane layer that was created in the template. Linetype DASHED has longer dashes than linetype HIDDEN. The Cutting_Plane layer has a different color than the Hidden_Line layer to help distinguish it. Also, cutting plane lines are printed as thick lines, so the lineweight for the layer is set to 0.6 mm.

Creating Dashed Lines

Set layer **Cutting_Plane** as the current layer.

Be sure that Snap is turned on and set to 0.25.

On your own, use the **Line command** to add a **horizontal dashed cutting plane line** in the top view of the boss that passes through the center of the holes in the top view between points A–A in Figure 9.6.

Now add a **vertical dashed cutting plane** line through the center of the top view of the boss between points B–B.

Save your drawing at this time.

The lines on layer Cutting_Plane should extend beyond the edges of the object by about 0.5 units as shown in Figure 9.6.

Figure 9.6

Drawing the Leaders

The Leader command lets you construct complex leaders. A leader is a line ending in an arrowhead (or sometimes a dot) that is used to locate specific notes and drawing information for an item. Leaders should generally be drawn at some angle other than horizontal or vertical.

AutoCAD provides three different commands for creating leaders:

Leader- starts with an arrowhead or dot and creates the leader line and a short ending segment (called the landing line) which you can connect to text, tolerance, block or other drawing objects.

QLeader- quick leader starts with an arrowhead or dot and creates the leader line and a short landing line segment and text, tolerance or a block object.

MLeader- multileader consists of an arrowhead, a horizontal landing, a leader line or curve, and either a multiline text object or a block. Unlike Leaders and Qleaders, multileaders may start arrowhead first, leader landing first, or content first. The settings for a multileader can be saved as a named style to make it easy to reuse the settings. (You will learn more about multileaders in Tutorial 13.)

Leaders can have annotative properties, so that they update as the zoom scale for the viewport changes.

Next you will make a new MLeader style and use MLeader as a quick way to add line segments ending in arrows for the cutting plane lines.

Making a Multileader Style (MLEADERSTYLE command)

Similar to creating a dimension style, the Multileader Style Manager lets you set and save the appearance of the leader. Use the ribbon Annotate tab, Leaders panel.

> *Click: **the small arrow from the right corner of the Leaders panel** to show the Multileader Style Manager*

The Multileader Style manager appears on your screen as shown in Figure 9.7

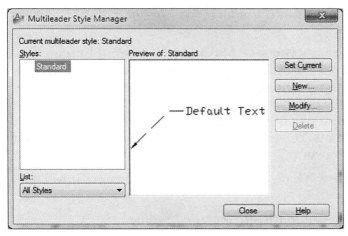

Figure 9.7

> *Click: **New***
>
> *Type: **CuttingPlaneArrows** as the name of your new style*
>
> *Do not select Annotative*
>
> *Click: **Continue***

Figure 9.8

Use the Modify Multileader Style dialog box to set up the appearance for your special cutting plane line leader.

The Leader Format tab lets you select the shape for the leader line: Splined or Straight, so that you can make a curved leader or straight lines (like the leaders you have drawn so far). You will leave this set to straight. The Arrowhead pull-down lets you select the style of arrowhead, including none. You can also specify a user arrow style from a file you select, which is useful for Architectural drawings that use stylish arrows and labels for their cutting plane lines. Leave the settings for color, arrow size, etc. set to the defaults.

*Click: **Leader Structure tab** so that it appears uppermost as shown in Figure 9.8.*

The Leader Structure lets you set a Maximum Number of Leader Points. The default is 3. This allows you to draw leaders with two line segments and then move on to the text prompt portion of the command. You can set the number higher to make more complicated leaders; however, most engineering leaders are straight line leaders with only two segments. You can define the angles at which the leader segments must be drawn.

The new leader style will have a maximum of two segments. It will not use a landing line.

*Click: **to unselect Automatically include landing***

Notice the image tile at the right updates to show no landing line.

*Click: **Content tab***

The Content tab appears on top. as shown in Figure 9.9. The pull down list for Multileader type allows you to select from: Mtext, Block and None. The default option is Mtext; you have a similar option to create text with QLeader. It lets you create multiple lines of text. Choosing

Block lets you select a block to be added to the end of the leader, as you will in Tutorial 13. The None option lets you draw a leader line with no text added to the end. You will use the None option to end the Leader command when you draw the leaders for cutting plane lines.

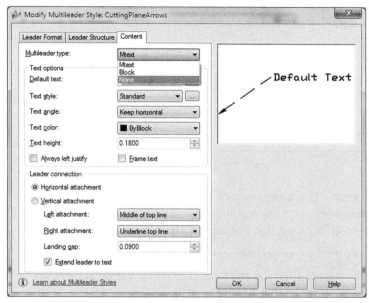

Figure 9.9

*Click: **None** from the pull down list for Multileader type*

The choices disappear and the image tile updates show a line and arrow.

*Click: **OK** to exit the Modify Multileader Style dialog box*

*Click: **Set Current** to make this the current style*

*Click: **Close** to exit the Multileader Style Manager dialog box*

Now you are ready to draw some arrow and line segments on to the ends of the cutting plane lines. Draw the lines on layer Cutting_Plane. After drawing the leaders, you add text labeling the cutting plane lines, using the Text command. You will start the leader with the landing line on the cutting plane and pick second the end with the arrow.

On your own, turn **Ortho on.**

*Click: **Multileader button***

Specify leader landing location or [leader arrowHead first/Content first/Options] <Content first>: *use Snap and select the end of line A-A*

Specify leader arrowhead location: *click past the end of line A-A*

The line ending in an arrow appears in your drawing, see Figure 9.10.

Repeat these steps to create a leader for the other end of cutting plane line A-A and for the ends of line B-B.

Use the Text command to add the label A to both ends of cutting plane line A–A.

Add the label B to both ends of cutting plane line B–B.

When completed, your leader lines should look like the ones shown in Figure 9.10.

Tip: *If you see the option [leader **Landing first**/Content first/Options] instead of [leader arrowHead first/Content first/Options], you will need to type **L** [Enter] to select to start with the landing line first. Otherwise the arrow will be first.*

Tip: *The Leader command will not draw the arrows if the first line segment of the leader is too short. The first line segment must be longer than the current arrowhead size. You can set the arrowhead size with the dimensioning variables that you learned to use in Tutorial 7.*

Tip: *You can easily insert arrowheads at the end of a cutting plane line by making your own arrowhead block. A quick way to make a block for arrowheads is to explode a leader line and make a block from its arrowhead. You can also use a Polyline with a zero starting width and larger ending width to create an arrowhead from scratch.*

Tip: *Use a crossing box to make selecting the hidden lines in the front view easier.*

Figure 9.10

Next, you will remove the unnecessary lines from the front view. When you draw a section view, you do not want to see the lines that represent intersections and surfaces on the outside of the object.

Use **Zoom** to enlarge the view to help select the points.

Use the **Erase** command to remove the *runout* (or curve that represents the blending of two surfaces) labeled 1 in Figure 9.10.

Use **Trim** to remove the portion of the line to the left of point 2.

Use the **Erase** command to remove the solid line from point 3 to point 4, which defines the surface in front of the boss.

Your drawing should be similar to that in Figure 9.11.

Figure 9.11

Changing Hidden Lines to Visible

When you section the drawing, the interior details become visible. You will use the Layer Control to change the layer of the hidden lines to VISIBLE.

Select: *all the hidden lines in the front view (their grips appear)*

Click: *to pull down the Layer Control*

Click: on Layer VISIBLE to move the selected lines to that layer

Press: [Esc] to unselect the objects

Now all the hidden lines in the front view have been changed to layer VISIBLE. Your screen should now be similar to Figure 9.12.

Figure 9.12

If you have zoomed your drawing, use Zoom Previous to return to the original size. You are almost ready to add the hatching to the drawing. The hatching will fill the areas of the drawing where the solid object was cut by the cutting plane.

Hatching for sections should be on its own layer and should be plotted with a thin line. Having the hatch on its own layer is useful so that you can freeze it if you do not want it displayed while you are working on the drawing. In the drawing you started from, a separate layer for the hatching has already been created. Its color is red, and its linetype is CONTINUOUS.

Click: HATCH to set it current using the Layer Control

Using Hatch

Hatching uses a series of lines, dashes, or dots to form a pattern. The Hatch command fills an area with a pattern or solid fill. It creates *associative hatching*, which means that, if the area selected as the hatch boundary is changed, the hatching updates to fill the new area. Associative hatching is the default for the Hatch command. If you update the selected boundary so that it no longer forms a closed area, the hatching will no longer be associative. Hatch helps you choose the boundary for the pattern by selecting from its various boundary selection options.

To activate Hatch, select the Hatch button from the Draw toolbar.

Click: **Hatch button**

The Hatch Contextual tab appears across the top of your screen as shown in Figure 9.13. The Associative check box in the Options area at the right of the dialog box should indicate that associative hatching is turned on.

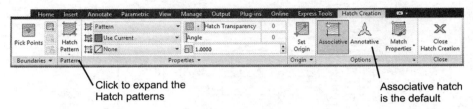

Figure 9.13

Selecting the Hatch Pattern

You can select predefined hatch patterns from the Pattern area. ANSI31 is the default hatch pattern. It consists of continuous lines angled at 45° and spaced about 1/16" apart, and is typically used to show cast iron materials. It is also used as a general pattern when you do not want to use the hatch pattern to specify a material. To select the ANSI31 pattern,

Move your cursor over different areas of the drawing. Notice that as you do so, a preview of the hatch pattern shows filling that boundary.

You can also select a different hatch pattern by clicking on its swatch tile (showing a picture of the hatch pattern). Notice the small scroll bars to the right of the swatches. You can use them to scroll to see more hatch patterns. To show a larger selection at once,

Click: **the image tile on the Ribbon Gallery - Hatch All Patterns**

The expanded hatch patterns, shown in Figure 9.14 appears on your screen. You can use it to preview hatch patterns by looking at a sample of their appearance.

Figure 9.14

There are many standard hatch patterns available. In addition to predefined hatch patterns, you can use *custom hatch patterns* that you previously created and stored in the file *acad.pat* or another *.pat* file of your own making. You can make *user-defined hatch patterns* more complex by setting the linetype for the layer on which you will create the hatch. Remember to refer to the AutoCAD online help for more information about any of the commands described in these tutorials.

After you have looked at some of the hatch patterns,

Click: ANSI31 as the hatch pattern

Angling the Hatch Pattern

The Angle input allows you to specify a rotation angle for the hatch pattern. You can do so by typing a value, or dragging the slider to change the angle. The default is 0 degrees, or no rotation of the pattern. In the hatch pattern you selected, ANSI31, the lines are already at an angle of 45°. Any angle you choose in the Angle area will be added to the chosen pattern; for example, if you added a rotation angle of 10 degrees to your current pattern, the lines would be drawn at an angle of 55 degrees.

Try some values and test the appearance by moving your cursor over the drawing to show the effect on the previewing hatch. Leave the default value of **0** ° for now.

Angle slider   Transparency slilder

Figure 9.15

Hatch Transparency

You can use the slider to make the hatching more or less transparent. If you will be hatching over the top of other drawing entities, changing the transparency can be helpful. For now, leave it set to 0.

Scaling the Hatch Pattern

The Scale input increases or decreases the sizing of the hatched pattern. The hatch pattern is similar in some ways to a linetype. Hatch patterns are stored in an external file, with the spacing set at some default value. Usually the default scale of 1.0000 is the correct size for drawings that will be plotted full scale, resulting in hatched lines that are about 1/16" apart. If the views will be plotted at a smaller scale, half-size for instance, you will need to increase the spacing for the hatch by setting the scale to a larger value so that the lines of the hatch are not as close together. For this drawing, you will not need to change the scale of the hatch pattern. Hatch patterns can also be annotative, so that multiple scales versions of the pattern are stored.

Click and drag to use the slider or try entering some values and inspect their previewed appearance on your drawing.

When you are done return the **scale to 1**.

Tip: *Hatch can have an annotative property so that its scale is based on the Viewport Scaling Factor.*

Note: *In previous versions of AutoCAD, it was possible to space the hatch lines too closely together, causing performance problems. Now there is a limit to prevent creating a huge number of hatch lines in a single operation. You can change the maximum allowed number of hatch lines with the HPMAXLINES system variable.*

Warning: *Be cautious when specifying a smaller scale for the hatch pattern. If the hatch lines are very close together, the AutoCAD software will take a long time calculating them.*

Gradient Fills

A *gradient fill* fills an area with a smooth transition between darker and lighter shades of one color, or transitions between two colors. While gradients are not frequently used in engineering drawings, they can add the appearance of shading or interest to logos, maps, and other graphics.

*Click: **Gradient** from the Properties area of the Hatch contextual tab as shown in Figure 9.16*

Figure 9.16

Options for gradient patterns are now available on the contextual ribbon. Buttons at the left of the color selectors let you choose whether you are using a one or two color gradient.

This button is used to turn off the second color for gradient patterns

Figure 9.17

*Click: **the image tile to expand the** patterns as shown in Figure 9.18*

Figure 9.18

On your own, experiment with the colors and styles of gradient. Preview them by moving your cursor over some areas inside the drawing. Do not add any gradient fills to your drawing at this time.

Return the selection to **Pattern** (as opposed to Gradient). Make sure that the **ANSI31** pattern is still selected.

You can also make hatches and gradients transparent. One useful application for gradient or solid colors is to make them transparent when filling large areas in color maps, charts, and architectural drawings.

Options for Hatch Boundaries

The Boundaries area at the right side of the Hatch Creation tab lets you select among the different methods used to specify the area to hatch. *Pick Points* allows you to click inside a closed area to be hatched. *Select Objects* lets you select drawing objects to form a closed boundary for the hatching. Clicking the small downward arrow to expand the Boundaries panel lets you select more options for the creation of the hatch boundary.

Click: **to expand the Boundaries area**

Click: **to expand the options for Retaining Boundary objects** *as shown in Figure 9.19*

Figure 9.19

You have the option to retain the hatch boundary and have it created using a polyline, or to retain the boundary and have it be created as a region (you will learn more about regions in later tutorials). You can also choose not to retain the hatch boundary.

In order to easily update the hatch when you make changes to the drawing objects, you will retain the hatch boundary.

Click: **Retain Boundaries - Polyline**

You also use the boundary area to choose whether to place the hatch in the drawing by directly clicking points inside the areas to hatch, or to select objects in the drawing.

When you clicked the Hatch button, in addition to the ribbon changing to show the contextual tab, the command prompt shows options. You should still see the command prompt line for the hatch command active. Use the settings option as follows:

Plick internal point or [Select objects/seTtings]: *T [Enter]*

The Hatch dialog box which was available in previous versions of AutoCAD appears on your screen as shown in Figure 9.20. If you have the ribbon turned off you will see this dialog box instead of the Create Hatch contextual tab.

Figure 9.20

*Click: **the right facing arrow at the bottom right of the dialog box** to show more options*

Figure 9.21 shows additional options for creating hatch boundaries. Notice that these can be accessed from the contextual tab also. By clicking the Retain boundaries box, you can save the AutoCAD generated hatch boundaries as one of two different types of objects: a polyline or a region (a region is a 2D enclosed area). When determining the hatch boundary, the software analyzes all the objects on the screen. This step can be time-consuming if you have a large drawing database. To define a different area to be considered for the hatch boundary, you would click the New button in the Boundary set area. You would then return to your drawing, where you could select the objects to form the new set. Using implied Windowing works well for this procedure.

You can use the Islands area to change the way islands inside the hatch area are treated. Observe the pictures above the radio buttons that describe the options. The selection Normal causes islands inside the hatched area to be alternately hatched and skipped, starting at the outer area. Choosing Outer causes only the outer area to be hatched; any islands inside are left unhatched. You can also choose Ignore; then, the entire inside is hatched, regardless of the structure. Leave this area of the dialog box set to Normal.

Figure 9.21

*Click: **Cancel** to exit the Hatch and Gradient dialog box*

On your own, explore the **Help** for the Hatch command. **Review the options for setting a Gap Tolerance** and **setting the Hatch Origin Points. Close the Help screen** to return to the command prompt. The contextual tab for hatch should still be on your screen.

Adding the Hatch Pattern

You use the Pick Points method to specify the area to fill with the hatch pattern. (To use the Select Objects method, you would return to your drawing and click on the objects that form the boundary.) The program will determine the boundary around the areas you clicked. (If there are islands inside the area that you did not want hatched, you would use Remove Islands to choose them after you have clicked the area to be hatched.) When you are finished selecting, you will press [Enter] to indicate that you are finished selecting and want to continue with the Hatch command.

You can use any standard selection method to select the objects. Refer to Figure 9.22 as you make selections.

Tip: *Turn Grid off before previewing, as it can make reading the hatch pattern difficult.*

Tip: *You can pick Create Separate Hatches from the Options area of the contextual tab if you would like each area you pick to be created as a separate hatch, so that they can be edited individually later.*

Figure 9.22

The following command prompt should still be on your screen.

Click internal point or [Select objects/seTtings]: *click a point inside the area labeled C*

The perimeter of the area that you have selected is highlighted and you see the hatch pattern filling inside that boundary. The prompt continues,

Click internal point or [Select objects/seTtings]: *click area D*

Click internal point or [Select objects/seTtings]: *click area E*

Click internal point or [Select objects/seTtings]: *click area F*

Click internal point or [Select objects/seTtings]: *[Enter]*

The areas that you selected becomes hatched in your drawing. Your drawing should now look like the one in Figure 9.23.

Figure 9.23

Creating the Side Section View

Make more room to the right of the existing views to draw the side section view.

On your own, use Pan Realtime (you can press and hold the mouse scroll wheel to drag the view close to the left hand side of the viewport.

Reorient the Side View

One of the alternative positions for a side view is rotated and lined up with the top view. You will use the Rotate button from the ribbon Home tab, Modify panel to reorient the side view so that you can align it with the top view, as shown in Figure 9.21.

On your own, verify that **Snap** is on.

Click: ***Rotate button***

Select objects: ***select all of the objects in the side view with implied Crossing***

Select objects: *[Enter]*

Specify base point: ***click the top left corner of the side view***

Specify rotation angle or [Copy/Reference] <0>: ***90 [Enter]***

Now you will align the rotated side view with the top view. You will enter the selection option, P to reselect the previous selection set.

Click: ***Move button***

Select objects: ***P [Enter]***

Select objects: *[Enter]*

Specify base point or [Displacement] <Displacement>: ***click the upper left corner of the rotated object***

Specify second point or <use first point as displacement>: ***click a point on the snap that lines up with the top line in the top view***

Your drawing should now look like that in Figure 9.24.

Figure 9.24

On your own, turn **Snap off**.

Use the **Erase** command to remove the unnecessary hidden lines (those for the counterbored hole and lines 1 through 5) from the rotated object.

Change the hidden lines for the countersunk hole in the rotated side view to layer **VISIBLE**. The countersunk hole is the only one that will show in the section view. Your drawing should now look like Figure 9.25

Tip: *Although you won't always be instructed to do so, remember to save your work frequently while creating drawings. The AutoCAD autosave feature saves automatically to a file named auto.sv$. You set the time interval for the autosave feature with the system variable Savetime. The default is to save every 120 minutes. You would not want to lose two hours of work, so you should set Savetime to save automatically at shorter intervals. To make such a change, type SAVETIME at the command prompt and enter the new number in minutes. However, do not rely on automatic saves. Save your file whenever you have made a major change that you want to keep or about every 10 minutes otherwise.*

Figure 9.25

Next, use the **Trim** command on your own to remove the visible line that crosses the outer edge of the boss. When you are finished trimming, your drawing should look like Figure 9.26.

Figure 9.26

Now you are ready to add the hatching.

Click: **Hatch button**

Check to be sure that pattern **ANSI31** is still the current pattern.

Click internal point or [Select objects/seTtings]: **click inside areas D and E labeled in Figure 9.26 [Enter]**

The hatching in your drawing should look like that in Figure 9.27.

Save and Plot your drawing on your own. Before you plot, be sure to switch to paper space. Update the scale noted for the drawing to .75:1. If you need help plotting, refer to Tutorials 3 and 5.

Tip: *You may need to use Zoom Window to enlarge the area on the screen. When you are finished erasing and changing the lines, use Zoom Previous to return the area to its original size.*

Tip: *If the View Cube is on, it may be in your way for creating the hatch. If so, use the ribbon View tab, Windows panel to expand the User Interface selections and turn it off as shown*

Figure 9.27

Solid Fill

Sometimes you want areas of the drawing to be filled in with a solid color instead of a hatch pattern or gradient. The Hatch command also lets you solidly fill and area. Use solid fill sparingly in your drawings because some printers and plotters do not show it correctly. Many engineering drawings are still printed in one color, and large gray areas do not improve the drawing. You will add a rectangle on layer DIM and add solid hatch inside it.

Return your drawing to **Model space** if it is not selected.

Make **DIM** the current layer.

*Click: **Rectangle button***

Draw a small rectangle overlapping the lower right of the front section view as shown in Figure 9.28.

Figure 9.28

Click the Select button as
the method for defining the
hatch boundary

Click on Solid as the
hatch type

Figure 9.29

*Click: **Hatch button***

The contextual tab for hatch creation appears on your screen. This time instead of selecting inside the boundaries to hatch, you will use the option to Select objects.

*Click: **Select button** from the Boundaries area (Figure 9.29)*

*Click: **Solid** from the Hatch types on the Properties panel*

Click internal point or [Select objects/seTtings]: ***click on the edge of the new rectangle [Enter]***

The rectangle is filled with a solid color, similar to Figure 9.30. The rectangle is on layer DIM, so it is blue.

Figure 9.30

Using Draworder

The Draworder option can be used to specify which object is on top when objects overlap.

*Click: **to pin the Modify panel** so it stays expanded.*

*Click: **to expand the Draworder flyout** as shown in Figure 9.31*

Tip: *You can also click on the Draworder command from the Modify II toolbar, or by clicking Tools, Display Order from the Classic menu bar to change the draw order for objects that overlay.*

Tip: *If you have trouble selecting hatches and solid fills, try clicking on their edges, not in the middle of the area.*

Figure 9.31

Click: **Send to Back**

Select objects: ***pick the edge of the blue box [Enter]***

The solid blue hatch color should now be behind the section hatch as in Figure 9.32. Use Zoom Window for a closer view if needed.

Figure 9.32

On your own, practice with the other draworder options: Send to Back, Bring to Front, etc. When you are done, restore the previous Zoom if you changed it.

You can also click on hatches and make them transparent using the slider from the contextual tab.

Erase the rectangle and solid hatch.

Change the current layer back to **HATCH**.

Changing Associative Hatches

The hatching is associative. In other words, it automatically updates so that it continues to fill the boundary when you edit the boundary by stretching, moving, rotating, arraying, scaling, or mirroring. You can also use grips to modify hatching that you've inserted into the drawing.

Next, you will stretch the top and front views of the drawing; the hatching will automatically update to fill the new boundary. Refer to Figure 9.33 for the points to select to create a crossing box.

Figure 9.33

Make sure that you are in model space.

Click: ***Stretch button***

Select objects to stretch by crossing-window or crossing-polygon. . .

Select objects: ***click point 1***

Specify opposite corner: ***click point 2***

Select objects: ***[Enter]***

Specify base point or [Displacement] <Displacement>: ***use object snap to select the lower right corner of the front view (point 3)***

Specify second point or <use first point as displacement>: ***turn Snap off and turn Ortho on, then click to the right of the previous location***

Figure 9.34

The objects selected by the crossing box are stretched, as shown in Figure 9.34. The hatching updates to fill the new boundary. You will now use the Hatchedit command to change the angle of the hatching. Because the angled edge of the countersunk hole is drawn at 45°, you will change the angle of the hatch pattern so that the hatch is not parallel to features in the drawing. (Having the hatch run parallel or perpendicular to a major drawing feature is not good technical drawing practice.) You will edit the hatch in the front view.

Click: **the hatching in the front view** *(it will appear highlighted)*

The Hatch Editor appears on your screen similar to Figure 9.35.

Figure 9.35

Tip: You can double-click on an existing hatch to edit it quickly.

Tip: You can create open, irregular hatch boundaries by typing the -Hatch command at the command prompt and selecting the W for the draW option. Irregular hatch boundaries are useful for hatching large areas where you do not want to fill the entire area—for example, to represent earth around a foundation on an architectural drawing, or in mechanical drawings to hatch only the perimeter of a large shape instead of filling in the entire area.

Its appearance is identical to the Create Hatch contextual tab. You can use this tab to edit hatching already added to your drawing.

On your own, use the angle slider to increase the hatch angle by about 15 degrees.

The hatching updates so that it is angled an additional 15 degrees.

Press: [Esc] to deselect the hatch in the front view

Click: the hatching in the side view to select it

Again the Hatch Edit contextual tab returns to your screen.

The final result of changing the hatch angles is shown in Figure 9.36.

On your own, set layer TEXT current.

Use **Dtext** to label the section views SECTION A–A and SECTION B–B.

Place the text directly below the section views, as shown in Figure 9.36.

Save and close your *bossect.dwg* drawing.

Figure 9.36

You have completed the section view portion of this tutorial. Next, you will learn how to create auxiliary views.

Auxiliary Views

An *auxiliary view* is an orthographic view of the object that has a line of sight different from the six *basic views* (front, top, right-side, rear, bottom, and left-side). Auxiliary views are most commonly used to show the true size of a slanted or oblique surface. Slanted and oblique surfaces are *foreshortened* in the basic views because they are tipped away from the viewing plane, causing their projected size in the view to be smaller than their actual size. An auxiliary view shows a surface true size when its line of sight is perpendicular to the surface.

You will learn to create auxiliary views first using 2D methods. You can easily project 2D auxiliary views from the basic orthographic views by rotating the snap or by aligning a new User Coordinate System.

Figure 9.37 shows three views of an object and an auxiliary view.

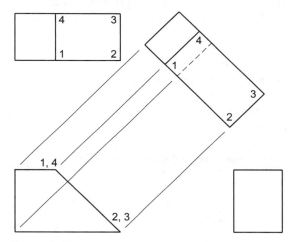

Figure 9.37

The surface defined by vertices 1–2–3–4 is inclined. It is perpendicular to the front viewing plane and shows on edge in the front view. Both the top and side views show foreshortened views of the surface.

The true size of surface 1–2–3–4 is projected in the auxiliary view by drawing projection lines perpendicular to the edge view of the surface, in this case the angled line in the front view. The width of the surface is measured from a *reference surface*, and transferred to the auxiliary view to complete the projection. Note that, as with the front, top, and side views, the auxiliary view shows the entire object as viewed from the line of sight perpendicular to that surface, causing the base of the object to show as a hidden line. Auxiliary views often use partial views that only show the surface of interest.

Drawing Auxiliary Views Using 2D

Open the drawing **adapt4.dwg**, provided with the data files.

Save your drawing as **auxil1.dwg**.

The orthographic views for the adapter appear similar to Figure 9.38.

Figure 9.38

You will create an auxiliary view showing the true size of the inclined surface. The surface is labeled 1–2–3–4–5–6–7–8 in Figure 9.38. For this tutorial, you will erase the top view and use the front and side views to project the auxiliary view.

Click: **Erase button**

Select objects: **use a window to select the top view**

Select objects: **[Enter]**

Your drawing will look like Figure 9.39.

Figure 9.39

Click: **Model tab** to show only model space

Click: Show/Hide **Lineweight button** from the status bar to hide the lineweights if they are shown.

On your own, turn **Snap off** and turn **Osnap Intersection on**. You will use object snaps to select the intersections in the next steps.

Aligning the UCS with the Angled Surface

Next, you will create a new UCS aligned with the angled surface to help you project lines perpendicular from the edge view of surface 1–2–3–4–5–6–7–8.

You can type the command UCS and use its options to create new user coordinate systems. A new feature in AutoCAD 2012 is the ability to *drag* the UCS icon to reorient the coordinate system. You will use the dragging method in the next steps.

>*Click:* **on the UCS icon in the lower right of the drawing area** *so that its grips appear as shown in Figure 9.40*
>
>*Click the square grip at the origin to select it.*
>
>**Drag the UCS icon and click intersection A in Figure 9.39**

Figure 9.40

When you have finished aligning the UCS, it should appear similar to Figure 9.41.

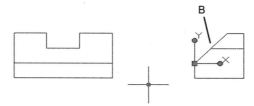

Figure 9.41

Next you will align the X axis with the angled surface. The grips should still be active on the UCS icon.

>*Click the circular grip at the end of the X axis to select it.*
>
>**Drag the X-axis and click intersection B**

The UCS icon should now be oriented as shown in Figure 9.42

Figure 9.42

Set **PROJECTION** as the current layer.

Turn **Ortho** on.

Make sure that Snap is off.

Now you will draw rays from each intersection of the object in the side view into the open area of the drawing above the front view. You will click Ray from the Draw panel; if you need help creating rays, refer to Tutorial 4.

Click: **Ray button** *from the ribbon Home tab, Draw panel*

Specify start point: ***click intersection 1***

Specify through point: ***with Ortho on, click a point above and to the left of the side view***

Specify through point: *[Enter]*

Restart the **Ray** command and draw projection lines from points **2 through 5** in the right-side view.

Click: **Line button**

On your own, turn on **Snap** and use it to draw a reference line perpendicular to the projection lines. The location of this line can be anywhere along the projection lines, but it should extend about 0.5 unit beyond the top and bottom projection lines.

Your drawing should look like that in Figure 9.43.

Figure 9.43

Note that the back edge of the slot (labeled A) and the lower right corner (labeled B) in the side view align with the projection lines through the corners of the angled surface (C and D) to produce a single projection line. If C and D did not align on the projection lines already created, you would need to project them also.

The width of the object is known to be 3. Next, offset a line 3 units from and parallel to the reference line.

Click: **Offset button**

Specify offset distance or [Through/Erase/Layer] <Through>: *3 [Enter]*

Select object to offset or [Exit/Undo] <Exit>: ***click the reference line, as shown in Figure 9.43***

Specify point on side to offset or [Exit/Multiple/Undo] <Exit>: *click a point anywhere to the left of the reference line*

Select object to offset or [Exit/Undo] <Exit>: *[Enter]*

Your drawing should look like the one in Figure 9.44.

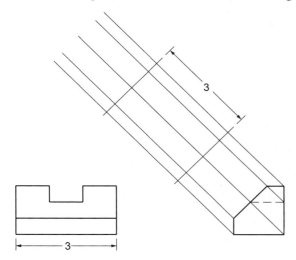

Tip: *If you did not know the dimensions, you could use the Distance command (available from the Tools menu under Inquiry) with the Intersection object snap in the front view to determine the distance.*

Figure 9.44

Add the width of the slot on your own by using **Offset** to create two more parallel lines, I unit apart.

Your drawing should look like that in Figure 9.45.

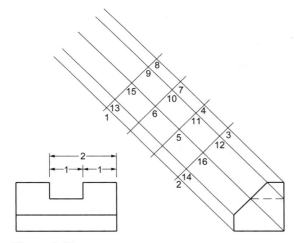

Figure 9.45

Next, you will draw the visible lines in the drawing over the top of the projection lines. Be sure to draw the correct shape of the object as it will appear in the auxiliary view. Refer to Figure 9.40 for your selections.

Set **VISIBLE** as the current layer.

Use **Snap to Intersection** when selecting points in the following steps.

*Click: **Line button***

Specify first point: *click the intersection of the projection lines at point 1*

Specify next point or [Undo]: *click point 2*

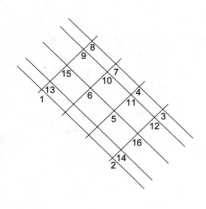

Specify next point or [Close/Undo]: *click point 3*

Specify next point or [Close/Undo]: *click point 4*

Specify next point or [Close/Undo]: *click point 5*

Specify next point or [Close/Undo]: *click point 6*

Specify next point or [Close/Undo]: *click point 7*

Specify next point or [Close/Undo]: *click point 8*

Specify next point or [Close/Undo]: *C [Enter]*

Now you will restart the Line command and draw the short line segments where the two short top surfaces of the object intersect the slanted front surface:

Command: *[Enter] to restart the Line command*

Specify first point: *click point 9*

Specify next point or [Undo]: *click point 10*

Specify next point or [Undo]: *[Enter]*

Command: *[Enter] to restart the Line command*

Specify first point: *click point 11*

Specify next point or [Undo]: *click point 12*

Specify next point or [Undo]: *[Enter]*

Next, you will add the line representing the back edge of the slot.

Command: *[Enter] to restart the Line command*

Specify first point: *click point 10*

Specify next point or [Undo]: *click point 11*

Specify next point or [Undo]: *[Enter]*

Now you will add the line showing the intersection of the vertical front surface with the angled surface.

Command: *[Enter] to restart the Line command*

Specify first point: *click point 13*

Specify next point or [Undo]: *click point 14*

Specify next point or [Undo]: *[Enter]*

Next you will set the layer for hidden lines and draw the hidden lines for the bottom and back surfaces.

Set **HIDDEN_LINES** as the current layer using the Layer Control

Command: *L [Enter] the alias for the Line command*

Specify first point: *click point 15*

Specify next point or [Undo]: *click point 16*

Specify next point or [Undo]: *[Enter]*

Next freeze the projection layer so that those lines do not appear.

*Click: **Freeze icon adjacent to layer PROJECTION** (so that it looks like a snowflake)*

Click: **Trim button**

On your own, trim the portion of the hidden line that coincides with the visible line from point **5** to point **6**.

When you have finished, your screen should look like Figure 9.46.

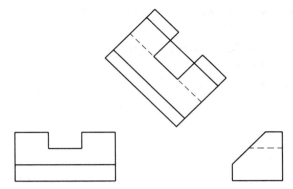

Figure 9.46

Adding Visual Reference Lines

Next, you will add two visual *reference line*s to your drawing from the extreme outside edges of the surface shown true size in the auxiliary view to the inclined surface in the side view. The lines will provide a visual reference for the angles in your drawing and help show how the auxiliary view aligns with the standard views. You can extend a centerline from the primary view to the auxiliary view or use one or two projection lines for the reference lines. In this case, as there are no centerlines, you will create two reference lines. Leave a gap of about 1/16" between the reference lines and the views.

> *Click:* **Thaw button for PROJECTION layer** *(so that it looks like a sun)*
>
> *Select:* **the two rays that project from the ends of the angled surface** *so that their grips appear*
>
> *Click:* **to pull-down the Layer Control list**
>
> *Click:* **THIN layer,** *so that the selected lines change to that layer*

Refer to Figure 9.47 if you are unsure which lines to select.

The rays should change to layer THIN. You can verify this result visually because the lines will turn red, the color for layer THIN.

Linetype Conventions

Two lines of different linetypes should not meet to make one line. You must always leave a small gap on the linetype that has lesser precedence. In the case of the visible and the reference lines, the reference line should have a small gap (about 1/16" on the plotted drawing) where it meets the visible line. In the case of the visible and the hidden lines, the hidden line should have a small gap (about 1/16" on the plotted drawing) where it meets the visible line. You can use the Break command to do this.

Tip: *You could offset the edge of the object by 1/16 in each view and use Trim to create the gap between the lines, but it is probably fastest and accurate enough, just to use the grips and make the gap by eye.*

Tip: *You could use Draworder and bring the visible lines to the front. The length of the hidden line is more accurate if it is not trimmed, but it is difficult to produce the gaps in the hidden line exactly where they are wanted without breaking it.*

Click: **to freeze layer PROJECTION**

Click: **Break button** *from the ribbon Home tab, Modify toolbar*

On your own, create a gap of about 1/16" between each view and the reference lines.

Create a similar gap where the hidden line extends from the visible line, forming the front of the slot in the auxiliary view.

Thaw layer PROJECTION and erase the extra portions of the rays where they extend past the side and auxiliary views.

Your drawing should look like the one in Figure 9.47.

Figure 9.47

To restore the world coordinate system, the default where X is to the right and Y is upward, you will use the short-cut menu.

> **Hover the cursor over the UCS icon so that it becomes highlighted** *(do not click on it).*

> *Right-click:* **to show the shortcut menu**

> *Click:* **World**

The UCS icon returns to its original location and the world coordinates are restored to use.

On your own, **save** and **close** your drawing.

Curved Surfaces

Now you will create an auxiliary view of the slanted surface in a cylinder drawing like the one you created at the end of Tutorial 6. The drawing has been provided for you as *cyl3.dwt* in the data files that came with this book.

On your own, begin a new drawing.

Use *cyl3.dwt* as a template.

Name your new drawing *auxil3.dwg*.

You return to the AutoCAD drawing editor, showing the orthographic views of the cylinder with the slanted surface (Figure 9.48).

Figure 9.48

The drawing shows the front and side views of the slanted surface but not the true shape of the surface. You will draw a *partial auxiliary view* to show the true shape of the surface. Partial auxiliary views are often used because, in the auxiliary view, the inclined or oblique surface chosen is shown true size and shape, but other surfaces are foreshortened. As these other surfaces have already been defined in the basic orthographic views, there is no need to show them in the auxiliary view. A partial auxiliary saves time in projecting the view and gives a clearer appearance to your drawing.

Figure 9.49 shows an example. This drawing shows the front view of an object, along with two partial auxiliary views.

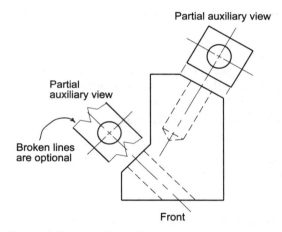

Figure 9.49   Example

Turn running Object Snap **Intersection** on.

Make sure the **grid** is on.

Turn **Ortho off**.

Make sure that **PROJECTION** is the current layer.

Figure 9.50

On your own, **drag the UCS** so that the origin is at point A, and the Y axis is aligned toward point B.

Your screen should be similar to Figure 9.51. Note that the crosshairs align with the inclined surface.

Figure 9.51

Next, copy the object in the side view and rotate it so that it aligns with the rotated grid and snap. Doing so makes projecting the depth of the object from the side view into the auxiliary view easy. Then you do not have to use a reference surface to make depth measurements, as you did in the previous drawing. The shapes in this drawing are simple, but these methods will also work for much more complex shapes.

> For the next steps you will use **Ortho** and **Snap**. Be sure that they are turned on. Refer to Figure 9.45 for the points to select.

Click: ***Copy button***

Select objects: ***use a window to select the entire side view***

Select objects: ***[Enter]***

Specify base point or [Displacement] <Displacement>: ***click the intersection labeled Base point***

Specify second point of displacement or <use first point as displacement>: ***click a point above and to the right of the side view***

Specify base point or displacement: ***[Enter]***

A copy of the side view appears on your screen, as shown in Figure 9.52.

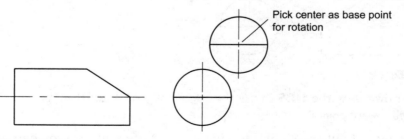

Pick center as base point for rotation

Figure 9.52

Now you are ready to rotate the copied objects so that they align with the snap and can be used to project the auxiliary view. You will use the Rotate button from the ribbon Home tab, Modify panel and type in the angle, which is 56°. If you were not given this information you can use the angular dimension command, or the Measuregeom command to determine it.

Click: ***Rotate button***

Select objects: ***use Window or Crossing to select the copied objects***

Select objects: ***[Enter]***

Specify base point: ***click the intersection of the centerlines of the copied objects***

Specify rotation angle or [Copy/Reference] <0>: ***56 [Enter]***

The objects that you copied previously should now be rotated into position so that they align with the snap and grid. Your drawing should look like that in Figure 9.53.

Figure 9.53

Now you will change the copy onto layer PROJECTION because it is part of the construction of the drawing, not something you will leave in the drawing when you are finished. You will freeze layer PROJEC-TION when you have finished the drawing.

On your own, change the copied objects to layer PROJECTION.

The objects that you selected are changed onto layer PROJECTION. Their color is now magenta, which is the color of layer PROJECTION. Next, you will draw projection lines from the front view to the empty area where the auxiliary view will be located.

Make sure that Ortho and the Intersection running object snap are turned on.

Figure 9.54

Refer to Figure 9.54 for the points to select.

   Click: **Ray button**

   Specify start point: **click the intersection labeled A**

   Specify through point: **click a point above the front view**

   Specify through point: **[Enter]**

   Command: **[Enter]** *to restart the Ray command*

   Specify start point: **click the intersection labeled B**

   Specify through point: **click a point above the front view**

   Specify through point: **[Enter]**

Figure 9.55 shows an example of these lines.

Figure 9.55

   On your own, project rays from the intersections in the copied side view so that your drawing looks like the one in Figure 9.56.

   Click: **VISIBLE** *as the current layer*

Figure 9.56

Drawing the Ellipse

Because the object appears as a circle in the side view and is tilted away in the front view, the true shape of the surface must be an ellipse. You will select the Ellipse button from the Draw toolbar to create the elliptical surface in the auxiliary view. Refer to Figure 9.50 for your selections.

Click: **Ellipse button**

Specify axis endpoint of ellipse or [Arc/Center]: **C [Enter]**

Specify center of ellipse: **click the intersection labeled Center**

Specify endpoint of axis: **click intersection 1**

Specify distance to other axis distance or [Rotation]: **click intersection 2**

The ellipse in your drawing should look like the one in Figure 9.57. You will need to trim the lower portion of it to create the final surface.

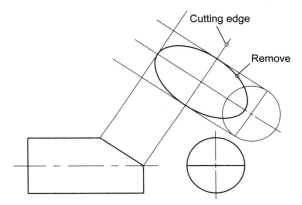

Cutting edge

Remove

Figure 9.57

You will use the Trim command to eliminate the unnecessary portion of the ellipse in the auxiliary view.

Click: **Trim button**

Select cutting edges: **click the cutting edge in Figure 9.51**

Select objects: **[Enter]**

Select object to trim or shift-select to extend or [Fence/Crossing/Project/Edge/eRase/Undo]: **click on the ellipse to the right of the cutting edge**

Select object to trim or shift-select to extend or [Fence/Crossing/Project/Edge/eRase/Undo]: **[Enter]**

The lower portion of the ellipse is now trimmed off.

Change the two projection lines from the front view onto layer THIN on your own.

Use the Break command to break them so that they do not touch the views.

Draw in the final line across the bottom of the remaining portion of the ellipse on layer VISIBLE.

Freeze layer PROJECTION to remove the construction and projection lines from your display.

Tip: *If the surface in the side view were an irregular curve, you could project a number of points to the auxiliary view and then connect them with a polyline. After connecting them, you could connect them in a smooth curve, using the Fit Curve or Spline option of the Edit Polyline command. Although this method would also produce an ellipse, the Ellipse command is quicker.*

When you are finished, your screen should look like Figure 9.58.

Figure 9.58

Save and **close** your drawing.

You have completed Tutorial 9.

Key Terms

associative hatching	custom hatch pattern	partial auxiliary view	runout
auxiliary view	cutting plane line	pictorial full section	section view
basic view	foreshortened	reference line	user-defined hatch pattern
crosshatching	gradient fill	reference surface	

Key Commands

Distance	Ray
Edit Hatch	Savetime
Ellipse Center	UCS 3 Point
Hatch	

Exercises

Redraw the given front view and replace the given right side view with a section view. Assume that the vertical centerline of the front view is the cutting plane line for the section view. The letter M after an exercise means that the given dimensions are in millimeters.

9.1 High-Pressure Seal

9.2 Valve Cover

9.3M Pulley

9.4 Double Cylinder

Use 2D techniques to draw this object; the grid shown is 0.25 inch. Show the front view as a half section and show the corresponding cutting plane in the top view. On the same views, completely dimension the object to the nearest 0.01 inch. Include any necessary notes.

6" WALL THICKNESS THROUGHOUT

Ø 3.25'

4.0'

Ø10"

8.0'

2.6'

7.0'

7.0'

3.5'

9.5 Manhole Junction

Draw standard orthographic views and show the front view in section.
Wall thickness is 6 inches throughout. The 10-inch hole is through the
entire manhole junction (exits opposite side).

5.0

1.0

2.5

1.25

.25

.5

.5

1.5

ø1.0
ø .5

.75

.25

1.5

.5

1.0

9.6 Plate

Use 2D to construct the top view with the cutting plane shown and show the front view in section.

9.7 Support Bracket

Create a drawing of the object shown with a plan view and full section front view. Note the alternate units in brackets; these are the dimensions in millimeters for the part.

9.8 Shaft Support

Redraw the given front view and create a section view. Assume that the vertical centerline of the shaft in the front view is the cutting plane line for the section view.

9.9 Turned Down Slab Detail
Use 2D methods to create the drawing shown. Use Boundary Hatch to fill
the area with the pattern for concrete. Make irregular areas to fill with patterns
for sand and earth.

Use the 2D techniques you have learned in the tutorial to create an auxiliary view of the slanted surfaces
for the objects that follow. The letter M after an exercise number means that the given dimensions are in
millimeters.

9.10 Stop Block

9.11 Bearing

BLOCKS, DESIGNCENTER, AND TOOL PALETTES

Introduction

You can unify a collection of drawing objects into a single symbol using the Block command. Using blocks helps organize your drawing and makes updating symbols easy. Text objects called attributes can be associated with blocks. These attributes can be visible or invisible. You can extract attribute information to an external database or spreadsheet for analysis or record keeping. (You will learn more about attributes in Tutorial 13.) The use of blocks has many advantages. You can construct a drawing by assembling blocks that consist of many small details. This way objects that appear often only need to be drawn once and inserted as needed. Inserting blocks rather than copying basic objects results in smaller drawing files, which saves time in loading and regenerating drawings. Blocks can also be nested, so that one block is a part of another block.

In this tutorial, you will learn to use the Block and Insert Block commands, while creating reusable symbols used in drawing electronic logic circuits. Using Write Block, you will make the symbols into separate drawings that you can add to any drawing. You will use the Design-Center to access blocks, layers, and other named entities from your existing drawings. Finally, you will learn to create custom tool palettes and toolbars to which you can add your block symbols and save your custom work space.

The AutoCAD *Group* command lets you group objects into named selection sets. You can also form *selectable groups*. When a group is selectable, clicking on one of its members selects all the members of the group that are in the current space and not on locked or frozen layers. An object can belong to more than one group. Groups are another powerful way of organizing the information in your drawing. In many ways groups are like blocks, but groups differ because of their special use for selecting objects as named sets.

One case in which you might use blocks and groups together is in an architectural drawing. You could create each item of furniture—a table, chair, etc.—as a separate block and then insert it multiple times into the drawing. You could use several different layers to draw each block. You could then name all the tables as a group called TABLES and all the chairs as a group called CHAIRS. The TABLES and CHAIRS groups could belong to a group named FURNITURE. Unlike a block, which acts as a single object, you can still move or modify items in groups individually, but you can also quickly select the group and modify it as a unit.

Objectives

When you have completed this tutorial, you will be able to

1. Use the Block, Write Block, Insert Block, and Donut commands.

2. Use the DesignCenter™.

3. Add blocks and commands to a Tool Palette.

4. Add your block symbols to toolbar buttons.

5. Create a logic circuit diagram using blocks.

6. Create named groups.

7. Create your own toolbars.

8. Customize your workspace.

Starting

Begin the AutoCAD program and open the drawing file *electr.dwg* provided with the datafiles. Save the drawing and name it *eblocks.dwg*. When you have finished, it should appear as in Figure 10.1.

Figure 10.1 shows six symbols used in drawing electronic logic circuits: the *Buffer, Inverter, And, Nand, Or,* and *Nor gates.* You will make each symbol into a block.

Figure 10.1

Using the Block Command

A *block* is a set of objects formed into a compound object or symbol. You define a block from a set of objects in your current drawing. You specify the *block name* and then select the objects that will be part of the block.

The block name is used whenever you insert the compound object (block) into the drawing. Each insertion of the block into the drawing, the *block reference*, can have its own scale factors and rotation. The software treats a block as a single object. Select a block for use with commands such as Move or Erase simply by clicking any part of the block, like you would any other drawing object.

You can take blocks apart into their individual objects by using the Explode or Xplode commands, but doing so removes the blocks' special properties.

A block can be composed of objects that were drawn on several layers with several colors and linetypes. The layer, color, and linetype information of these objects is preserved in the block. Upon insertion, each object is drawn on its original layer with its original color and linetype, regardless of the current drawing layer, object color, and object linetype.

There are three exceptions to this rule.

1. Objects that were drawn on layer 0 are generated on the current layer when the block is inserted, and they take on the characteristics of that layer.

2. Objects that were drawn with color BYBLOCK inherit the color of the block (either the current drawing color when they are inserted or the color of the layer when color is set by layer).

3. Objects that were drawn with linetype BYBLOCK inherit the linetype of the block (either the current linetype or the layer linetype, as with color).

Blocks are stored only in the current drawing and you can use them only in the drawing in which they were created. To use a block in another drawing, you need to use the Write Block command or the Windows Clipboard. You can use blocks in other drawings by copying vectors (graphical objects) to the Windows Clipboard and pasting them into another drawing, which results in a block. In addition, you can insert the drawing containing a block into another drawing. When you insert a drawing as you did in Tutorial 4 with the subdivision drawing, *subdivis.dwg*, any blocks it contains are then defined in the drawing in which it is inserted.

Unlike using the Windows Clipboard to copy a block, or inserting a file containing a block, using the Write Block command saves the selected block or drawing objects as a separate drawing file. This block file can then be inserted into any drawing.

Zoom up the area of the drawing showing the And gate so that your screen is similar to Figure 10.2.

Figure 10.2

You will use the Create button from the ribbon Home tab, Block palette to create a block from the objects making up the And gate on the screen. Be sure to select Create Block and not Insert Block on the same palette. When typing the command, enter BLOCK. Refer to Figure 10.2 to help you select point 1.

Turn on running object snap **Endpoint**. Turn off any other modes from the status bar.

Click: **Create button** *from the Block palette*

A Block Definition dialog box appears, similar to Figure 10.3.

Figure 10.3

The dialog box allows you to type in a block name, select a base point, select objects to be used in that group, and view existing blocks. The Objects area of the dialog box allows you to select whether the items you select to make the block will be retained in your drawing (as individual objects), converted to a block (as a single object), or deleted.

Leave the Objects radio buttons set to **Convert to block**.

You can also add a description, and specify the default unit system you are using to define the sizes of the features in the block. These things will help you later find and size the blocks when you insert them into drawings.

Finally, blocks can be annotative, like the text, dimensions, and hatch you used in earlier drawings.

Next you will type the block name, select a base point, and finally select the objects to be used.

Type: **AND** *for the Name*

Click: **Pick Point** *(located in the Base Point area of the dialog box)*

Be sure to choose a base point that will be useful when you insert the block in another drawing. If you do not select a base point, the default base point coordinates (0,0,0) or whatever other coordinates appear in the dialog box will be used. Refer to Figure 10.2 and use Snap to Endpoint to select the base point.

Specify insertion base point: *click endpoint 1*

When you return to the dialog box, you will choose to Select objects.

Click: **Select objects button**

Select objects: *use implied Crossing to select all of the objects making up the And gate, including the name AND [Enter]*

Click: **Unitless** *as the Block Unit type under Settings*

Type: **Electronic AND gate** *as the description*

Click: **OK**

You are returned to the drawing editor and now have a block of the And gate to be used in later drawings.

Click: **Zoom Previous**

This will restore the original view of the drawing, where you can see each symbol.

Click: **Create block button**

On your own, **create a block for each of the other electronic logic symbols.**

Name the blocks **NAND, OR, NOR, INVERTER, and BUFFER.**

Select the right-hand endpoint of the lead from each electronic logic gate as the base point.

To see how you can use blocks within the current drawing, you will insert the And block you created.

Inserting a Block

The Insert Block command inserts blocks or other drawings into your drawing. When inserting a block, you use a dialog box to specify the block name, the insertion point (the location for the base point you selected when you created the block), the scale, and the rotation for the block. A scale of 1 causes the block to remain the original size. The scaling factors for the X-, Y-, and Z-directions do not have to be the same. However, using the same size ensures that the inserted block has the same proportions, or aspect ratio, as the original. Blocks (even those with different X-, Y-, and Z-scaling factors) can be exploded back into their original objects with the Explode command. A rotation of 0° ensures the same orientation as the original. You can also use Insert Block by typing INSERT at the command prompt.

You will select Insert Block from the ribbon Home tab, Block panel and use the dialog box to insert the And gate into your drawing.

Click: **Insert button** *from the Block palette*

The Insert dialog box appears on your screen, as shown in Figure 10.4.

Tip: *You can use the Design-Center to import blocks from existing drawings into your current drawing.*

Figure 10.4

*Click: **AND** from the list that pulls down adjacent to Name*

The dialog box lets you select whether you will be returned to your drawing to specify the Insertion point, Scale, and Rotation or whether you will type in a value for these (or use the defaults). You will leave the Scale factor set to 1 for the X, Y, and Z coordinate directions. This way the block will retain the same size in the drawing as where it was created. Also leave the Rotation set to an angle of 0 degrees so that the block retains its original angle.

The Specify On-screen feature allows you to click the location for the block from your screen after you exit the dialog box. Otherwise, you must type in the coordinates for its location in the dialog box.

Be sure that in the Insertion area the box to the left of **Specify On-screen** has a check in it.

To exit the dialog box and begin specifying the insertion parameters on screen,

*Click: **OK***

The And block appears, attached to the crosshairs by its endpoint, the base point you specified. Continue with the Insert command.

Specify insertion point or [Basepoint Scale/X/Y/Z/Rotate/PScale/PX/PY/PZ/ PRotate]: *click anywhere to the right of the logic symbols*

The And block is added to your drawing.

On your own, try to erase only one of the lines of the newly added block.

Press [Esc] to **cancel** the Erase command without erasing anything.

Note that the entire block behaves as one object. In Tutorial 7, when you added associative dimensions to your drawing, they were also blocks. That's why they behave as a single object, even though they are a collection of lines, polylines, and text. Before you can change individual pieces of a block, you must use the Explode command, as you did with Xplode in Tutorial 7. However, exploding takes away a block's special properties.

Tip: *You can reenter the Block Definition dialog box and update the selections for any of the blocks in the drawing. To do this, pick the Create block button and expand the list of names in the dialog box to select the block you want to redefine. Make any necessary changes to the dialog box and then pick OK.*

Using Explode

A block behaves as a single object. The Explode command replaces a block reference with the collection of simple objects the block comprises.

Explode also turns 2D and 3D polylines, associative dimensions, and 3D mesh back into individual objects. When a 3D solid object is exploded, it becomes a collection of surfaces.

When you explode a block, the resulting image on the screen is identical to the one you started with, except that the color and linetype of the objects may change. That can occur because properties such as the color and linetype of the block return to the settings determined by their original method of creation, either BYLAYER or the set color and linetype with which they were created. There will be no difference unless the objects were created in layer 0 or with the color and linetype set to BYBLOCK, as specified in the list at the beginning of this tutorial.

You will use the Explode command to break the newly inserted And block into individual objects for editing.

Click: **Explode button** from the ribbon Home tab, Modify panel

Select objects: **click any portion of the newly inserted And block**

Select objects: **[Enter]**

The block is now broken into its component objects.

On your own, try to **erase** a line from the block.

Notice that now you can erase one line at a time, rather than the whole block.

Erase the newly added AND block.

Using Write Block

The block you just created is only defined within the current drawing. You can use the Write Block command to make it into a separate drawing for use in other drawings. A drawing file made with the Write Block command is the same as any other drawing file. You can open it and edit it like any other drawing. You can use any AutoCAD drawing as a block and insert it into any other drawing, as you did in Tutorial 5 when inserting the subdivision drawing. This is a great tool you can use when creating AutoCAD drawings.

You will use the Write Block command to write the AND block that you created to a new AutoCAD drawing file called *and-gate.dwg*. The alias for the WBLOCK command is W.

Command: **W [Enter]**

The Write Block dialog box similar to that shown in Figure 10.5 appears on the screen.

Figure 10.5

You can select the source information for the Wblock by clicking one of the following three radio buttons:

- **Block:** Click on the name of a block that already exists in the current drawing. The objects that make up the specified block are written to the drawing file being created.

- **Entire drawing:** This saves the entire current drawing to the name specified as the Destination file name (as the Save command does), except that unused named objects, layers, and other definitions are eliminated.

- **Objects:** Clicking this allows you to specify the objects and the base point, similar to the Make Block options. You can choose whether the items you select are retained, deleted, or converted to blocks in the current drawing. The selected objects are written to the drawing file name that you specify in the Destination area.

In the Source area,

Click: **Block button**

Select: **AND** *as the block name*

The middle area of the dialog box appears grayed out. Next set the destination file and default units for the block. You will name the new file *and-gate*. You do not need to include the file extension; the *.dwg* extension is automatically added. (Be sure to use the *c:\work* directory for the new file to keep your hard drive organized.)

Type: **AND-GATE** *for the File name*

Click: **the ellipsis button** *to the right of File name and path to navigate to* **c:\work** *as necessary*

Click: **Unitless** *for the Insert units*

Click: **OK**

Warning: *Do not give the write block the same name as an existing drawing. If you do, you will see the message "This file already exists. Replace existing file?" Select No unless you are certain that you no longer want the old drawing file.*

Tip: *Write Block does not save views, User Coordinate Systems, viewport configurations, unreferenced symbols (including block definitions), unused layers or linetypes, or text styles. This compresses your drawing file size by getting rid of unwanted overhead.*

The block that you created, named AND, has been saved to the new AutoCAD drawing file *and-gate.dwg*.

> On your own, use the **WBlock** command to create separate drawing files for each of the other blocks that you created. Name them *or-gate*, *nor-gate*, *nand-gate*, *inverter*, and *buffer*.

Using DesignCenter and Tool Palettes

Next you will use the DesignCenter and Tool Palettes to manage blocks so that you can add them easily to your drawings. The DesignCenter is an easy way to save time on drawings by copying and pasting layer definitions, layouts, and text and dimension styles between drawings. DesignCenter allows you to:

- Browse for drawings or symbol libraries on your computer, your network, or on web pages.
- View definitions for blocks and layers and insert, attach, copy or paste them into the current drawing.
- Update (redefine) a block definition.
- Make shortcuts to drawings, folders, and web pages that you use frequently.
- Add xrefs, blocks, and hatches to drawings.
- Open drawing files in a new window.
- Drag drawings, blocks, and hatches to a convenient tool palette.

> Start a new drawing from the **proto.dwt** template provided with the datafiles. Name it **hfadder.dwg**.

The ribbon Insert tab, Content palette shown in Figure 10.6 provides access to the DesignCenter, and search tools to find information from external sources to quickly add to your drawing. Notice that at the left end of the insert tab, you can also access the Block commands.

Figure 10.6

Click: **DesignCenter button** *from the ribbon Insert tab, Content palette*

The DesignCenter appears on your screen similar to Figure 10.7.

Tip: *You can use Write Block to export part of any drawing to a separate file. This action can speed up your computer's response time by keeping file sizes smaller. When you are working in an extremely large file, but just need to work on a certain part of it, use Write Block to export that area to a new file. Work on the new, smaller file that contains only the part of the drawing you need. When done, use Insert Block to reinsert the finished work in the larger drawing. You will have to explode it after inserting it before you can edit it.*

Tip: *You can click and drag on the corner of the dialog box to resize it.*

Tip: *You can also show the contents of a drawing by double-clicking on its thumbnail pictured in the list at the right.*

Figure 10.7

On your own, use the Folder List area to show the list of files in your **c:\work** directory.

The DesignCenter shows a list of all of the files that are available in the selected directory. You can drag and drop named drawing objects, such as layers, blocks, text and dimension styles, layouts, linetypes, and xrefs into your drawing. Next, you will select drawing *mysubdiv.dwg* so you can drag one of its layers into your current drawing.

*Click: **drawing mysubdiv.dwg from tree list at left** (if you don't have this drawing use the datafile named subdiv2.dwt)*

You should now see a list of the types of named objects that are available from within the Mysubdiv drawing as shown in Figure 10.8.

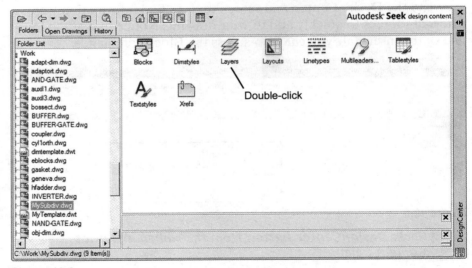

Figure 10.8

*Double-click: **on the Layers button** in the DesignCenter*

The DesignCenter changes to show the list of layers that are available inside drawing Mysubdiv (see Figure 10.9). You will drag and drop layer Points into the current drawing.

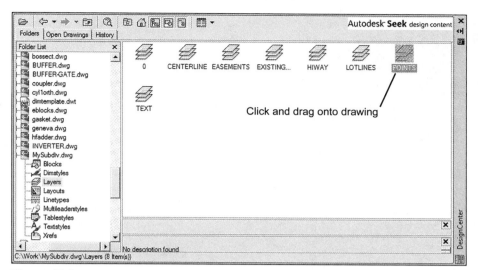

Figure 10.9

Drag layer Points to your current drawing.

Click: **Layer Control**

You should see that your current drawing now has a new layer named Points as shown in Figure 10.9. It has all the same properties as the layer Points from drawing Mysubdiv, is locked, and has color blue.

Next you will turn on the Tool Palettes and then add your electronic gates to it. The Palettes panel is show in Figure 10.11.

Tool Palettes button

Figure 10.11

Click: **Tool Palettes button** *from the ribbon View tab, Palettes panel*

You should see the Tool Palettes appear on your screen as shown in Figure 10.12. The Tool Palettes are an easy way to quickly add hatches and blocks to your drawing without having the entire DesignCenter open. A tool palette is not backward compatible. A new tool palette cannot necessarily be used in an older version of AutoCAD.

Tip: *You do not need to close the Design Center to view the layers. Leave it open as you will need it in the next steps.*

Figure 10.10

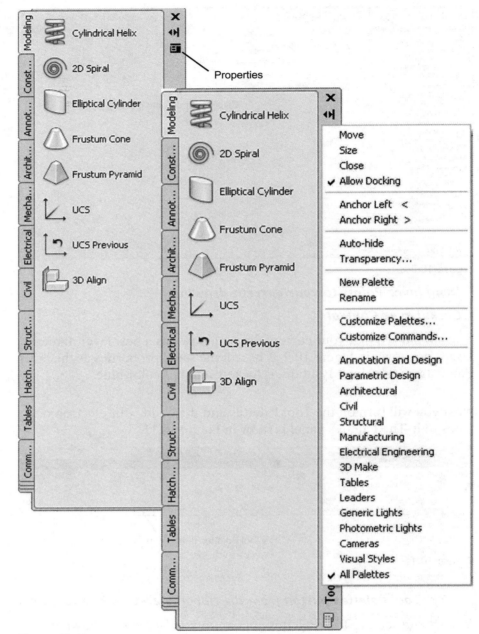

Figure 10.12

*Right-click: **on the Properties button at the top right of the Tool Palettes to pop up the menu choices.***

The pop up menu appears as shown in Figure 10.12. You will use it to add a new tab to the Tool Palettes for your electronic blocks.

*Click: **New Palette***

*Type: **Electronic** when the text cursor appears and press [Enter]*

A new tab has been added to the Tool Palettes. It is shown in Figure 10.13. You will drag and drop your electronic gate drawings onto this new Tool Palette.

Figure 10.13

On your own, use the **DesignCenter** and **drag and drop** the logic gate drawings onto the Tool Palette as shown in Figure 10.13.

Continue until you have added all 6 logic gates so that your Tool Palette is similar to Figure 10.13.

Close the DesignCenter on your own.

Next you will add the Explode command to this tool palette. You can drag tools (command buttons) onto a palette when the Customize User Interface dialog box is open.

*Right-click: **on a blank area of the tool palette***

*Click: **Customize commands** from the menu that pops up*

The Customize dialog box appears on your screen.

On your own, drag a copy of the Explode command from the dialog box onto the tool palette as shown in Figure 10.14.

Close the Customize dialog box when you have finished.

The Explode command is added to the tool palette as in Figure 10.14.

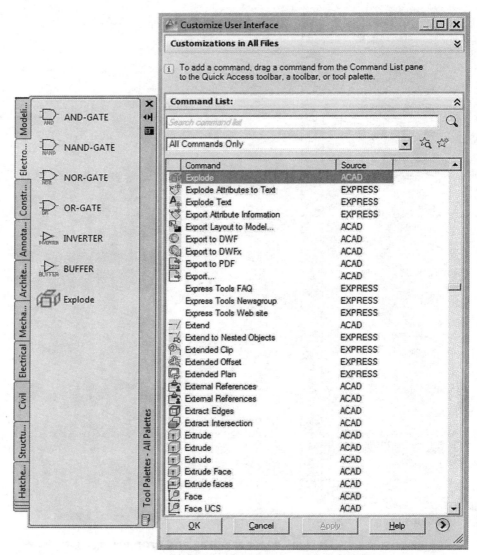

Figure 10.14

Tip: *The Minsert command lets you insert a rectangular array of blocks. It can be useful when you're laying out drawings that have a pattern, such as rows of desks or rows of electronic components. Typing the command MULTIPLE and pressing enter allows you to make any command repeat multiple times without restarting it. The Divide and Measure commands also allow you to insert blocks. The Divide command divides an object that you select into the number of parts that you specify. You can either insert a point object where the divisions will be (as you did in Tutorial 5), or you can select the Block option and specify a block name. The Measure command works in much the same way, except that instead of specifying the number of divisions that you want to use, you specify the lengths of the divisions. Use the on-line Help facility to get more information about these commands.*

Now you have learned to create a customized AutoCAD tool palette. You can create your own blocks and add them to other tool palettes. You can also program your own commands onto toolbars and buttons or modify existing toolbars and buttons using the techniques that you will learn later in this tutorial.

You are ready to try adding some of the logic blocks to your drawing by dragging and dropping them from the Tool Palettes.

Drawing the Half-Adder Circuit

You will use the new tool palette you created to draw a half-adder circuit with electronic logic symbols.

Switch to paper space and use the Edit Text command to change the text in the title block to HALF-ADDER CIRCUIT and type your name. Specify NONE for the scale, as electronic diagrams usually aren't drawn to scale.

Switch back to model space when you are finished.

On your own, set the current layer to **THIN** and **Snap** to **0.1042** so that it will align with the spacing between the leads on the logic symbols that you created.

Use the Electronic tool palette on your own to insert the logic symbols as shown in Figure 10.15.

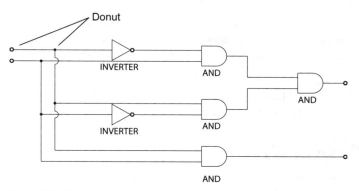

Figure 10.15

Use the **Line** and **Arc** commands with **Snap to Endpoint** to connect the output from one logic circuit to the inputs of the next as shown.

You will use the Donut command to make the filled and open circles for connection points.

Using Donut

The Donut command draws filled circles or concentric filled circles. See Figure 10.16. Donut is found on the ribbon Home tab, expanded Draw panel. The Donut command requires numerical values for the inside and outside diameters of the concentric circles, as well as a location for the center point. If you enter a zero value for the inside diameter, a solid dot appears on the screen. The diameter of the dot will equal the stated outside diameter value. Next, you will draw some donuts off to the side of your logic circuit drawing.

 Click: **Donut button,** *from the ribbon Home tab, Draw panel*

   Specify inside diameter of donut <0.5000>: *[Enter]*

Specify outside diameter of donut <1.0000>: *[Enter]*

Note that a doughnut-like shape is now moving with your cursor. The Center of donut prompt is repeated so that you can draw more than one donut. Select points on your screen.

   Specify center of donut or <exit>: *select a point off to the side of your drawing*

   Specify center of donut or <exit>: *select another point*

   Specify center of donut or <exit>: [Enter] to exit the command

On your own, **erase** the donuts that you drew to the side.

Restart the Donut command and set the inside diameter for the donut to **0**.

Set the outside diameter to **0.075**.

Draw the solid connection points for the logic circuit that you see in Figure 10.15

Figure 10.16

Next add the open donuts at the ends of the lines.

Start the Donut command and set the inner diameter to **0.0625** and the outer diameter to **0.075**.

Create four donuts on the side of your drawing.

Place the four donuts by using the **Move** command so that each donut is attached at its outside edge, not its center. Use **Snap to Quadrant** to select the base point on the donut and then **Snap to Endpoint** to select the endpoint of the line.

When you have drawn and placed all the connection points, your drawing should look like that in Figure 10.15.

Freezing the TEXT2 Layer

The drawing *electr.dwg*, which you used to create the blocks for the logic gates, contained different layers for the text, lines, and shapes of the logic gates. You can freeze or turn off layers to control the visibility within parts of a block. You will freeze the text in the blocks because it is there to help identify the blocks while you are inserting them but would not ordinarily be shown on an electronic circuit diagram. The text in the blocks is on layer TEXT2. The text in the title block is on layer TEXT. You will use Layer Control to freeze the layer that holds the text showing the name of the type of gate.

Use the **Layer Control** list that appears on your screen to **freeze layer TEXT2.** The names of the gates should disappear from the screen.

Save your drawing on your own before continuing.

Your drawing should look like Figure 10.17.

Figure 10.17

Creating Object Groups

Another powerful method of organizing objects is to use named groups. You can select these groups for use with other commands. You will select Group Manager from the Home tab Group panel (Figure 10.18).

Figure 10.18

Tip: *You can quickly change blocks by redefining them. If you redefine a block, the appearance of all the blocks with that name will update. To redefine a block, make the changes you want to the block. Then use the Block command to save it as a block again, retaining the same file name. You will be prompted that the block already exists and asked if you want to redefine it. The appearance of all existing blocks that have the same name as the redefined block will update.*

Tip: *You can also quickly create unnamed groups using the Group palette on the Home tab.*

🔲 *Click:* **Group Manager button**

The Object Grouping dialog box appears on your screen, as shown in Figure 10.19.

Figure 10.19

You will create a new group named EXISTING- CIRCUIT comprised of the upper Inverter and And gate and their leads. Groups can be selectable, not selectable, named, or unnamed. When a group is selectable, the entire group becomes selected if you click on a member of the group when selecting objects. You can return to the dialog box and turn Selectable off at any time.

Type the following information into the Group Identification area of the dialog box.

Group Name: **EXISTING-CIRCUIT**

Description: **Portions of the Existing Circuit**

Make sure Selectable is checked.

Click: **New**

You return to your drawing for the next selections.

Select objects for grouping: **click the upper Inverter and upper And gate and the two leads to the left of each of them**

Select objects: **[Enter]**

The dialog box returns to your screen as shown in Figure 10.20 so that you can continue creating groups.

Figure 10.20

You will group the remainder of the circuit and give it the group name NEW-CIRCUIT.

> *Type:* **NEW-CIRCUIT** *as the Group Name*
>
> *Click:* **New**
>
> *Select all the remaining objects to form the NEW-CIRCUIT group.*
>
> *Press:* **[Enter]** *when you are done selecting*
>
> *Click:* **OK** *to exit the dialog box*

Now, you are ready to try your groups with drawing commands. Remember, you can click on any member of a selectable group to select the entire group. You will change the linetype property for the NEW-CIRCUIT group to a HIDDEN linetype. To cause the Properties palette to appear on your screen,

> *Press:* **[Ctrl]+1** *to show the* **Properties palette**
>
> *Click:* **on one of the symbols from the NEW-CIRCUIT group**

The entire group becomes selected similar to Figure 10.21.

Figure 10.21

Click: **Hidden** *from the pull-down list for Linetype*

Click: **Windows Close button** *to remove the Properties dialog box from your screen*

Press: **[Esc] twice** *to unselect the objects*

The wiring diagram for the new portion of the circuit becomes dashed lines.

Click: **Undo** *from the Quick Access toolbar*

This will reverse this linetype change before you go on.

To be able to select each object individually, return to the Object Grouping dialog box on your own and turn Selectable off.

Your finished drawing should look like Figure 10.22.

Save and **plot** your drawing. Do not close the drawing yet.

Close the Tool Palettes if you have not already done so.

Figure 10.22

The DesignCenter and Tool Palettes are important tools for reusing your past work efficiently. Make the most of them! Reuse layers, blocks, dimension styles, and other named objects from your past drawings to create new drawings quickly.

Creating Custom Interfaces

Another way in which you can *customize* your AutoCAD software is by creating new toolbars and palettes and programming the existing toolbars and palettes to contain the commands you use most frequently. You can also reprogram existing buttons.

You can save customized user interfaces called workspaces which show the tools and palettes that you find useful. Using different workspaces for different tasks makes it quick to create the drawings you need. Follow the next steps to create a custom workspace.

Tip: *You can right-click on a workspace name and use the pop-up menu to pick Rename and change the workspace name if you missed overtyping the name.*

Figure 10.23

Expand the workspace selections as shown in Figure 10.23.

Click: **Customize**

The Customize User Interface dialog box appears on your screen.

Right-click: **Workspaces as shown in Figure 10.24**

Click: **New, Workspace**

Figure 10.24

A new workspace named Workspace1 is added to the list below the AutoCAD Default workspace.

Type: **MyWay** *as the name for your workspace, overtyping the name Workspace1*

Figure 10.25

Figure 10.25 shows the dialog box as it appears after the new workspace is added. Next, customize your workspace, *MyWay*, by selecting which standard interface items are shown on it.

> *Click:* **Customize Workspace button** *from the upper right of the dialog box in the Workspace Contents area as shown in Figure 10.25.*

The items in the right side of the dialog box become active. Next, select items from the left side of the dialog box to add to your workspace.

> On your own, **select some of the ribbon tabs** by clicking them so they appear checked as shown in Figure 10.26. You will notice them add to the Ribbon Tabs in the area at the right where your workspace is shown. When you have finished selecting the tabs to add,

> *Click:* **Done** *from Workspace Contents at the right of the dialog box*

Figure 10.26

Warning: *Be sure to add the Workspaces toolbar or you will have trouble switching back to the default workspace quickly.*

Next, you will create your own toolbar for the logic symbols that you created. You will program the buttons on the new toolbar to insert the logic symbols. To create a new toolbar,

Right-click: **on Toolbars** *in the top left window to show the pop-up menu (you may have to collapse some of the times in the tree or scroll to see it)*

Click: **New, Toolbar**

Toolbar1 is added to the end of the list of toolbars shown in the dialog box, as in Figure 10.27.

On your own, rename Toolbar1 to **Logic**.

Click: **Apply**

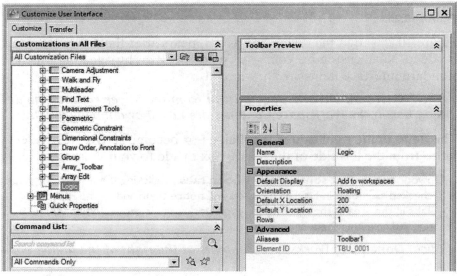

Figure 10.27

Tip: *When you create a toolbar, it is added by default to all workspaces. This is controlled by the On By Default item in the Properties window for the toolbar.*

You will see a small toolbar appear on your screen. (It does not have any buttons on it, so it may be hard to notice. You may have to move the dialog box around as it may be behind it.) It should be similar to Figure 10.28.

Figure 10.28

To create a new command, you will use the Command List area at the bottom left of the dialog box.

*Click: **New button** to the right of Categories*

Command1 is added to the list of commands that appear in the lower left of the dialog box.

> On your own, rename Command1 in the list in the lower left to And-gate as shown in Figure 10.29.

Figure 10.29

Next you will program the command appearance and select the button icon file.

The input box to the right of Name in the Properties area allows you to specify the name of the command that you are creating. This name will appear as the tool tip for the button exactly as you type it. You use the input box to the right of Description to enter the help line for the button, which will appear in the status bar at the bottom of the screen. The area to the right of Macro lets you type in the AutoCAD command sequence that you want to use when you click on the button. Do not add any spaces between ^C^C and the first command you type. A space represents pressing [Enter] or [Spacebar].

You will program the button to insert your and-gate block into your current drawing. When you click the button, the Insert Block command will be invoked to insert the specified block.

Using Special Characters in Programmed Commands

There are some special characters that you can use in programming the toolbars. One of these is ^C. If you put ^C in front of the command name you are programming, it will cancel any unfinished command when you select its button from the toolbar. In programming menus and buttons, putting cancel twice before a command is often a good idea in case you have left a subprompt active (so that it would take two cancels to return to the command prompt). Putting cancel before the Insert Block command is useful because you cannot select this command during another command. Do not add cancel before the toggle modes or transparent commands (a ' must precede them) because, if you execute cancel before you use them, you can't use them during another command.

A space or [Enter] is automatically added to the end of every command you program for the buttons. This way the command is entered when you select the button. You can enter a string of commands, or a command and its options, by separating them with a space to act as [Enter]. You can use the following special characters to program the toolbar buttons:

Character	Meaning
space	[Enter]
;	[Enter]
^Z	-At the end of a line, suppresses the addition of a space to the end of a command string
+	-At the end of a command string, allows it to continue to the next line
−	-In front of a command name, causes it to operate at the command line (not using a dialog box)
\	Pauses for user input
/	-Separates directories in path names, because \ (backslash) pauses for user input
^V	Changes current viewport
^B	[Ctrl]-B Snap mode toggle
^C	[Ctrl]-C Cancel
*^C^C	-At the beginning of a line, automatically restarts command sequence (repeating)
^D	[Ctrl]-D Coordinates toggle
^E	[Ctrl]-E Isoplane toggle
^G	[Ctrl]-G Grid mode toggle
^O	[Ctrl]-O Ortho mode toggle

An __ (underscore) preceding a command or option automatically translates AutoCAD keywords and command options for use with foreign-language versions.

Tip: *You can use the Action recorder from the Manage tab to quickly save macros.*

Click: **in the input box to the right of Name**

Type: **AND-GATE**

Click: **in the input box to the right of Description**

Type: **INSERTS AND-GATE SYMBOL**

Click: **to the right of ^C^C, for Macro**

Type: **–INSERT c:/work/AND-GATE.dwg**

Click: **to the right of Small Image**

Type: **c:\datafile2012\And.bmp** *(or click ... and browse for the file)*

Click: **to the right of Large Image**

Type: **c:\datafile2012\And.bmp** *(or click ... and browse for the file)*

When you have finished making the selections, the dialog box appears as shown in Figure 10.30.

Figure 10.30

Click: **in the text box next to Macro**

Click: **... (the ellipsis to the right of the Macro area)**

The Long String editor appears on your screen as shown in Figure 10.31. You can use it to see and edit long macros for commands. Your command to insert the And-gate should look like the figure.

Click: **OK** *to exit the Long String Editor*

Tip: *The block or file that you are inserting must be in the current path or you must specify where the block is located by adding the path name ahead of the block name. (You can change the current path in the Preferences dialog box.) The back slash has a special meaning in this dialog box: pause for user input. Therefore, when you add a path to a macro, you use the forward slash instead of the backslash to separate the directories (e.g., c:/work/and-gate.dwg). Finally, you can create a block library drawing and insert it into the drawing so that all the blocks are available in the current drawing prior to using the Logic toolbar that you just created.*

Tip: *You may need to add the*

Tip: *You may need to add the path to where your and-gate drawing is stored (i.e., ^C^C-Insert c:/work/and-gate). You must use a forward slash in the path. Do not add spaces between the ^C^C and the Insert command. Do not forget to type the hyphen (-) in front of the insert command so the command will run at the command prompt.*

Figure 10.31

Scroll down in the image list in the Button Image area if needed click the new *And.bmp* icon if it does not already appear as shown in Figure 10.30 then,

Click: **Edit** *below the Button Image tile at the top right*

Figure 10.32

The Button Editor dialog box appears on your screen as shown in Figure 10.32. (When the Toolbars dialog box is not open, if you double-click with the right button on an icon, the Toolbars dialog box opens and then the Button Editor dialog box opens.) The button editor works much like many paint-type drawing programs.

Each little box in the button editor represents a pixel, or single dot, on your screen. You can select the drawing tool from the buttons at the top of the editor. The color of the drawing tool is selected from the colored buttons at the right of the editor.

The And-gate button image was provided with the datafiles, but you can see how you could create your own button images using the button editor.

Click: **Close**

Now you are ready to drag your command onto the Logic toolbar you created.

Click: **the Logic toolbar** *in the upper left portion of the dialog box*

Drag the And-gate command onto it *from the Command List as shown in Figure 10.33.*

Click: **the Logic toolbar again** *(if needed) to see the preview in the top right*

Figure 10.33

Click: **Apply**

Click: **OK** *to close the Customize User Interface dialog box*

When you click Apply, your selections are applied to the toolbar. You should now see the And-gate icon that you made appear on your Logic toolbar as shown in Figure 10.34.

Figure 10.34

All the dialog boxes should now be closed. Close Tool Palettes if necessary to see the drawing editor.

Click: ***And-gate button*** *from your new toolbar*

The And gate should now be attached to the crosshairs, ready for insertion into your drawing.

> Position it as you like in your drawing and then click. Press [Enter] for the remaining prompts for scale and rotation.

The And-gate should appear in your drawing.

> On your own, close all drawings.

Tip: *If the And gate doesn't move with the cross hairs, press the [Esc] key and try it again. If that doesn't fix the problem, return to the button properties dialog and check to see that you have the command entered with the correct syntax.*

Start a new drawing from the default template *acad.dwt*

Your new workspace, MyWay is the default. (If it is not select it from the Quick Access toolbar.) It shows the ribbon with the tabs you selected when you customized it. To switch back to a standard workspace,

Click: **Workspace Switching button** *from the status bar as shown in Figure 10.35*

Figure 10.35

Use the menu that appears to switch to the **2D Drafting and Annotation** workspace (see Figure 10.36).

Figure 10.36

Click the [X] to close the Logic toolbar.

Exit the AutoCAD program.

You have completed Tutorial 10.

Key Terms

And gate	block reference	group	Nor gate
block	Buffer gate	Inverter gate	Or gate
block name	customize	Nand gate	selectable group

Key Terms

Block	Customize Workspace	Explode	Object Group
Customize User Interface	DesignCenter	Insert Block	Tool Palettes
	Donut	Multiple Insert	Write Block

Exercises

10.1 Stress Test Circuit
Create this circuit board layout, using Grid and Snap set to 0.2. Use donuts and polylines of different widths to draw the circuit.

10.2M Decoder Logic Unit

10.3 Floor Plan

Draw the floor plan shown for the first floor of a house. Create your own blocks for furniture and design a furniture layout for the house.

10.4M Arithmetic Logic Unit

Create blocks for the components according to the metric sizes shown. Use the blocks that you create to draw the circuit shown.

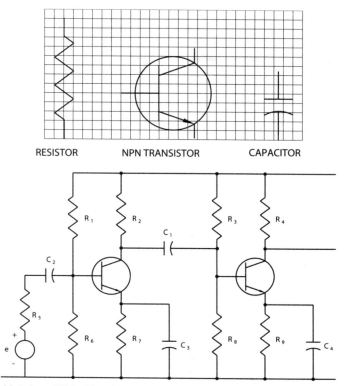

RESISTOR   NPN TRANSISTOR   CAPACITOR

10.5 Amplifier Circuit
Use the grid at left to draw and create blocks for the components shown. Each square equals 0.0625. Use the blocks that you create to draw the amplifier circuit.

GATE VALVE   PUMP   FLOW ARROW

CHECK VALVE   REDUCER   CONTROL VALVE

PIPING SYMBOLS

10.6 Piping Symbols
Draw the piping symbols at right to scale; the grid shown is 0.2 inch (you do not need to show it on your drawing). Use polylines 0.03 wide. Make each symbol a separate block and label it. Insert all the blocks into a drawing named pipelib.dwg.

10.7 Office Plan

Draw the office furniture shown and create blocks for DeskA, DeskB, ChairA, ChairB, and the window. Use the floor plan shown as a basis for creating your own office plan.

10.8 Wood Screws

Create blocks for each of the wood screws shown. The grid gives their proportions. Make the diameter of each 1.00 so that you can easily determine the scale needed for inserting them at other sizes.

10.9 Mechanical Fasteners

Draw the hex head bolt, square head bolt, regular hex nut, and heavy hex nut according to the proportions shown. Make each into a block. Base the dimensions on a major diameter (D) of 1.00, so when you insert the block you can easily determine the scaling factor.

INTRODUCTION TO SOLID AND SURFACE MODELING

11

Introduction

In Tutorials 1 through 10 you learned how to use the AutoCAD software to model objects in two dimensions. When you create a multiview drawing, it is a model of the object that contains enough information within the various views to give the person interpreting it an understanding of the complete 3D shape. Your drawings have been composed of multiple two-dimensional (2D) views, which are used to convey the information. Now you will learn to use the AutoCAD program to create 3D models.

AutoCAD 3D models are of three types: wireframe, surface, and solid. *Wireframe modeling* uses 3D lines, arcs, circles, and other graphical objects to represent the edges and features of an object. It is called wireframe because it looks like a sculpture made from wires. *Surface modeling* takes 3D modeling one step further, adding surfaces to the model so that it can be shaded and hidden lines can be removed. A surface model is like an empty shell: There is nothing to tell you how the inside behaves. *Solid modeling* is the term for creating an accurate 3D model that describes a volume contained by the surfaces and edges making up the object. A solid model is most like a real object because it represents not only the lines and surfaces, but also the volume contained within. In this tutorial you will first learn to create solid models and then how to create surface models.

Using the computer, you can represent three dimensions in the drawing database by using X-, Y-, and Z-coordinates. When you create a solid model, in some ways it is as if the actual object were stored inside the computer. Benefits of solid models include: easier interpretation; rendering (shading) so that someone unfamiliar with engineering drawings can visualize the object easily; 2D views can be generated directly from them; and the solid's *mass properties* can be analyzed. The need to create a physical prototype of the object may even be eliminated.

Creating a solid model is somewhat like sculpting the part in clay. You can add and subtract material with *Boolean operators* and create features by *revolution* and *extrusion*. Of course, when modeling with the AutoCAD software, you can be much more precise than when modeling with clay. At first, the software's solid modeling may look much like wireframe or surface modeling. The reason is that wireframe representation often is used in solid modeling and surface modeling to make many drawing operations and selections quicker. When you want to see a more realistic representation, you can shade or hide the back lines of solid models and surface models.

Objectives

When you have completed this tutorial, you will be able to

1. Change the 3D viewport.

2. Work with multiple viewports.

3. Set individual limits, grid, and snap for each viewport.

4. Create and save User Coordinate Systems.

5. Set Isolines to control model appearance.

6. Create model geometry using primitives, extrusion, and revolution.

7. Use Boolean operators to add, subtract, and intersect parts of your model.

8. Use region modeling.

9. Create basic surface models.

Starting

Launch **AutoCAD**.

Begin a **new drawing** based on the AutoCAD default template drawing *acad.dwt.* Save your new drawing as *block.dwg.*

Check to see that you are in model space. The limits should be set to 12 X 9.

Set the **grid** to **2** and turn it on.

Use **Zoom All** so that the grid area fills the screen.

The regularly spaced grid should appear every 2 units, filling your screen. When you are working in 3D, the grid can help you relate visually to the current viewing direction and coordinate system.

The 3D Modeling Workspace

The 3D Modeling workspace customizes the ribbon with tabs and panels providing useful tools for 3D modeling. Since you will be creating 3D models, you will switch to this workspace. As you have seen in Tutorial 10, it is easy to customize the workspace should you want to add additional tools and commands.

Click: ***3D Modeling*** *workspace from the workspace pull-down list*

The ribbon changes to show the tabs and panels for the 3D Modeling workspace as shown in Figure 11.1.

Tip: *If the Materials Browser is turned on, you can set it to Autohide so that it takes up less space when yuou are not using it.*

Figure 11.1

3D Coordinate Systems

The AutoCAD software defines model geometry using precise X-, Y-, and Z-coordinates in what is called the *World Coordinate System (WCS)*. The WCS is fixed and is used to store both 2D and 3D drawing geometry in the database. Its default orientation on the screen is a horizontal X-axis, with positive values to the right, and a vertical Y-axis, with positive values above the X-axis. The Z-axis is perpendicular to the computer screen, with positive values in front of the screen. The default orientation of the axes is shown in Figure 11.2.

Figure 11.2

While creating 2D geometry, you have been using this default WCS. You have been looking straight down the Z-axis, so that a line in the Z-direction appears as a point. When you do not specify the Z-coordinate, the AutoCAD software uses the default elevation, which is zero. This method made creating and saving 2D drawings easy.

Creating 3D Objects

The AutoCAD software provides several methods for creating model geometry including *primitives*, extrusion, and revolution. Primitives are basic shapes (e.g., boxes, cylinders, and cones) that can be joined to form more complex shapes. You will create a solid 3D box. Later in this tutorial you will learn how to join shapes by using Boolean operators and how to create other shapes with extrusion and revolution.

The Box command enables you to draw a solid rectangular prism. You can draw a box by specifying the corners of its base and its height, its center, corner, and height, or its location and length, width, and height. Figure 11.3 shows the information you specify to draw a box using these methods. The default method of defining a box is to specify two corners across the diagonal in the XY-plane and the height in the Z-direction.

Figure 11.3

You will draw a solid box by specifying the corners of the base and then its height.

*Click: **Box button** from the Home tab, Modeling panel*

Specify corner of box or [CEnter] <0,0,0>: *2,2,0 [Enter]*

Specify corner or [Cube/Length]: *8,6,0 [Enter]*

Specify height or [2Point]: *3 [Enter]*

On your own, turn off the grid.

Your screen should be similar to Figure 11.4. The box appears, but you are still looking straight down the z-axis at it, so it appears as a rectangle.

Figure 11.4

Setting the Viewpoint

When creating 3D geometry, it is useful to view the XY-plane from different directions, to see the object's height along the Z-axis. You can do so using the ViewCube. First make sure that it is turned on.

*Click: **Window, User Interface** from the ribbon View tab (Figure 11.5)*

Verify that **ViewCube** and **Navigation Bar** are on.

ViewCube

Navigation Bar

Figure 11.5

The ViewCube and Navigation Bar appear on your screen. The View-Cube is surrounded by a circle with N, E, S, W (North, East, South, West) labeled at its quadrants. At the center of the ViewCube is a target cube which is shown from your view point. At present you should be looking straight down the z-axis, showing the center cube from the top, so that it appears as a square, labeled "Top".

Figure 11.6 shows the ViewCube enlarged, with its features identified.

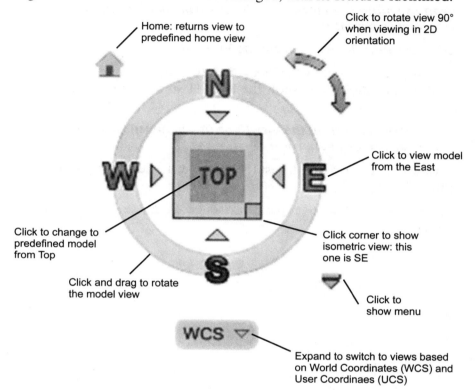

Figure 11.6

Click and drag your cursor inside the circle to rotate the view.

Notice the view rotate around the pivot point shown on the screen.

Click: **TOP** *from the ViewCube*

The view returns to show a top view with the x-axis aligned horizontally.

Click: **the lower right (SE) corner of the ViewCube** *see Figure 11.6*

The viewing direction changes as shown in Figure 11.7.

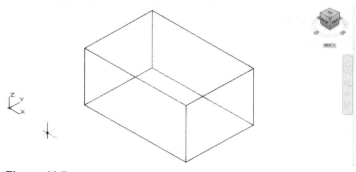

Figure 11.7

Note that your view has changed. You are no longer looking straight down on the XY-plane. Your view is now from an angle. The ViewCube updates to show the central cube as viewed from the direction you selected. Notice the changed appearance of the UCS icon. It updates to reflect the new viewing direction, still showing you the directions for the x, y, and z-axes. The cursor also updates to a 3D appearance.

Move your cursor over the circle in the ViewCube and click and drag to rotate the view. (The circle is transparent until you move your mouse over it.)

*Click: the **RIGHT** surface from the ViewCube*

The view changes to show the box you drew from the right side. The ViewCube updates now to show the RIGHT surface of the central cube.

*Click: **Home icon** from the ViewCube (it will appear transparent, until your cursor passes over it)*

The view updates to a Southwest (SW) isometric view as shown in Figure 11.8.

*Experiment with the ViewCube on your own. When you are done, reselect the **Home view**.*

Figure 11.8

*Right-click: **on the ViewCube** (or click the small downward arrow) to show the menu*

The pop-up menu appears. You can use it to quickly change from parallel to perspective projection, set the current view as Home, and change the settings for the ViewCube.

*Click: **ViewCube Settings***

The ViewCube Settings dialog box appears similar to Figure 11.9.

Figure 11.9

Notice that you can change the position, size, opacity, and the behavior of the ViewCube. You can also choose whether or not the view is automatically zoomed to the extents when using the ViewCube to change your viewing direction. In addition, notice that by default, Keep Scene Upright is selected. This prevents confusion that you may have when the view is shown from below the object, looking from a negative z-direction toward the origin. For now, leave these settings at the defaults. If you have changed anything, select Restore Defaults.

If desired, use the slider to increase the opacity for the ViewCube, so that it shows more clearly on your screen.

Close the ViewCube Settings dialog box on your own.

Click: on 2D Wireframe from the View tab, Visual Styles panel to expand the Visual Styles as shown in Figure 11.10

Figure 11.10

On your own, **click on each of the visual styles** to see the effect on your drawing of the box. Then,

Click: ***Conceptual** as the visual style*

Your screen should look like Figure 11.11. Keep in mind that in the screens in this book are shown with a white background color. The default is to show a dark background.

Figure 11.11

User Coordinate Systems

A *User Coordinate System (UCS)* is a set of X-, Y-, and Z-coordinates that you define to help you create your 3D models. You can define your own UCS, which may have a different origin and rotation from the WCS and may be tilted at any angle with respect to it. UCSs are helpful because your mouse moves in only two dimensions, and UCSs let you orient the basic drawing coordinate system at any angle in the 3D model space of the drawing, so you can continue using your mouse or other pointing device to draw easily. You can define any number of UCSs, give them names, and save them in a drawing, but only one can be active at a time.

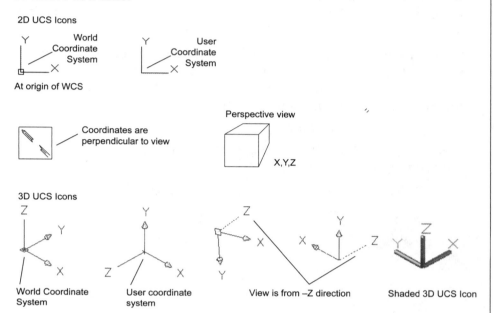

Figure 11.12

Tip: *Recall from Tutorial 9 that you can click and drag the UCS icon as a quick way of aligning a new user coordinate system.*

The UCS Icon

The UCS icon appears in the lower left of the screen. It will help you to orient yourself when looking at views of the object. The monitor screen is essentially flat so, even if the object is a 3D solid model in the database, only 2D views of it can be represented on the monitor. Because wireframe models look the same from front and back or from any two opposing viewpoints, keeping track of which view you are seeing on the screen is especially important.

Figure 11.12 shows some of the appearances of the 2D and 3D UCS icons. When you are displaying the 2D UCS icon, it is always drawn in the XY-plane of the current UCS. The arrows at the X- and Y-ends always point in the positive direction of the X- and Y-axes of the current UCS.

A special symbol may appear instead of the UCS icon to indicate that the current viewing direction of the UCS is edgewise. (Think of the X- and Y-coordinate system of the UCS as a flat plane like a piece of paper; the viewing direction is set so that you are looking directly onto the edge of the paper.) In this case you can't use most of the drawing tools, so the icon appears as a box containing a broken pencil. Take special note of this icon.

The 3D UCS icon shows the X-, Y-, and Z-axis directions. When the Z-axis is viewed from the negative direction, it appears dashed. A box at the intersection of the X-, Y-, and Z-axes indicates the World Coordinate System is active.

A plus sign in the lower left of the icon indicates that the icon is positioned at the origin of the current UCS. When you start a drawing from the *acad.dwt* template, the origin (0,0,0) of the drawing is in the lower left of the screen. If the UCS were at the origin, it would be partially out of the view; thus the default for the 2D UCS icon is not at the origin. You can use the UCSICON command to reposition the icon so that it is at the origin of the X-, Y-, and Z-coordinate system.

The *perspective icon* replaces the UCS icon when perspective viewing is active; it appears as a cube drawn in perspective. Many commands are also limited when perspective viewing is in effect. Next explore the options for setting the appearance of the UCS icon.

Command: **UCSICON [Enter]**

Enter an option [ON/OFF/All/Noorigin/ORigin/Selectable /Properties] <ON>: **P [Enter]**

The UCS icon dialog box appears as shown in Figure 11.13.

Figure 11.13

You can use this dialog box to switch between the 2D and 3D appearance of the UCS icon. You can also set the size, color, linewidth, and arrowhead appearance for the icon. Test the effect of various settings on the image tile shown in the dialog box. When you are finished, leave the appearance set to show a 3D UCS icon.

Click: *Cancel to exit the UCS icon dialog box*

Using Layers

Next you will create three new layers, one to contain the solid model, another for the viewports, and the third for the drawing's border.

On your own, use the Layer Properties Manager to **create the following layers**:

- MYMODEL   Blue   Continuous   Non-plotting
- VPORT   Magenta   Continuous
- BORDER   White   Continuous

Set layer **VPort** as the current layer.

Click on the 3D Box you drew and change it onto layer MYMODEL. Its color changes to blue.

Creating Multiple Viewports

Next, you will create viewports to show several views of the object at the same time. This way you can create just one solid model and produce a drawing with the necessary 2D orthographic views directly from that 3D model. Having several views also can make creating the model easier, as you can quickly switch between views to draw on different model surfaces. You have already used a single paper space viewport for printing and plotting in Tutorial 5. Now you will create four viewports and then change them so that they contain four different views of the model. You can think of the four separate viewports as four separate TV screens, each one of them showing the model. Each TV screen (viewport) can show a different view of the game (similar to watching the same televised event on several different stations at once). When watching several televisions, each cameraperson is looking at the game from a different angle, producing a different view on each TV set. Yet there is only one real event being televised. Multiple viewports work the same way. You can have many AutoCAD viewports, each of which contains a different view of the model, but there is only one model space and each object in it need be created only once. You will create paperspace viewports in layer VPORT.

Click: **Layout1 tab** *(from near the status bar)*

When you switch to Layout1, note the triangular paper space icon in the lower left of your screen as shown in Figure 11.14. Now you are ready to arrange views of your model, text, and other objects as you would on a sheet of paper.

If necessary, use Zoom All so that the paper space layout fills the graphics area.

Tip: *The type of viewports created depends on whether you are in model space or paper space. Paper space (or layout) viewports are called floating viewports, because they can be arranged on top of each other or with space between them. You can also create viewports in model space. These are called tiled viewports because they must always abut one another like floor tiles. In these tutorials you will use floating viewports. Tiled viewports can be a useful modeling tool. Experiment with them on your own.*

Figure 11.14

You will erase the current viewport which was created automatically when you switched to the Layout1 tab. Then you will create four viewports in its place. Check to make sure you are in paper space.

*Click: **Erase button***

Select objects: ***the magenta viewport border***

Select objects: ***[Enter]***

The viewport and objects showing in it disappear from your layout. The block you created is still there; you just cannot see it without a viewport to "look through." You will make four new viewports in which to show it. You use the VPort command to create viewports. You will use the New button from the Viewports panel on the ribbon View tab.

 *Click: **Named button** from the Viewports panel of the View tab*

The Viewports dialog box appears on the screen similar to Figure 11.15. You can use its New Viewports tab to select from preconfigured viewport arrangements, or use the Named Viewports tab to select from named viewport configurations you create ahead of time.

*Click: **New Viewports** tab*

*Click: **Four: Equal** from the Standard Viewports area*

*Click: **3D** from the Setup drop-down list*

*Click the **upper left image** tile, where View "Top" is listed and use the Visual Style drop down from the lower right of the dialog box to select **Wireframe**.*

*Use the same process to set the **lower left** and **lower right** viewports to the **Wireframe** visual style.*

*Leave the **upper right** viewport set to the **Conceptual** visual style.*

*Click: **OK** to return to the drawing for the remaining selections*

Named Viewports

Rectangular

Viewports ▾

Figure 11.15

You will place the viewports inside the area that you want to plot full size, centered on your page, as you did in Tutorial 5. You may find that the following values work for your printer. If you used a different setting in Tutorial 5, apply the one that works for your printer.

Specify first corner or [Fit] <Fit>: *.25,.25 [Enter]*

Specify opposite corner: *10.25,7.75 [Enter]*

Four viewports appear on your screen, each containing a different view of the object. The upper right viewport shows the shaded conceptual style object and the other viewports show the top, front, and right side views with no shading. Your screen should be similar to Figure 11.16.

Figure 11.16

Next, you will set the scale for the viewports so that the drawing views are at the same scale.

Selecting the Active Viewport

To make the upper left viewport active, you will move the arrow cursor until it is positioned in the top left viewport and then click.

*Double-click: **anywhere in the upper left viewport***

The crosshairs will appear in the viewport and the viewport becomes highlighted. This indicates that it is now the active viewport.

You can only draw and click to select points in a viewport when it is active. After you create something, whatever you created is visible in all other viewports showing that area of the WCS, unless the layer that the object is on is frozen in another viewport. (You can freeze layers in specific viewports.) You can start drawing something in one viewport and finish drawing it in another. Keep in mind that, you are using a certain viewport to access model space, but there is only one model space.

Tip: *You can press [Ctrl]-R to toggle the active viewport. This action is helpful when you are unable to pick in the viewport for some reason.*

Each viewport can contain its own setting for Grid, Snap, and Zoom (or Viewport Scale). The status bar lists the Viewport Scale.

*Click: **1:2** from the list of Viewport Scales*

The top view of the box fits into the viewport at half scale (Figure 11.17).

Figure 11.17

*Double-click: **anywhere in the lower left viewport** to make it active*

The crosshairs appear in the lower left viewport and its border becomes highlighted. This viewport shows the front of the object, as though you had taken the top view and tipped it 90° away from you. (Imagine that the original Y-axis is projecting straight into your monitor.) The object is again too large to fit in the viewport well. Unless an enlarged detail is necessary, all of the views are typically shown to the same scale, except for perhaps the pictorial view. To set the Viewport Scale,

*Click: **1:2** from the Viewport Scale on the status bar*

Now you see the entire front view of the object in the viewport at half size related to the paper units (similar to Figure 11.18.)

Notice that the XY coordinates of the UCS are aligned to be parallel to each of the top, front and side views. The world coordinate system (WCS) is parallel to the bottom surface of the block. You see the WCS in the upper right viewport. When you double-click to make a viewport active, your drawing's current XY-plane automatically changes to align with that viewing direction (not the WCS). This is a convenient feature to help you create 3D drawings. Think about what would happen if it did not. It would be like looking at a piece of paper edgewise at eye level and then trying to draw on it. If the user coordinates are "on edge" in your view, you can not easily click points to draw objects.

*Double-click: **inside the lower left viewport to make it active***

*Click: **1:2** from the Viewport Scale on the status bar*

Save your drawing *block.dwg* at this time.

Viewports Using Different UCSs

The ability to display more than one UCS at a time in different viewports is controlled by system variable UCSVP. When UCSVP is set to 1 in a viewport, the UCS last used in that viewport is saved with the viewport and is restored when the viewport is made current again. The Top, Front, and Right Side oriented viewports have the UCSVP variable preset to 1 during their creation.

When UCSVP is set to 0 in a viewport, its UCS is always the same as the UCS in the current viewport. The UCSVP variable for the upper right (isometric view) is set to 1 by default. You will set this variable to 0 in the upper right viewport only, so that it always displays the current UCS. This is useful so that you can use this isometric view to see how your current UCS (drawing plane) is aligned with the model.

Double-click: ***the upper right viewport*** *to make it active*

Command: ***UCSVP [Enter]***

Enter new value for UCSVP <1>: ***0 [Enter]***

Double-click: ***inside the lower right viewport to make it active***

Notice the UCS X-Y plane becomes parallel to the front surface of the object. You can also see this change in the isometric view shown in the upper right viewport.

Notice also that a small ViewCube shows in the active viewport.

Click: ***the small downward arrow near the small ViewCube in the lower right viewport (near Unn...)***

Short-cut menu selections appear as shown in Figure 11.18. The UCS used in the viewport is unnamed.

Figure 11.18

Do not change the UCS in the lower right viewport.

Tip: *If you have trouble lining up the views, use the Pan command to make them line up approximately while you are working. To line them up exactly, use MVSETUP and use the Align option. Select Horizontal or Vertical alignment. Then pick a point in one viewport (using Snap to Endpoint or some other object snap) and pick a point that should align in the other viewport (again using an object snap). The view in the viewport that you pick second will be shifted to align with the point you selected in the first viewport. You can use Pan in the first viewport to position the view where you want it before you begin the MVSETUP command.*

Tip: *The scale in the isometric viewport need not match the scale in the top, front, and side orthographic views. Isometric views are often shown at a different, visually pleasing scale.*

Double-click: to make the upper left viewport active

Your screen should look similar to Figure 11.19.

Selection Cycling button

Figure 11.19

Now the current UCS X-Y plane is parallel to the top view in the upper left viewport. The default AutoCAD XY-plane is considered to be the *plan view* of the WCS. A plan view is basically a top view, which may sound familiar if you have worked with architectural drawings.

Next, you will add a cylinder to the drawing. Later, you will turn the cylinder into a hole using the Subtract command.

Creating Cylinders

You create cylinders by specifying the center of the circular shape in the XY-plane and the radius or diameter, then giving the height in the Z-direction of the current UCS. The Elliptical option allows you to specify an elliptical shape instead of circular and then give the height.

Instead of giving the height, you can use the Cylinder command's Center of other end option to specify the center of the other end by clicking or typing coordinates.

Set layer **MYMODEL** as the current layer.

Click: **Cylinder button** *from the ribbon Home tab, Modeling panel*

Specify center point for base of cylinder or [Elliptical] <0,0,0>: *4,4 [Enter]*

Specify radius for base of cylinder or [Diameter]: *.375 [Enter]*

Specify height of cylinder or [Center of other end]: *3 [Enter]*

Tip: *The PLAN command produces a view looking directly onto the current UCS.*

Tip: *If you do not specify a Z-coordinate, it is assumed to be your current elevation, which should be 0.*

Selection Cycling

When two solids overlap as the box and cylinder do, it can be difficult to select the internal one. Selection cycling is often useful when working in 3D as objects often overlap, which makes selecting difficult.

The Selection Cycling button located on the status bar makes it easy to click the object you want.

There are two ways that selection cycling operates. One way is to show a list of possible objects when an ambiguous area is clicked. The other way is to use a keyboard short-cut (Shift+spacebar+click) to toggle between the items on the screen when selecting in an area where there are multiple objects. Selection cycling can also be turned off.

One way to control the selection cycling mode used is the Drafting Settings dialog box.

 Right-click: **Selection Cycling button** on the status bar to show the short-cut menu

Click: **Settings**

The Drafting Settings dialog box appears with the Selection Cycling tab uppermost as shown in Figure 11.20.

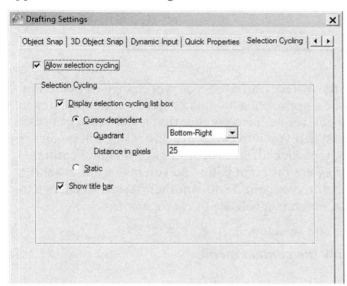

Figure 11.20

> On your own, verify that Allow selection cycling is checked and that Display selection cycling list box is checked.

You can set the list to either appear at the cursor or at a static location.

> Leave these settings as you see in Figure 11.20.

Click: **OK** (to close the Drafting Settings dialog box)

Click: **Selection Cycling button** from the status bar to turn it on

Click: **to make the lower right viewport active**

Click: **on the top line of the box where the lines of the box and cylinder meet**

Move your cursor over items in the Selection list (Figure 11.21). Notice that an object becomes highlighted on the screen when it is the active item on the selection list.

Try the keyboard shortcut on your own. Press **[Shift]+[spacebar]** to toggle between the different entities near your cursor location.

On your own, use one of these methods to select the cylinder..

Figure 11.21

Now that you have the cylinder selected, you will change its color. For many drawings the best approach is to make objects on separate layers and use the layer to determine the color, but that is not always the case with solid modeling. When you join two solids, the result will be on the layer of the first item clicked, unless you change it later. Features are easier to see if they are different colors, so you may want to set the color for an object before you join it with another object. To change the color of the cylinder, which you will use to create a hole,

While the cylinder is still selected,

Right-click: **to show the context menu**

Click: Properties

Click: **Red** from the Properties dialog box Color list

Click: **[X] to close** the Properties dialog box

Press: **[Esc]** to unselect the cylinder

 Click: **to turn off Selection Cycling button** from the status bar

The cylinder should be changed to the new color. Your screen should look like Figure 11.22.

Tip: *You can press [Ctrl]-1 to pop up the Properties dialog box.*

Tip: *You can change the color of a single face of a model by using the Solidedit command and then selecting the Face and Color options. You can use a similar method to recolor single edges.*

Isolines button

Figure 11.22

Now you have a box and a cylinder, each occupying the same space. Although they could not do so in the real world, in the drawing data base these two objects are both occupying the volume inside the cylinder.

Setting Isolines

Before you continue, you will set the variable called Isolines. This variable controls the wireframe appearance of the cylinders, spheres, and tori (3D "donuts") on the screen. You can set the value for Isolines between 4 and 2047, to control the number of tessellation lines used to represent rounded surfaces. Displayed on a curved surface, tessellation lines help you better visualize the surface. The number of *tessellation lines* that you set will be shown on the screen, representing the contoured surface of the shape. The higher the value for Isolines, the better the screen appearance of rounded wireframe shapes will be. The default setting of 4 looks poor but saves time in drawing. The highest setting may look best, but more time is needed for the calculations, especially for a complex drawing.

You will set the value to 12. You can change the setting for Isolines and regenerate the drawing at any time. You can use the Isolines command from the View tab, Visual Styles panel. You will use the Regenall command to regenerate all of the viewports to show the new setting for Isolines.

> Command: ***ISOLINES [Enter]***
>
> Enter new value for ISOLINES <4>: *12 [Enter]*
>
> Command: ***REGENALL [Enter]***

The cylinder should be redrawn with more tessellation lines, similar to Figure 11.23.

Tip: *The Facetres variable adjusts the smoothness of shaded objects and objects from which hidden lines have been removed. Its value can range from .01 to 10. Viewres controls the number of straight segments used to draw circles and arcs on your screen. Viewres can be set between 1 and 20000. You can type these commands at the command prompt and set their values higher to improve the appearance of rendered objects.*

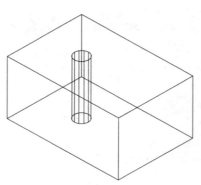

Figure 11.23

Next you will use the Boolean operator Subtract to remove the cylinder from the box so that it forms a hole.

Building Complex Solid Models

You can create complex solid models with Boolean operators, which find the *union* (addition), *difference* (subtraction), and *intersection* (common area) of two or more sets. These operations are named for Irish logician and mathematician George Boole, who formulated the basic principles of set theory. In the AutoCAD software the sets can be 2D areas (called regions), they can be surfaces (like an empty shell) or they can be 3D solid models. Often *Venn diagrams* are used to represent sets and Boolean operations. Figure 11.24 will help you understand how the Union, Subtract, and Intersection commands work. The order in which you select the objects is important only when you're subtracting (i.e., A subtract B is different from B subtract A). Keep in mind that when objects are on different layers, the solid resulting from a Boolean operation will reside on the layer of the first item clicked.

A Union B   A Subtract B   A Intersect B

Figure 11.24

Next you will remove the volume of the cylinder from the box, thereby forming a solid model with a hole in it. You will use the Subtract command from the Home tab, Solids Editing panel (you can also select it from the Solids tab, Booleans panel).

⬚ *Click:* **Subtract button**

Select solids, surfaces and regions to subtract from...

Select objects: *click the 3D box and then press [Enter]*

Select solids, surfaces and regions to subtract...

Select objects: *click the cylinder and then press [Enter]*

The resulting solid model is a rectangular prism with a hole through it. If you selected the items in the wrong order (i.e., clicked the cylinder and subtracted the box from it) the result would be a null solid model or one that has no volume. If you clicked both the box and the cylinder and then pressed [Enter], the command would not work unless you selected something else to subtract. If you make a mistake, you can back up by typing U [Enter] at the command prompt to use the Undo command and then try again.

Note that you can now see that the cylinder has formed a hole in the block. The color inside the hole is red and the rest of the block is blue. Your drawing in the upper right viewport should look like Figure 11.25.

Figure 11.25

You will make the isometric view in the upper right use the wireframe appearance. Objects are easier to select when they are not shaded. Also, overlapping solids are much easier to see when they are not shaded.

Using the Viewport Controls

By default, near the upper left of the active viewport is a series of labels, called the Viewport control. These labels also act as menus used to maximize the viewport, set to a named view, or change the visual style.

Make the **upper right viewport current** if it is not already.

*Click: **on Conceptual** from the Viewport control to show the Visual Styles short-cut menu as shown in Figure 11.26*

*Click: **Wireframe***

The upper right viewport changes to wireframe display.

Figure 11.26

Tip: *If your hole formed by subtracting the cylinder does not go all of the way through the 3D box, this may be because the height of both parts is exactly the same. At times, this will leave a thin surface over the top of the hole. If this has happened, undo the Subtract operation. Click on the cylinder and use its grips to drag it to extend beyond the box. When the cylinder is subtracted, the excess portion will be removed during subtraction.*

Tip: *The Viewport controls may be hard to see if you are using a white background and you have not set them to a darker color. Use the Options dialog box Display tab. Pick Colors... and select a medium color for the Viewport control.*

Save your drawing, *block.dwg*, before continuing.

Saving your work after you've completed a major step and before you go on to the next step is useful. That way, if you want to return to the preceding step, you can open the previous version of the drawing, discarding the changes that you have made. This is useful when a sequence cannot easily be undone.

Creating Wedges

Now you will add a Wedge primitive to the drawing and then subtract it from the main block. The Wedge command has two options: Corner (the default) and Center. Drawing a wedge by specifying the corner first lets you draw the rectangular base of the wedge, and prompts you for two points that define the diagonal of the rectangular base. The height you enter starts at the first point specified for the base and gets smaller in the X direction toward the second point. The Center option asks you to specify the center point of the wedge you want to draw.

 Click: **Wedge button**

Specify first corner of wedge or [CEnter]: *8,6 [Enter]*

Specify corner or [Cube/Length]: *6,2 [Enter]*

Specify height or [2Point] <0.5000>: *3 [Enter]*

Now you will use the Boolean operators to subtract the wedge from the object.

Click: **Subtract button**

Select solids, surfaces and regions to subtract from...

Select objects: *click the box with the hole and press [Enter]*

Select solids, surfaces and regions to subtract...

Select objects: *click the wedge and press [Enter]*

With the wedge subtracted, your drawing should look like that in Figure 11.27.

Figure 11.27

Next, switch to the Hidden visual style to remove hidden lines from the upper right view.

Be sure that the upper right viewport is active.

*Click: **Wireframe** from the View control to show the menu*

*Click: **Hidden** as shown in Figure 11.28.*

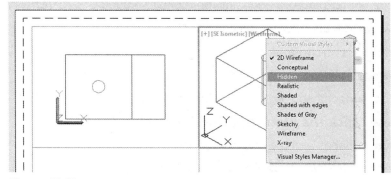

Figure 11.28

The 3D object will appear on your screen with the hidden lines removed. The shape in the upper right viewport should look like that in Figure 11.29.

Figure 11.29

You will continue to work with wireframe representation for the isometric view.

*Click: **Hidden** from the View control to show the menu*

*Click: **Wireframe** to return to that representation*

Creating Cones

The cone primitive creates a solid cone, defined by a circular or elliptical base and tapering to a point perpendicular to the base. It is similar to the cylinder primitive that you have already used. The circular or elliptical base of the cone is always created in the XY-plane of the current UCS. The height is along the Z-axis of the current UCS.

Now you will create a cone using the cone primitive and then subtract it from the block to make a countersink for the hole. It will have a circular base and a negative height. Specifying a negative height causes the cone to be drawn in the opposite direction from a positive height (i.e., in the negative Z-direction).

Click: **Cone button**

Specify center point of base or [3P/2P/Ttr/Elliptical]: *4,4,3 [Enter]*

Specify base radius or [Diameter] <1.0000>: *.625 [Enter]*

Specify height or [2Point/Axis endpoint/Top radius] <3.0000>: *–.75 [Enter]*

On your own, change the color for the **cone** to **Green**.

Next, subtract the cone to make a countersink for the hole.

Click: **Subtract button**

Select solids, surfaces and regions to subtract from...

Select objects: *click the block and press [Enter]*

Select solids, surfaces and regions to subtract...

Select objects: *click the cone and press [Enter]*

Click: **Xray** *from the View control*

The upper right viewport now displays a transparent view of the shaded object. Your screen should look like Figure 11.30.

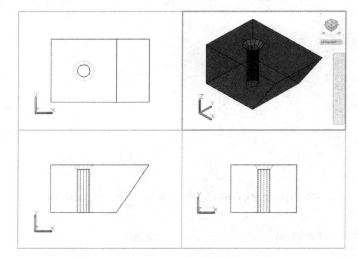

Figure 11.30

Next, you will use the cylinder primitive to add a rounded surface to the top of the block.

Creating User Coordinate Systems

As you have seen, you can have more than one coordinate system. The object is stored in the WCS, which stays fixed, but you can use the UCS command to create a User Coordinate System oriented any way you want. The UCS command allows you to position a User Coordinate System anywhere with respect to the WCS. You can also use it to change the origin point for the coordinate system and to save and restore named coordinate systems. You will create a new UCS that aligns with the left side of the block. This will make it easy to select back edges,

Make sure the **upper right viewport** is active.

Right-click: ***Object Snap button***

Click: ***Settings to show*** *the Drafting Settings dialog box*

Click: ***Clear All*** *from the Object Snap tab*

Click: ***Endpoint*** *and* ***Midpoint***

Click: ***OK***

Click: ***Wireframe*** *from the View control*

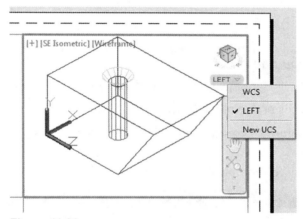 *Click:* ***3 Point button*** *from the Home tab, Coordinates panel*

Specify new origin point <0,0,0>: ***target endpoint 1 in Figure 11.31***

Specify point on positive portion of X-axis <3.0000,2.0000,0.0000>: ***target endpoint 2 (the back corner)***

Specify point on positive-Y portion of the UCS XY plane <1.0000,2.0000,0.0000>: ***target endpoint 3***

Now the UCS is aligned with the left surface of the object.

Figure 11.31

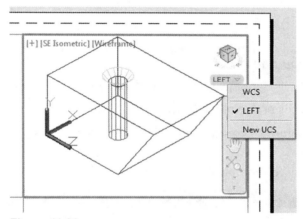

Figure 11.32

You will save the new UCS that you created parallel to the left side of the part and give it a name so that you can select it again later.

Command: ***UCS [Enter]***

Current ucs name: *NO NAME*

Specify origin of UCS or [Face/NAmed/OBject/Previous/View/World/X/Y/Z/ZAxis] <World>: ***NA [Enter]***

Enter an option [Restore/Save/Delete/?]: ***S [Enter]***

Enter name to save current UCS or [?]: ***LEFT [Enter]***

Notice the new UCS named LEFT appears on the Named UCS drop down list near the ViewCube. You can click on the named UCS (LEFT) to show the short-cut menu shown in Figure 11.32. In addition to typing the UCS command as you did above, you can also select New UCS from this menu.

Next, you will use the Cylinder button and choose to draw a cylinder by specifying its center. Refer to Figure 11.33 for the points to select.

You will use the object snaps for Midpoint and Endpoint to aid in selecting locations from the object.

Figure 11.33

> On your own, make sure that running object snap is turned on. Verify that the upper right viewport is active.

Click: **Cylinder button**

Specify center point for base of cylinder or [Elliptical] <0,0,0>: ***click the midpoint of the back top line A***

Specify radius for base of cylinder or [Diameter]: ***click endpoint B***

Specify height or [2Point/Axis endpoint]: *1 [Enter]*

> On your own, use **pan** and **zoom** if necessary to fit the model in the upper right viewport.

Your drawing should look like the one shown in Figure 11.34.

Figure 11.34

Next, use the Boolean operator Union to join the cylinder to the block.

Click: **Union button**

Select objects: *click the new cylinder and the block [Enter]*

Click: **Conceptual** *from the View control*

Save your completed *block.dwg* drawing.

The joined objects are shown in Figure 11.35.

Figure 11.35

Plotting Solid Models from Paper Space

Change to **paper space** on your own by typing PS [Enter] at the command prompt, using the Model/Paper button, or double-clicking outside the viewport borders.

When you have done so, the paper space icon appears.

Next you will insert a simple title block like you created in Tutorial 5. *TitleBlockA.dwg* is provided with the datafiles for the book.

Click: **Insert** *from the Insert tab, Block panel*

Click: **Browse...**

Navigate to your *Datafiles2012* directory and select **TitleBlockA.dwg**.

Figure 11.36

From the Insert dialog box, use **Specify On-screen, Scale 1.0000** and **Angle 0** as shown in Figure 11.36

Click: OK

You return to your drawing for the remaining prompt.

Specify insertion point or [Basepoint/Scale/Rotate]: *use Object Snap Endpoint to target the lower left corner of the lower left viewport*

The titleblock appears in your drawing as shown in Figure 11.37.

On your own, complete the title block with your information.

Save your drawing.

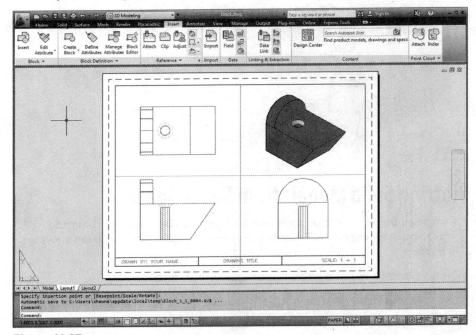

Figure 11.37

Next, set the top, front, and side views to the Hidden visual style.

Double-click: inside the top left viewport to make it active

Click: Hidden from the View control

On your own, change the two lower viewports to use the Hidden visual style.

Three viewports should now show views with the back lines removed. Use the techniques you learned in Tutorial 5 to plot your drawing.

On your own, switch to **paper space**. **Plot** the drawing limits at a scale of 1=1.

The orthographic views that you have drawn should be exactly half-size on the finished plot because the Viewport Scale was 1:2. Your plotted drawing should be similar to that in Figure 11.38.

Figure 11.38

Saving Your Multiview Setup as a Template

Next you will switch back to model space, so that when the template is saved, the 3D model space will be active.

*Double-click: **inside the top right viewport** to switch to model space inside that viewport*

The UCS icons are restored to all the viewports.

On your own, **freeze** layer **VPort**.

The magenta viewport borders, but you can still use the viewports and switch to them.

Now you will erase the object and save the basic settings to use as a template for new 3D drawings. Type the alias for Erase.

*Command: **E [Enter]***

Select objects: ***click the solid block object you have drawn***

Select objects: ***[Enter]***

It is erased from all viewports.

> **Tip:** *Switch to paper space and use Zoom All if necessary so that the paper area fills the graphics window. Be sure to switch back to model space.*

> **Tip:** *If you want to see the viewports, you can thaw the layer VPORT and make it a non-plotting layer, so that it will not print.*

Figure 11.39

On your own, in the upper right viewport, restore the World Coordinate System, by clicking WCS as shown in Figure 11.39.

Next you will use Save As to create a template file named *soltemplate.dwt*.

Click: **Save As**

Click: **AutoCAD Drawing Template .dwt** *in the Files of Type area*

Name the file **soltemplate.dwt.**

Description: **3D template with 4 viewports**

Select: **English** *as the measurement units*

Click: **OK**

Click: **to close the current drawing**

Creating Solid Models with Extrude and Revolve

Next, you will learn how to create new solid objects using the extrusion and revolution methods.

Click: **New button**

Use the drawing *proto-3D.dwt* provided with your datafiles or *soltemplate.dwt* that you just created.

Use **Save As** and name the new drawing **extrusn.dwg**.

Make sure layer MYMODEL is the current layer.

Click: **the upper right viewport to make it active. Select the WCS from the View control for this viewport.**

Set **Grid** and **Snap** to **.5** each and turn them on.

Your screen should be similar to Figure 11.40.

Figure 11.40

Tip: *Each viewport can have a different grid setting. In later figures, the grid is turned off to make it easier to see.*

Because you started your new drawing from the solid modeling template, the viewports already exist. The viewports themselves are on layer VPORT, which is currently frozen. You can still make each viewport active by clicking inside it.

You will draw the H shape shown in Figure 11.41 using the 2D Polyline command. The coordinates have been provided to make selecting the points to match the tutorial easier for you.

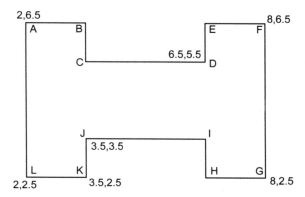

Figure 11.41

Click: **Polyline button** *from the Home tab, Draw panel*

    Specify start point: ***click point A***

Current line-width is 0.0000

Specify next point or [Arc/Halfwidth/Length/Undo/Width]: ***click points B-L in order***

Specify next point or [Arc/Close/Halfwidth/Length/Undo/Width]: ***C [Enter]***

You will set the fillet radius to 0.25 and then use the Fillet command's Polyline option to round all the corners of the polyline. Use the alias for the Fillet command.

Command: ***F [Enter]***

Select first object or [Undo/Polyline/Radius/Trim/Multiple]: ***R [Enter]***

Specify fillet radius <0.0000>: ***.25 [Enter]***

Select first object or [Undo/Polyline/Radius/Trim/Multiple]: ***P [Enter]***

Select 2D polyline: ***click the polyline you just created***
12 lines were filleted

Tip: *If you did not close your object by typing C, you will get the message 11 lines were filleted. In this case, undo the last two commands and redraw your H shape, closing the polyline with the Close option.*

Tip: *If the upper right viewport is not shaded, make it active and then set its visual style to a shaded one. Be sure to make the top left viewport active when finished.*

On your own, use the Snap spacing to **draw the two circles** shown in Figure 11.42.

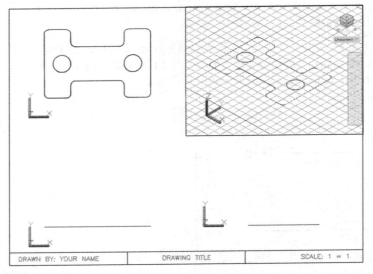

Figure 11.42

Region Modeling

You can also use the Boolean operators with the closed 2D shapes made by circles, ellipses, and closed polylines. You can convert closed 2D shapes to *regions*, which essentially are 2D models, or areas. Expand the Draw panel to select the Region button. Region modeling and extrusion can be combined effectively to create complex shapes.

Turn **Snap off** on your own to make selecting easier.

Click: **Region button** *from the Home tab, Draw panel*

Select objects: *use implied Crossing to click the polyline and both circles; then press [Enter]*

3 loops extracted

3 regions created

Now you are ready to subtract the two circles from the polyline region to form holes in the area.

Click: **Subtract button**

Select solids, surfaces and regions to subtract from...

Select objects: *click the polyline region and press [Enter]*

Select solids, surfaces and regions to subtract...

Select objects: *click the circles and press [Enter]*

Now there is only one region, which has two holes in it. Notice that in the shaded view in the upper right viewport, the circles now appear as holes in a shaded flat region, as shown in Figure 11.43.

Tip: *Using the Boundary or Pedit commands to join objects into a closed polyline is an effective way to create 2D shapes to extrude. You can also use the Join command to connect line segments.*

Figure 11.43

Extruding a Shape

Now you can extrude this shape to create a 3D object. Extrusion is the process of forcing material through a shaped opening to create a long strip that has the shape of the opening. The Extrude command works similarly to form a 3D shape. Closed 2D shapes such as splines, ellipses, circles, donuts, polygons, regions, and polylines can be given a height, or extruded to create solids.

Polylines must have at least three vertices in order to be extruded. You can specify a taper angle if you want the top of the extrusion to be a different size than the bottom. You can use the Path option to extrude a shape along a path curve that you have previously drawn. Path curves can be lines, splines, arcs, elliptical arcs, polylines, circles, or ellipses. (You may encounter problems when trying to extrude along path curves with a large amount of curvature and where the resulting solid would overlap itself.)

The Mode option is used to control whether a solid or surface is created by the extrusion. The variable, Surfacemodelingmode controls the type of surface created (either NURBS or procedural).

The Direction options lets you specify two points to give the length and direction of the extrusion with two specified points. The points cannot be in the same plane as the shape to be extruded.

The Path option lets you select an object to extrude the shape along. When you select the path, it automatically locates to the centroid of the profile shape you selected to extrude.

Taper angle lets you angle the extrusion inward or outward as it is formed. A positive number causes the taper to be inward; a negative number causes the taper to be outward.

The Expression option of the Extrude command allows you to enter an equation for the height of the extrusion. Use the symbols below to enter expressions:

Operator	Function
( )	Group expressions
^	Exponent
*,	Multiply
/	Divide
+	Add
–	Subtract

Read more about the details of any of the commands, using the Help feature.

The Extrude button appears on the Modeling panel. You will use the Mode option to check that the extrusion will create a solid, and then extrude the region you created in the last steps.

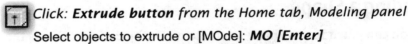 *Click:* **Extrude button** *from the Home tab, Modeling panel*

Select objects to extrude or [MOde]: **MO [Enter]**

Closed profiles creation mode [SOlid/SUrface] <Solid>: **[Enter]**

Select objects to extrude or [MOde]: **click the region and press [Enter]**

Specify height of extrusion or
[Direction/Path/Taper angle/Expression] <0>: **1 [Enter]**

The extruded solid should look like Figure 11.44.

On your own, **save** your drawing, *extrusn.dwt.*

Figure 11.44

Next you will save the drawing with a new name and use it to create a solid using revolution techniques.

 Click: **SaveAs button**

Browse to your */Work* directory and save the new drawing with the name **revolutn.dwg**.

Check that the name of the drawing shown in the title bar is revolutn.dwg.

Erase the previous solid created by extrusion.

Make sure that Snap is on and that Object Snap is turned off.

Creating Solids by Revolution

Creating a solid model by revolution is similar in some ways to creating an extrusion. You can use it to sweep a closed 2D shape about a circular path to create a symmetrical solid model that is basically circular in cross section. You can revolve closed polylines, polygons, circles, ellipses, closed splines, donuts, and regions to form solid objects. You can also use revolution to create surfaces.

Use the 2D Polyline command on your own to draw a closed shape like that shown in Figure 11.45.

Figure 11.45

Now you will revolve the polyline about an axis to create a solid model. You don't need to draw the axis line; you can specify it by two points. The Revolve button is on the Home tab, Modeling panel.

 Click: **Revolve button**

Select objects to revolve or [MOde]: *click the polyline*

Select objects to revolve or [MOde]:*[Enter]*

Specify axis start point or define axis by [Object/X/Y/Z] <Object>: *click one endpoint of the bottom line*

Specify endpoint of axis: *click the other endpoint*

Specify angle of revolution or [STart angle/Reverse/EXpression] <360>: *[Enter]*

Aligning the Views

Next, you will use the Pan Realtime command and Mvsetup to help align the views in the lower left, lower right, and upper left viewports.

Click: **the lower left viewport to make it active**

Click: **Pan Realtime button or use the mouse scroll wheel to pan**

On your own, **pan** the view so that the solid appears centered in the lower left viewport.

Press: **[Esc]** *if needed to exit the Pan command*

Your screen should now be similar to Figure 11.46.

Figure 11.46

Next, you will type the command Mvsetup and align the lower right and upper left views relative to the lower left viewport using Object Snap Quadrant. Use Figure 11.46 to help in making the selections.

On your own, be sure that Object Snap is turned on, with **Quadrant** selected.

Type: **MVSETUP [Enter]**

Enter an option [Align/Create/Scale viewports/Options /Title block/Undo]: *A [Enter]*

Enter an option [Angled/Horizontal/Vertical alignment /Rotate view/Undo]: *H [Enter]*

Specify basepoint: *select point 1, using the AutoSnap Quadrant marker to help*

Specify point in viewport to be panned: *select the lower right viewport and point 2, using the AutoSnap Quadrant marker*

The view in the lower right viewport should align with the view in the lower left viewport relative to the points you selected. Continue with the command to align the upper left viewport vertically.

Enter an option [Angled/Horizontal/Vertical alignment /Rotate view/Undo]: *V [Enter]*

Specify basepoint: *select point 3 using the AutoSnap Quadrant marker to help*

Specify point in viewport to be panned: *select the upper left viewport and point 4, using the AutoSnap Quadrant marker to help*

On your own, use Zoom Extents and Pan Realtime to fit the pictorial view in the upper right viewport.

Save your drawing.

When you are done, your drawing should look similar to Figure 11.47.

Tip: *If the V (vertical) option line is not active, then press the return button to reactivate MVSETUP and choose align again.*

Figure 11.47

Click: **Save As**

Name your new drawing **intersect.dwg**.

On your own, **erase** the solid model that you just revolved.

Using the Boolean Operator Intersection

Like the Union and Subtract Boolean operators, Intersection lets you create complex shapes from simpler shapes. Intersection finds only the area common to the two or more solid models or regions that you have selected. You will create the shape shown in Figure 11.48 by creating two solid models and finding their intersection.

Figure 11.48

First, you will select to work in the lower left viewport and create a UCS parallel to this viewport.

Click: **the lower left viewport to make it active**

Click: **View** *from the Home tab, Coordinates panel*

A UCS is created parallel to the view in the lower left viewport. Notice the X-Y plane is now parallel to the view.

On your own, set the **grid** to **.5** and turn it **on** in the lower left viewport.

Next, you will create the shape of a surface in the front view that you will extrude to create the angled face and notch. You will use the Polyline command to create a polyline that defines the shape of the object in the front view.

Click: **Polyline button**

Specify start point: *2.5, 0 [Enter]*

Current line-width is 0.0000

Specify next point or [Arc/Close/Halfwidth/Length/Undo/Width]: *2.5,1.5 [Enter]*

Specify next point or [Arc/Close/Halfwidth/Length/Undo/Width]: *3.5,1.5 [Enter]*

Specify next point or [Arc/Close/Halfwidth/Length/Undo/Width]: *3.5,1 [Enter]*

Specify next point or [Arc/Close/Halfwidth/Length/Undo/Width]: *5,1 [Enter]*

Specify next point or [Arc/Close/Halfwidth/Length/Undo/Width]: *5,1.5 [Enter]*

Specify next point or [Arc/Close/Halfwidth/Length/Undo/Width]: *5.5,1.5 [Enter]*

Specify next point or [Arc/Close/Halfwidth/Length/Undo/Width]: *7,0 [Enter]*

Specify next point or [Arc/Close/Halfwidth/Length/Undo/Width]: *C [Enter]*

After you've drawn the shape of the object in the front view, you may need to Pan so that you can see it in the top and side views.

When you have finished, your drawing will look like the one shown in Figure 11.49.

Figure 11.49

Now extrude this shape to form a solid model.

Click: **Extrude button**

Select objects to extrude or [MOde]: *click the polyline [Enter]*

Specify height of extrusion or [Direction/Path/Taper angle /Expression] <-4.5000>: *–3 [Enter]*

The solid model shown in Figure 11.50 has been created. Next, you will make the upper right viewport active and enlarge that viewport to fill the drawing area. (Often when you are modeling it is useful to disable the paper space layouts temporarily and work only in the model view.)

Click: **the upper right viewport** *to make it active*

Click: **to turn the Grid and Snap off** *in the upper right viewport*

Tip: *The Delobj variable controls whether the 2D object is automatically deleted after being extruded or revolved. A value of 1 means delete the object that was used to create the other object (the circle that created the cylinder, for example); a value of 0 means do not delete the object. The default AutoCAD setting is 1 (delete).*

Click: **Maximize viewport button** *from the status bar*

Your screen should show a single view of the object.

Click: **Zoom Object button** *from the Zoom flyout*

Select objects: **click on the extruded shape**

The viewport and zoomed object fill the screen as in Figure 11.50.

Tip: *You can also use the [+]/ [-] from the Viewport control to maximize and minimize the viewport..*

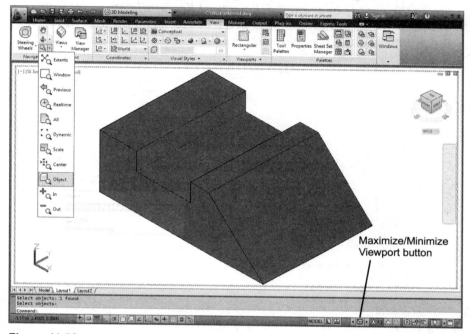

Figure 11.50

Command: *[Enter] to restart the Zoom command*

Specify corner of window, enter a scale factor (nX or nXP), or [All/Center/ Dynamic/Extents/Previous/Scale/Window/Object] <real time>: **.8x [Enter]**

The object is zoomed to 80% of the previous size Next you will create a new unnamed UCS parallel to the vertical back face of the object.

Click: **on the UCSicon** *to activate its grips*

On your own, use object snap Endpoint and drag the UCS icon to the front corner of the shape; then drag the X axis and Y axis to align with the back surface as shown in Figure 11.51.

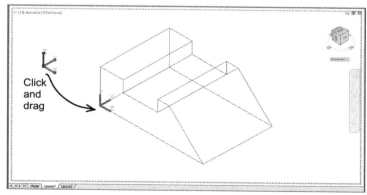

Figure 11.51

Next you will create the circular shape of the object.

Click: **Object Snap Tracking button** *from the status bar to turn it on.*

Verify that object snap **midpoint** is turned on.

Click: **Circle button**

Specify center point for circle or [3P/2P/TTR (tan tan radius)]: *hover the cursor over the bottom line until you acquire its midpoint; then hover the cursor over the back vertical line until you acquire its midpoint. Once both midpoints are tracked, position the cursor at the intersection of the two tracking lines and click (see Figure 11.52)*

Figure 11.52

Specify radius of circle or [Diameter]: *0.75 [Enter]*

The circle is drawn at the center of the back surface. You will use the Extrude command to elongate the circle into a cylinder.

Click: **Extrude button**

Select objects to extrude or [MOde]: *click the circle [Enter]*

Specify height of extrusion or [Direction/Path/Taper angle/Expression] <-3.0000>: *7 [Enter] (or move the mouse to drag the extrusion to a length past the right end of the solid)*

Your shapes should look like Figure 11.53.

Figure 11.53

Experiment by typing DELOBJ at the command prompt and changing the setting to 0. Create a polyline and extrude it in one direction using a taper angle. The original polyline will remain. Select it again and extrude it in the other direction using the same taper angle. This way you can create a surface that tapers in both directions.

Now you are ready to use the Intersection command to create a new solid model from the overlapping portions of the two solid models that you have drawn.

> Click: **Intersect button**

> Select objects: ***click the cylinder and the extruded polyline [Enter]***

> Use the viewport control to change to **Conceptual** shading.

> **Save** your *intersect.dwg* drawing. *Turn off Object Snap Tracking.*

The solid model is updated. Your drawing should look like Figure 11.54.

> **Close** *intersect.dwg.*

Figure 11.54

Creating Surface Models

Surfaces behave much like solids but are basically a shell, like a paper cup. Surface modeling tools are useful for irregularly shaped contours. You can convert the following objects into surfaces by using the CONVTOSURFACE command: 2D solids, regions, bodies, open polylines (with thickness and zero-width), lines with thickness, arcs with thickness, and planar 3D faces. To create a surface object from a solid you explode the solid.

Once you have created a surface you can use the editing commands such as union and subtract to create more complex surfaces. You can create a solid from a surface using the THICKEN command.

The AutoCAD software provides two types of surface modeling: procedural surfaces or NURBS. Which type is in use is controlled by the Surfacemodelingmode variable. Setting Surfacemodelingmode to 0 creates procedural surfaces during surface modeling commands. Setting it to 1 create NURBS surfaces instead. (You can convert from procedural surfaces to NURBS surfaces using the CONVTONURBS command.) NURBS surfaces may allow you more control over individual vertices making it easier to reshape the surfaces you create.

Start a new drawing from ***contrdat.dwg***, which was provided with the datafiles.

Name your new drawing ***surf1.dwg***.

The Viewport control shows the visual style Shaded with Edges.

*Click: **Surface tab** from the ribbon*

At this point your screen should show contours like Figure 11.55.

Figure 11.55

On the screen are 2D splines representing contours (lines of equal elevation on a contour map). The splines are at different heights along the Z-axis. The bottom line is at Z 200, the next at Z 220, the next at Z 240, and so on. You can create these contour lines on your own by drawing splines (or polylines) through your data points, joining points of equal elevation. Then use Move to relocate the resulting spline. Specify a base point of (0,0,0) and a displacement of (0,0,200) (or whatever your elevation may be).

Tip: *You can use the Elevation command to set the Z height at which new drawing objects will be created as you draw.*

Using Loft

Loft creates a surface or a solid between contours. These can also be the existing edges of a surface or solid. You must have at least two edges to create a loft.

Next you will create a loft surface (often called "lofting") between contour lines in the drawing.

*Click: **Loft button***

Current wire frame density: ISOLINES=4, Closed profiles creation mode = Surface

Select cross sections in lofting order or [POint/Join multiple edges/ MOde]: ***click contour lines 1 through 6 in order [Enter]***

6 cross sections selected

Enter an option [Guides/Path/Cross sections only/Settings] <Cross sections only>: ***[Enter]***

The lofted surface is created as shown in Figure 11.56.

Figure 11.56

Creating a Patch (SURFPATCH)

The top surface is still open. Loft creates a surface between contours so it has no way to form the very top. You can use the Surfpatch command to create a surface like a cap, using just a single closed loop.

Click: **Patch button**

> Continuity = G0 - position, bulge magnitude = 0.5

Select surface edges to patch or <Select Curves>: **click the top edge [Enter]**

Press Enter to accept the patch surface or [CONtinuity/Bulge magnitude/ CONStrain geometry]: **[Enter]**

The patch appears as a surface over the top loop as shown in Figure 11.57. Next you will use its handles to change the appearance of the patch.

Pick on the
Patch surface

Figure 11.57

Click: **the Patch surface** to show its editing features

Figure 11.58

The *3D gizmo* as shown in Figure 11.59 provides quick editing for surfaces and solids similar in a way to using grips with 2D objects. Like using grips, you can right-click the 3D gizmo to show the context menu and make selections from it.

The 3D UCS icon uses red associated with the x-axis, green with the y-axis, and blue with the z-axis. The 3D gizmo uses the same colors to identify the x, y, and z directions. Click and drag on one of the colored features to use the gizmo.

3D Move Gizmo   3D Rotate Gizmo   3D Scale Gizmo

Figure 11.59

Notice that if you use the gizmo to move the top surface patch, you will see a message "One or more surfaces are associated with a defining curve, surface, or parametric equation." You see the message because the patch was defined by the top edge of the lofted surface. You have the option to continue and break the associativity, or to cancel. If so, click Cancel.

> *Click the small blue downward arrow to show the Continuity options as shown in Figure 11.60*

> Click: *Tangent (G1)*

The patch surface curves to become tangent to the lofted surface. These continuity options were available when you created the patch surface, but as you have just seen, you can still access them easily after the surface has been created.

Figure 11.60

Creating Mesh Models

You can also use the AutoCAD software to create mesh models. Mesh models and surface models are different types of objects and have different editing features. Many 3D objects can be converted to mesh models using the Smooth Object (MESHSMOOTH) command.

AutoCAD mesh models are composed of a faceted polygonal mesh that approximates curved surfaces. Mesh modeling can be more difficult to use than solid modeling and provides less information about the object. The reason is that only the surfaces and not the interior volumes of the object are described in the drawing database. You must edit the mesh that creates surface models differently. However, mesh modeling is well suited to applications such as modeling 3D terrain for civil engineering applications.

In general you should not mix solid modeling, surface modeling, and wireframe modeling for the same model, as you can't edit them in the same ways to create a cohesive single structure. Select the single method that is best for your application.

Because using Box, Wedge, Pyramid, Cone, Sphere, Dome, Dish, Torus, Revolved Mesh, and Tabulated Mesh is basically similar to the method you used earlier in the tutorial to create solid models, these tools are not covered here. Instead, on your own, refer to AutoCAD Help for further information about creating these shapes.

Next, you will learn to create a 3D Mesh, an Edge Mesh, and a Ruled Mesh. Understanding how to create these objects will allow you to create a wider variety of shapes that are especially useful for modeling 3D terrain, such as mountainous topography.

> **Erase** the two surfaces that you created leaving only the contour lines (or start a new drawing from the datafile, *contrdat.dwg*.
>
> If needed, change the viewpoint and use Zoom to see the lines clearly.

The commands to create meshes can be selected from the ribbon Mesh tab. When you have finished, your screen should look like Figure 11.61.

Figure 11.61

Creating a Ruled Mesh

Using the Ruled Surface selection, you can create a surface mesh between two graphical objects. The objects can be lines, points, arcs, circles, ellipses, elliptical arcs, 2D polylines, 3D polylines, or splines. The objects can either be both open (like lines) or both closed (like circles). Points can be connected to either open or closed objects.

Controlling Mesh Density

The mesh comprising a surface is defined in terms of a *matrix* of M and N vertices; M and N specify the column and row locations of vertices. Two system variables control the density of the mesh for creating surfaces. *Surftab1* controls the density of the mesh in the M direction, and *Surftab2* controls the density of the mesh in the N direction. The larger the value for Surtab1 and Surftab2, the more tightly the generated mesh will fit the initial objects selected. As with other commands, increasing the density of the mesh increases the time for calculation and display of the object.

The Surftab1 variable controls the density of the mesh for Ruled Meshes because they are always a 2 X Surftab1 +1 mesh. To set the value for Surftab1,

> Command: **SURFTAB1 [Enter]**
>
> Enter new value for SURFTAB1 <6>: **40 [Enter]**

Next, you will create a ruled surface between the two bottom splines. Use the Mesh tab, Primitives panel to select Ruled Surface (Rulesurf). Refer to Figure 11.62 for the lines to select.

 Click: **Ruled Surface** *from the Mesh tab, Primitives panel*

Select first defining curve: *click curve 1*

Select second defining curve: *click curve 2*

The ruled mesh will be added between the two splines as shown in Figure 11.62.

Figure 11.62

On your own, repeat the command for Ruled Meshes between curves 2 and 3, 3 and 4, 4 and 5, and 5 and 6.

You may need to zoom in so that you can select the red splines.

If you click on the blue mesh, you will not be able to use it as a defining curve. Note that for the upper curves, half the mesh for the ruled surface is connected to each curve. To create an accurate model, sometimes you must change Surftab1 to vary the mesh refinement to avoid so much interpolation.

When you have finished, the drawing will look like Figure 11.63.

Figure 11.63

Save and close your drawing.

Start a new drawing on your own from *edgsurf.dwg*.

Name your new drawing *surf2.dwg*.

On your own, make **MESH** the current layer.

Turn the **grid off**.

Your drawing should look like Figure 11.64.

Tip: *When you are picking the defining curves, pick in a similar location on each curve. If you pick on the opposite end of the second curve, the generated mesh will be intersecting.*

Tip: *Remember, 'Zoom is transparent and can be used during the command.*

Figure 11.64

You will use the four 3D splines shown on the screen to define an edge surface.

Creating an Edge Mesh

The Edge Mesh selection from the Mesh tab, Primitives panel creates a mesh defined by four edges you select. The mesh density for an edge surface is controlled by the Surftab1 and Surftab2 variables. The Edge Surface selection creates a *Coons patch mesh*. A Coons patch mesh is a *bicubic surface* interpolated between the four edges. First, you will set the values for Surftab1 and Surftab2 to control the mesh density. Then you will select Edge Surface from the Surfaces toolbar. Refer to Figure 11.64 for the splines to select.

Command: *SURFTAB1 [Enter]*

New value for SURFTAB1 <6>: *20 [Enter]*

Command: *SURFTAB2 [Enter]*

New value for SURFTAB2 <6>: *20 [Enter]*

Click: *Edge Surface from the Mesh tab, Primitives panel*

Select object 1 for surface edge: *click curve 1*

Select object 2 for surface edge: *click curve 2*

Select object 3 for surface edge: *click curve 3*

Select object 4 for surface edge: *click curve 4*

The edge surface appears in your drawing.

On your own, change the visual style for the view to **Shaded with Edges**.

Using the Steering Wheel

The handy Steering Wheel feature lets you quickly adjust your 3D view. It can be selected from the Viewport control as shown in Figure 11.65.

Click: *[-] from the Viewport control in the upper left*

Click: **Steering Wheel**

Figure 11.65

The Steering Wheel appears attached to your cursor as shown in Figure 11.66.

Figure 11.66

To use the steering wheel, move your cursor to highlight the steering tool you want to use and then press the mouse button while dragging to use the tool.

Try the **Orbit** feature on your own now.

As you press and drag with your mouse, while the orbit area is highlighted, the pivot point shows at the center of the object and dragging revolves the 3D viewpoint (Figure 11.67).

Figure 11.67

Experiment with the other modes on your own. When you are done, press [Esc] or click the small x in the upper right corner of the steering wheel to close it. Note that if you have the navigation bar turned on you can quickly access the steering wheel from it.

Save your drawing.

On your own, use **SaveAs** to save the drawing with the new name *surfnetwork.dwg*. Erase the edge mesh surface you created so that just the original four lines are left.

Creating a Network Surface

A network surface is similar to the edge mesh that you just created and similar to the lofted surface you created earlier. The network surface forms a surface between splines, 2D and 3D curves, and edge subobjects. A subobject is just that: a portion of an existing object, such as the edge of a model. To define a network surface, you first select the curves to define one direction (u or v) and then the curves defining the other direction.

Unlike the edge mesh and the lofted surface, the network surface does not have to be made from a closed boundary (although of course the boundary can also be closed). First you will use the 3D gizmo to move the lines apart and adjust their shapes.

Click on the **front line** so that its grips show and you see the 3D gizmo.

Use the 3D Move gizmo to move the line a slight distance away from the other three lines .

Click on the **right line** to show its grips and the 3D gizmo.

Click on one of the grips and use the 3D gizmo to **drag the grip** and reshape the line as you see in Figure 11.68.

Figure 11.68

Now you are ready to create the network surface.

Click: **Network** *from the Surface tab, Create panel*

Select curves or surface edges in first direction: **click the two vertically oriented lines one at each end [Enter]**

Select curves or surface edges in second direction: **click the two horizontally oriented lines [Enter]**

The network surface appears on your screen similar to Figure 11.69. If you see the message, "Can't create a network from the selected curves", move the curves closer together and try again.

On your own, **save** your drawing.

Figure 11.69

Creating 3D Mesh

The 3D Mesh command lets you construct rectangular polygon meshes by entering the X-, Y-, and Z-coordinates of the points in the mesh. First, you define the number of columns (M) and then the number of rows (N) for the mesh matrix. The values for M and N must fall between 2 and 256. After you define M and N, you are prompted to type the values for the vertices defining the mesh. You can often use an AutoLisp® program or script in conjunction with the 3DMesh command to automate creation of the mesh.

Next, you will define a rectangular mesh. You will erase the objects from the screen and use Save As to give the drawing a new name.

Click: **Erase button**

Select objects: **ALL [Enter]**

Select objects: **[Enter]**

Use **Save As** to save the empty drawing with the name *mesh.dwg*.

The name mesh appears in the title bar at the top of the current drawing.

Click: **3D Mesh** from the Mesh tab, Primitives panel

Enter size of mesh in M direction: **3 [Enter]**

Enter size of mesh in N direction: **3 [Enter]**

Specify location for vertex (0, 0): **0,0,0 [Enter]**

Specify location for vertex (0, 1): **15,0,1 [Enter]**

Specify location for vertex (0, 2): **30,5,2 [Enter]**

Specify location for vertex (1, 0): **0,15,0 [Enter]**

Specify location for vertex (1, 1): **18,18,3 [Enter]**

Specify location for vertex (1, 2): **30,15,0 [Enter]**

Specify location for vertex (2, 0): **0,30,2 [Enter]**

Specify location for vertex (2, 1): **15,30,0 [Enter]**

Specify location for vertex (2, 2): **30,34,3 [Enter]**

The mesh appears in your drawing. Use Zoom, Extents so that you can see the entire drawing.

Click: **Zoom Extents button**

Click: **Wireframe** from the View tab, Visual Styles panel

Your drawing should appear similar to Figure 11.70, although you won't see the coordinates of the vertices. Use the Orbiter and shade and spin the view on your own.

Figure 11.70

Now you know how to establish viewports and viewing directions and create and join the basic shapes used in solid modeling. With these tools you can create a variety of complicated shapes. In Tutorial 12, you will learn how to change solid models further, as well as to plot them. Practice creating shapes and working with the User Coordinate Systems on your own. You have now completed Tutorial 11.

Save and **close** all drawings before exiting the software.

Key Terms

3D gizmo	intersection	revolution	vector
arcball	mass properties	solid modeling	Venn diagrams
bicubic surface	matrix	surface modeling	viewpoint
Boolean operators	perspective icon	tessellation lines	wireframe modeling
Coons patch mesh	plan view	union	World Coordinate
difference	primitives	User Coordinate System	System (WCS)
extrusion	regions	(UCS)	

Key Commands

3DMesh	Front View	Region	Top View
3DWireframe	Hide	Revolve	UCS
Box	Intersection	Right View	Union
Cone	Isolines	Ruled Surface	Viewres
CONVTONURBS	Loft	SE Isometric View	View UCS
CONVTOSURFACE	Mview	Shademode	Vpoint
Cylinder	Mvsetup	Subtract	Wedge Center
Delobj	Named UCS	Surfacemodelingmode	Wedge Corner
Edge Surface	Network Surface	Surfpatch	World UCS
Extrude	Plan	Surftab1	
Facetres	Regenerate All	Surftab2	

Exercises

Use solid modeling to create the parts shown according to the specified dimensions.

11.1 Connector

R.25
BOTH ENNDS

R.50
TYPICAL

11.2 Support Base

11.3 Shaft Support

11.4 Angle Link

0.25

0.05

0.10

0.30

R0.05

1.65

0.70

R0.05

R0.15

0.20

0.35

Polyline used for revolution

0.80

Cut outs
for tower
are 36
degrees

Polygon base has 8 sides
and a 15 degree taper angle.
Thickness = 0.15

Top view of rook

11.5 Chess Piece

Create *the rook chess piece body by revolving a polyline. Use Subtract to remove box primitives to form the cutouts in the tower. Add an octagon for the base. Extrude it to a height of 0.15 and use a taper angle of 15°. (Use your soltemplate.dwt as the template from which you start the rook.) Draw the following shapes by using solid modeling techniques. The letter M after an exercise number means that the units are in millimeters.11.6M Bushing Holder*

82.5

R22.5

ø4

6

15

30

45

15

ø15 THRU
ø30 SFACE
3 DEEP

11.6M Bushing Holder

ø2.25

ø1.00 THRU
⌴ø1.60 ⦂ .44

2 X ø.50

.48

.48

1.60

2.25

.48

1.95

38

R.52 TYP

11.7 Shaft Support

5'0"

8'0"

3'0"

11.8 Balcony

Design a balcony like the one shown here, or a more complex one, using the solid modeling techniques you have learned. Use "two-by-fours" (which actually measure 1.5" x 3.5") for vertical pieces. Use Divide to ensure equal spacing.

Boxprimitive

Extruded ARCs

11.9 Bridge

Create the bridge shown. First, determine the size of the bridge that you want and the area to be left open with the arc. Use extrusion to create the arc. Add the structure of the bridge, making sure that the supports are evenly spaced and of sufficient height. (You can enter one-half of the supports and then use Mirror.)

11.10 Rock Plan

Use the information in the file rockplan.pts to create the plan and profile drawings for the railroad bed as shown below. The file has the information in the following order: point number, northing (the y-coordinate to the north from the reference point), easting (the x-coordinate to the east from the last reference point), elevation, and description. Start by locating each point at the northing and easting given. Extrapolate between elevations and draw polylines for the contour lines at 1' intervals. Make the contour lines for 95' and 100' wider, so that they stand out. Create a 3D mesh using the information in the file rockplan.pts modeling the terrain shown.

CHANGING AND PLOTTING SOLID MODELS

Introduction

You have learned how to create solid models and use multiple view-ports. In this tutorial you will learn to use the solid modeling editing commands to make changes and create a larger variety of shapes. You can create solid models for many engineering drawing needs. From these models you can directly generate two-dimensional (2D) ortho-graphic views that correctly show hidden lines. You will learn a method for controlling layer visibility that allows you to add centerlines so that they appear in a single view. You can also use this method for adding dimensions that appear only in a single viewport. In later tutorials you will learn how to apply solid modeling to create many different stan-dard types of engineering drawings.

Starting

Launch the AutoCAD 2012 software.

Open your drawing **block.dwg** that you created in Tutorial 11 or the datafile **solblock.dwg**.

Save it with the name **soledit.dwg**

Make the WCS current if it is not already.

Make the upper right viewport active.

Verify that you are using the 3D Modeling Workspace.

Your screen should be similar to Figure 12.1.

Figure 12.1

12

Objectives

When you have com-pleted this tutorial, you will be able to

1. Add a rounded fillet between two surfaces.

2. Add an angled surface or chamfer to your model.

3. Remove a portion from a solid.

4. List the solid informa-tion and tree structure.

5. Plot 2D views of the model with hidden lines shown correctly.

6. Control visibility of layers within each viewport.

Tip: *As you work through this tutorial, you may need to redraw or regenerate the drawing to eliminate partially shown lines or shading. Use Redraw to eliminate partially shown lines in a single viewport. Use RedrawAll to redraw all the viewports at the same time. The Redraw commands refresh the screen from the current display file. The Regen commands recalculate the display file from the drawing database and refresh the screen. Use Regen to regenerate the current view port or RegenAll to regenerate all the viewports at once.*

Tip: *To make selecting easier, remember the 'Zoom Window command. Transparent zooming allows you to zoom a view during another command. You can use it to enlarge an area to make selecting easier. To return the area to the original size, always use 'Zoom Previous, not 'Zoom All. To use the transparent version of Zoom, don't forget to add the apostrophe in front of the command (or select it from the View tab).*

Using Fillet on Solids

The Fillet command lets you add concave or convex rounded surfaces between plane or cylindrical surfaces on an existing solid model. You have already used it to create rounded corners between 2D objects. Now you will use it to create a rounded edge for the front, angled surface of the object. Refer to Figure 12.1 for your selection of line A.

Click: *Fillet button*

Select first object or [Undo/Polyline/Radius/Trim/Multiple]: *click on line A*

Enter fillet radius: *.5 [Enter]*

Select an edge or [Chain/Loop/Radius]: *[Enter]*

Your drawing with the rounded edge should look like Figure 12.2.

Figure 12.2

Next, you will undo the fillet and then use the Chamfer command to add an angled surface.

Command: *U [Enter]*

The fillet that you added to your drawing is eliminated.

Using Chamfer on Solids

The Chamfer command works on solid models in a way similar to the Fillet command, except that it adds an angled surface instead of a rounded one. Its Loop option allows you to add a chamfer to all edges of a base surface at once.

Click: *Chamfer button*

(TRIM mode) Current chamfer Dist1 = 0.0000, Dist2 = 0.0000

Select first line or [Undo/Polyline/Distance/Angle/Trim/mEthod/Multiple]: *click line A in Figure 12.1*

Base surface selection...

Enter surface selection option [Next/OK (current)] <OK>: *if the top surface of the object is highlighted, press [Enter]; if not, type N so that the next surface becomes highlighted; then when the top surface is highlighted, press [Enter]*

Specify base surface chamfer distance or [Expression]: *.75 [Enter]*

Specify other surface chamfer distance or [Expression] <0.7500>: *[Enter]*

Select an edge or [Loop]: *click line A in Figure 12.1 [Enter]*

Your screen should look like Figure 12.3.

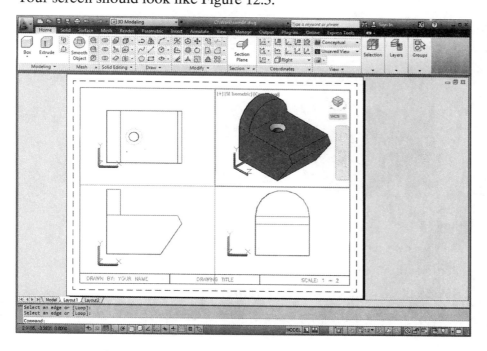

Figure 12.3

Command: *U [Enter]*

The chamfer that you added to your drawing is eliminated.

Using Slice

Using the Slice command, you can cut a solid using a specified *cutting plane*, also called the *slicing plane*. The cutting plane does not have to be an existing drawing entity. You can specify the cutting plane in several ways.

Option	Function
Object	Select an existing planar entity
Zaxis	Specify a point for the origin and a point that gives the direction of the Z-axis of the cutting plane
View	Align a plane parallel to the current view and through a point
XY, YZ, ZX	Choose a plane parallel to the XY-, YZ-, or ZX-coordinate planes and through a point
3points	Choose three points to define a plane

When you have specified the cutting plane, you are prompted to click a point on the side of the plane where you want the object to remain. The portion of the object on the other side is then deleted. You can choose

Tip: *When you are clicking on the solid model, you may have trouble at first deciding which surface to select because each wire of the wireframe represents not one surface, but the intersection of two surfaces. Many commands have the Next option to allow you to move surface by surface until the one you want to select is highlighted. If the surface you want to select is not highlighted, use the Next option until it is. When the surface you want to select is highlighted, press [Enter], You can also cycle through surfaces by pressing the [Ctrl] key when selecting.*

the Both sides option so that neither side is deleted.

In this example you will use the 3points option of the Slice Command to separate the rounded top surface from the block itself. Refer to Figure 12.4 for your selections.

Figure 12.4

On your own, turn running object snap **Endpoint** on.

Command: *SLICE [Enter]*

Select objects: *select the block [Enter]*

Specify start point of slicing plane or [planar Object/Surface/Zaxis /View/XY/YZ/ZX/3points] <3points>: *[Enter] to use the 3 points option*

Specify first point on plane: *use object snap and click endpoint A*

Specify second point on plane: *use object snap and click endpoint B*

Specify third point on plane: *use object snap and click endpoint C*

Specify a point on the desired side of the plane or [keep Both sides]: *[Enter]*

Select the **half-cylinder** that used to be the top surface of the block.

Tip: *To keep both sides of the sliced object, press [Enter] to accept the default value (keep Both sides). You can also type B [enter]*

It is now separate from the block. The grips and 3D gizmo appear as shown in Figure 12.5.

Figure 12.5

Next, you will move the half-cylinder up one unit in the Z-direction and then create a new rectangular piece beneath it.

Click: **Move button**

Select objects: ***click on the half-cylinder*** *that you separated from the block, unless it is already selected*

Select objects: ***[Enter]***

Specify base point or Displacement <Displacement>: ***0,0,1 [Enter]***

Specify second point of displacement or <use first point as displacement>: ***[Enter]***

The cylinder is moved upward 1 unit in the Z direction, as shown in Figure 12.6.

Tip: *If the half-cylinder does not move upward, check that you have the WCS active.*

Figure 12.6

Next you will create two boxes. For the first one, you will use object snaps and *point filters* to draw the box. Point filters allow you to target a point and select only the x, y, z, or xy, zy, or yz portion of its coordinates. The WCS should still be active. Use Figure 12.6 for your selections.

Click: **Box button**

Specify corner of box or [CEnter] <0,0,0>: ***click corner A using Object Snap Endpoint***

Specify other corner or [Cube/Length]: ***right-click to show the short-cut menu and use it to select Snap Overrides, Point Filters, XY***

.XY of: ***click corner B*** *from the upper block*

Specify other corner or [Cube/Length]: .XY of (need Z): ***.Z [Enter]***

.Z of: ***click corner B again,*** *this time to select the z-coordinate*

The box appears between the top surface of the block and the half cylinder as shown in Figure 12.7. Your object will appear shaded. The second box will be where you subtracted a wedge in Tutorial 11.

Double-click inside the active **upper right viewport** to zoom extents so that the entire object is visible inside the viewport.

Figure 12.7

Figure 12.8

Command: *[Enter] to restart the Box command*

Specify corner of box or [CEnter] <0,0,0>: *click corner 1 in Figure 12.7, using Object Snap Endpoint*

Specify corner or [Cube/Length]: *L [Enter]*

Specify length: *2 [Enter]*

Specify width: *4 [Enter]*

Specify height: *3 [Enter]*

Your objects will appear similar to Figure 12.8 except that they will be shaded. Note that the object is not centered well in all viewports. You will pan the view in the lower right viewport.

> Make the **lower right viewport active** and use **Pan** to fit the entire view inside the lower right viewport.

Next you will align the other viewports to the one you used pan to position.

Command: *MVSETUP [Enter]*

Enter an option [Align/Create/Scale viewports/Options/Title block/Undo]: *A [Enter]*

Enter an option [Angled/Horizontal/Vertical alignment/Rotate view/Undo]: *H [Enter]*

Specify basepoint: *use Object Snap Endpoint to click the lower left corner of the object in the lower right viewport*

Specify point in viewport to be panned: *make the lower left viewport active and then use Object Snap Endpoint to click the lower right corner of the object*

Enter an option [Angled/Horizontal/Vertical alignment/Rotate view/Undo]: *[Enter]*

Enter an option [Angle/Create/Scale viewports/Options/Title block/Undo]: *[Enter]*

Your screen should be similar to Figure 12.9.

Tip: *Many of the editing commands that you learned in the 2D tutorials are still effective in solid modeling. Try them when they seem useful.*

Figure 12.9

Now you will use Union to join the block and the new second box.

Click: **Union button**

Select objects: **use Crossing to select ONLY the block and the second box,** *using Figure 12.8 for reference*

Select objects: **[Enter]**

The two objects should now be joined, forming one object similar to that in Figure 12.10.

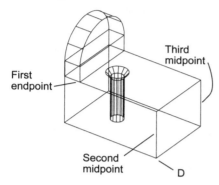

Figure 12.10

Now you will use the 3points Slice option again to slice an angled portion from the block. Select the Slice command from the Home tab, Solids Editing panel. Refer to Figure 12.10 for the three points.

Click: **Slice button**

Select objects: **select the block object**

Select objects: **[Enter]**

Specify start point of slicing plane or [planar Object/Surface/Zaxis/ View/ XY/YZ/ZX/3points] <3points>: **[Enter]** *to select 3points*

Specify first point on slicing plane by [Object/Zaxis/View/XY/ YZ/ ZX/3points] <3points>: **use Object Snap Endpoint and click the endpoint labeled First endpoint,**

Specify second point on plane: **use Object Snap Midpoint to select the midpoint of the front vertical edge labeled Second midpoint**

Specify third point on plane: **use Object Snap Midpoint and click the midpoint of the front vertical edge labeled Third midpoint**

Specify point on the desired side of the plane or [keep Both sides]: **click the bottom left corner, labeled D**

The upper portion of the block is cut off, leaving an angled surface, as shown in Figure 12.11.

Now use the Union command to join the three parts.

Click: **Union button**

Select objects: **use implied Crossing to select all three objects**

Select objects: **[Enter]**

Your drawing should look like that in Figure 12.12.

Figure 12.11

Figure 12.12

Next, you will add a 0.375 deep hole of diameter 0.5, perpendicular to the angled surface.

To create a hole perpendicular to the angled surface, you will align the UCS icon with the angled surface, creating a new user coordinate system. Refer to Figure 12.13.

Make the upper right viewport active

Turn on running Object Snap for Endpoint.

Click: on the UCS icon

Use object snap Endpoint while click and dragging the UCS icon to the lower left corner of the angled surface

Either continue to drag the UCS icon to align the X and Y axis with the slanted surface or click and drag the X-axis and the Y-axis to align with the slanted surface as shown.

The UCS changes so that it now aligns with the angled surface.

Next you will turn the shading off in the top right viewport so that you can see the back surfaces of the object, then use the Plan command to align your view so that you are looking straight down the Z-axis. The resulting view shows the XY-plane of the new UCS that you created in the previous step. The Plan command will fit the drawing extents to the viewport.

*Click: **Wireframe** from the View control for the upper right viewport*

Command: **PLAN [Enter]**

Enter an option [Current ucs/Ucs/World] <Current>: **[Enter]**

Turn the **Grid on**.

Figure 12.13

The view in the upper right viewport should now be directly perpendicular to the angled surface of the object. Your drawing should look like that in Figure 12.14.

Figure 12.14

Next, save the UCS and the view so you can restore them later.

> *Click: **on the small arrow by Unnamed** below the ViewCube to show the menu as seen in Figure 12.14*
>
> *Click: **New UCS***
>
> Specify origin of UCS or [Face/NAmed/OBject/Previous/View/World/X/Y/Z/ZAxis] <World>: ***NA [Enter]***
>
> Enter an option [Restore/Save/Delete/?]: ***S [Enter]***
>
> Enter name to save current UCS or [?]: ***ANGLE [Enter]***
>
> Command: ***VIEW [Enter]***

The View dialog box is shown in Figure 12.15. You will use it to create a new named view.

Figure 12.15

Click: **New** *from the View dialog box*

The New View dialog box appears on your screen. Use it to make the settings shown in Figure 12.16.

Figure 12.16

Type: **Angled View** *for the View name*

Select: **Still** *for the View type*

Click: **Current Display** *in the Boundary area*

Select: **ANGLE** *for* **UCS** *in the Settings area*

Notice that you can also set the visual style for the view, as well as the background color. You can use this also to make walkthrough, and cinematic as well as still views.

Click: **OK**

You return to the View dialog box.

Click: **OK**

Creating the Hole

You will use the cylinder primitive and then subtract it to create the hole. You will use Object Tracking to aid in the location of the cylinder.

Make sure that the running object snap **Midpoint** is active.

Turn the **Grid off** in the upper right viewport to easily see the selections.

Turn on **Object Tracking from the status bar**.

Click: **Cylinder button**

Specify center point for base of cylinder or [Elliptical] <0,0,0>: ***Hover the cursor over line 1, using Object Snap Midpoint as shown in Figure 12.17 to acquire the tracking point.***

Specify center point for base of cylinder or [Elliptical] <0,0,0>: ***positioning cursor along temporary tracking line that appears, type 1 [Enter] to specify a distance of 1 along the tracking line***

Specify radius for base of cylinder or [Diameter]: ***D [Enter]***

Specify diameter for base of cylinder: ***.5 [Enter]***

Specify height of cylinder or [Center of other end]: ***-.375 [Enter]***

On your own, change the color for the small cylinder you just created to Red.

Next, subtract the cylinder to form a hole in the object.

Click: **Subtract button**

Select objects: ***click the large block***

Select objects: ***[Enter]***

Select solids and regions to subtract...

Select objects: ***click the short cylinder you just created [Enter]***

Next return to World Coordinates in the upper right viewport..

Click: ***to expand the menu and choose WCS (near the ViewCube)***

Next, reset the viewpoint for the upper right viewport,

Click: ***on Angled View from the Viewport control to show the menu and choose SE Isometric.***

Set **Conceptual** for the upper right viewport visual style. Set the other three views to **Wireframe**.

Use **Save As** to name your drawing anglblok.dwg.

Your drawing should now look like Figure 12.18.

Figure 12.17

Figure 12.18

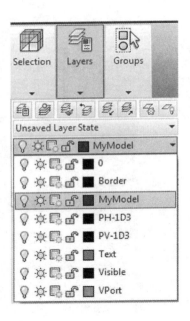

Plotting with Hidden Lines

To generate views that plot correctly using hidden lines, you can use the Setup Profile (SOLPROF) command to create a 2D projection, or *profile*, of each view. The Profile button is located on the Home tab, Modeling panel. When you use Setup Profile, separate layers for hidden and visible lines are automatically generated for each viewport. The tangential edges, or multiple lines, that make up circular features can also be automatically deleted. You will project a 2D profile of the object in each viewport using the Solid Profile command. First, expand and pin the Modeling panel from the Home tab. Next,

*Click: **in the upper left viewport so that it becomes active***

*Click: **Solid Profile button***

Select objects: ***click on an edge*** of the object in the upper left viewport

Select objects: ***[Enter]***

Display hidden profile lines on separate layer? [Yes/No] <Y>: ***[Enter]***

Project profile lines onto a plane? [Yes/No] <Y>: ***[Enter]***

Delete tangential edges? [Yes/No] <Y>: ***[Enter]***

You may now see lines drawn over the original colored lines that designate the edges of your model in the current viewport. The default color for the profile lines is white (which appears black on a light background). The new lines may be under the lines of the model, so that you cannot see them.

*Click: **to pull-down the list of layers***

You should now have two new layers that were created by the Solid Profile command during the last step. Solid Profile creates new layers for the lines of the profile, and the default color setting is white (or black). Because you responded "Yes" to the prompt for displaying hidden profile lines on a new layer, two new types of layers exist in the drawing—one for *visible profile lines* and one for *hidden profile lines*.

The AutoCAD software automatically names the layers for visible profile lines. The layer names for profiled visible lines start with the letters PV-. The layer names for profiled hidden lines start with the letters PH-. The remaining portion of the layer name is based on the handle number of the viewport that the object was profiled in. You will work more with these layers after you create profiles for the other views.

With the upper left viewport active, use the layer list and select the **freeze in current viewport** icon across from layer MyModel.

The colored model is frozen and removed from the screen in only the upper left viewport.

Next, you will create a 2D profile for the front view.

*Click: **the lower left viewport to make it active***

*Click: **Solid Profile button***

Select objects: ***click on an edge of the object in the lower left viewport***

Select objects: *[Enter]*

Display hidden profile lines on separate layer? [Yes/No] <Y>: *[Enter]*

Project profile lines onto a plane? [Yes/No] <Y>: *[Enter]*

Delete tangential edges? [Yes/No] <Y>: *[Enter]*

Use the **Freeze in Current Viewport** button to freeze layer MyModel in only the lower left viewport.

On your own, **repeat this process** for the lower right viewport.

Again, lines appear over (or under) the original colored lines in this viewport. When you have completed profiling the object in each viewport, you will see only white lines (which appear black on a light background) and colored tessellation lines on the screen, except in the shaded view, where they may be hard to see.

Controlling the Generated Layers

The layers that were created using the Solid Profile command were named with two parts: PV or PH, describing whether they were the visible or hidden profile lines, and a handle number for the viewport. To find the handle number for each viewport, switch to paper space and use the List command. Later you will use this information selectively to freeze and thaw the profiled lines for the desired layers.

On your own, switch to **paper space**.

Thaw layer Vport if it is not already thawed.

Note that the paper space icon, a triangle, is now displayed in the lower left corner of your screen. Next, you will list the information for the viewports. To select a viewport, you must click on its border and not just somewhere inside the viewport.

Command: *LIST [Enter]*

Select objects: ***click the border of the upper left viewport***

Select objects: *[Enter]*

The information shown in Figure 12.19 is displayed on your screen.

Figure 12.19

Write the handle number for the upper left viewport in the space provided on the next page. Handle numbers begin with hexadecimal number 1, which is assigned to the first object you draw, and then proceed with hexadecimal numbers for each additional entity.

Tip: *The AutoCAD software has a handy Quick Calculator (QUICKCALC) function that can be very useful in specifying points that would be impossible to specify by other drawing means. Whenever you see a prompt requesting input of a point, real number, integer, or vector, you can use the Quick Calculator or the transparent command 'CAL. 'CAL lets you write an expression in infix notation, such as 112*sin(30), at the prompt and the resultant value is used. You can also use Object Snap functions and acquire points from your drawing in combination with the Quick Calculator. This is very useful in creating complex models.*

Hexadecimal representation for decimal number 10 is A; 11 is B; and so on. The handle number that you see in your drawing may be different from that listed in Figure 12.19, depending on how you created each object in the drawing.

> *Click: **the Close button** to remove the text window*
>
> Command: *[Enter] to restart the List command*
>
> Select objects: ***click the border of the upper left viewport***
>
> Select objects: *[Enter]*

The information and handle number for the upper left viewport are listed on the text screen.

You may want to keep track of these numbers in order to easily freeze and thaw profile layers in any particular viewport.

> Write the handle numbers for the viewports on your own.
>
> Upper Left Viewport Handle Number: _____
>
> Lower Left Viewport Handle Number: _____
>
> Lower Right Viewport Handle Number: _____

Setting the Linetypes and Colors for Generated Layers

Now you will use the Layer Properties Manager to set the color and linetype for the new layers.

> *Click: **Layer Properties Manager button***

The Layer Properties Manager appears on your screen. Note that eight more layers are listed in the dialog box than were previously. These are the generated layers for the profiles that were created when you used the Solid Profile (SOLPROF) command. You will use the dialog box to set the color and linetype of the generated hidden line layers. Remember you can hold down the CTRL key in order to select more than one layer name at a time.

> *Click: **each of the layer names that start with PH-***
>
> *Click: **on Continuous** under the heading Linetype, across from one of the selected layers to show the Select Linetype dialog box*
>
> *Click: **Load***
>
> *Click: **Hidden** from the Load or Reload Linetypes dialog box*
>
> *Click: **OK***
>
> *Click: **Hidden***
>
> *Click: **OK** to exit the Select Linetype dialog box*
>
> *Click: **the Color box** across from one of the selected layers*
>
> *Click: **Blue***
>
> *Click: **OK** to exit the Select Color dialog box*

Click: *on Default to show the Lineweight listing*

Click: *0.30 mm*

Click: *OK*

You have finished setting the color blue and linetype HIDDEN for the generated hidden line layers. The PH- and PV- layers are frozen in the current viewport, which was done automatically when you generated the layers; otherwise, each 2D profile would appear in every viewport, creating a lot of confusion.

Using the techniques you have learned, set the lineweight for all **PV** layers to **0.60 mm**.

When you have made these changes the list of layers appears as shown in Figure 12.20.

Click: *[X] to exit the Layer Properties Manager box*

S...	Name	O...	Freeze	Lock	Color	Linetype	Lineweight	Tr...	Plot Style	Plot	New VP Fr...	Des
	0				white	Continuous	Default	0	Color_7			
	Border				white	Continuous	Default	0	Color_7			
	MyModel				blue	Continuous	Default	0	Color_5			
	PH-1D3				blue	HIDDEN	0.30 ...	0	Color_5			
	PH-1D7				blue	HIDDEN	0.30 ...	0	Color_5			
	PH-1DB				blue	HIDDEN	0.30 ...	0	Color_5			
	PV-1D3				white	Continuous	0.60 ...	0	Color_7			
	PV-1D7				white	Continuous	0.60 ...	0	Color_7			
	PV-1DB				white	Continuous	0.60 ...	0	Color_7			
	Text				red	Continuous	0.30 ...	0	Color_1			
	Visible				white	Continuous	0.60 ...	0	Color_7			
	VPort				mage...	Continuous	Default	0	Color_6			

Current layer: MyModel — Search for layer

Filters — All — All Used Layers — Invert filter

All: 12 layers displayed of 12 total layers

Figure 12.20

Your screen should look like Figure 12.21.

DRAWN BY: YOUR NAME — DRAWING TITLE — SCALE: 1 = 2

Figure 12.21

Adding the Centerlines

Next you will draw the centerlines for the front view. First you will create a new layer named CL-FRONT for the front view centerlines, using the Layers Properties Manager.

Click: **Layer Properties Manager button**

Click: **New button**

Type: **CL-FRONT**

Click: **the Color box** *to the right of the new layer*

Click: **Green** *from within the Select Color dialog box*

Click: **OK** *to exit the Select Color dialog box*

Click: **linetype CONTINUOUS** *to show the Select Linetype dialog box*

Click: **Load**

Click: **CENTER** *from the Load or Reload Linetypes dialog box*

Click: **OK**

Click: **CENTER**

Click: **OK** *to exit the Select Linetype dialog box*

Click: **to show the lineweight list** *for the new layer*

Click: **0.30 mm**

Click: **OK** *to exit the Lineweight dialog box*

Double-click: **on CL-FRONT** *to set it as the current layer*

Click: **[X]** *to exit the Layer Properties Manager dialog box*

On your own, make the **lower left viewport** active. Align the UCS to the front view.

Use the **Line** command to draw a centerline for the hole in the front view.

Switch to paper space and set **LTSCALE** to **.5** to adjust the centerline pattern.

When you have finished, your drawing should be similar to Figure 12.22.

Figure 12.22

What happened? The line that you drew appears in the other viewports. Anything you add in model space will be visible in all the views unless you specify otherwise. You can use Freeze/Thaw in the Current Viewport selection to freeze the layer in specific viewports so that the centerline does not appear in them.

Using Freeze/Thaw in Current Viewport

When you add lines such as centerlines and dimensions to 3D drawings, you usually have to create layers for each viewport. Using the Freeze/ Thaw in Current Viewport selection, you can turn off the visibility of the layers in the viewports in which you do not want the lines to show. The AutoCAD software did this for you with the generated layers for profile visible and profile hidden. You must control the visibility of layers that you create unless you want them to show in every viewport. Imagine putting dimensions in the front view and having them show up edgewise in the top and side views.

Click: **to make the upper right viewport active**

Click: **to pull down the layer list**

Click: **Current Viewport Freeze adjacent to layer CL-FRONT as shown in Figure 12.23.**

Figure 12.23

The centerline you drew should now be visible only in the front view.

Now that you have set the layer visibility,

Draw the centerline for the smaller hole on your own.

Next, you will use the Layer Properties Manager to create centerline layers for the top and side view. Then you will set their visibility and draw the appropriate centerlines.

Click: **the upper left viewport to make it active**

Click: **Layer Properties Manager button**

Use the Layer Properties Manager to create a new layer, **CL-TOP.**

Set the linetypes to **CENTER** and the colors to **green.**

Make layer CL-TOP current by double-clicking it. When you have finished, exit the dialog box.

Draw the top view centerlines.

Your drawing should be similar to the one in Figure 12.24. You can also create dimensions that appear in only one viewport by controlling layer visibility as you did for the centerlines.

DRAWN BY: YOUR NAME   DRAWING TITLE   SCALE: 1 = 2

Figure 12.24

On your own, **save** your drawing.

Switch to paper space and use the techniques you have learned to plot the drawing.

Close all drawings and exit the AutoCAD software.

You have now completed Tutorial 12.

Tip: *Try various values for LTScale until you are pleased with the results.*

Key Terms

cutting plane	hidden profile line	slicing plane
handles	profile	visible profile line

Key Commands

Calculator	Fillet	Setup Profile
Chamfer	List	Slice

Exercises

12.1 Angled Support
Create this figure as a 3D solid model. Create necessary views and plot with correct hidden lines and centerlines.

12.2 Gland
Create a 3D solid model of the part shown in the orthographic views.

12.3 Step Model
Construct a solid model of this object. Grid spacing is 0.25 inch. Use a viewpoint of (3,–3,1) in the upper right viewport.

12.4M Rack
Create a 3D solid model of this metric part.
Create solid models for the objects shown. Show
the necessary orthographic views in the correct viewports.
Use **SOLPROF** to generate hidden lines.

12.5 Rod Holder

12.6 Gear

12.7 Router Guide

12.8 Slide Support

12.9 Spacer

CREATING ASSEMBLY DRAWINGS FROM SOLID MODELS

13

Introduction

In previous tutorials you created solid models of objects and projected 2D views to create orthographic drawings. To make a set of working drawings using solid modeling, you will create an assembly drawing of a clamp, similar to the one shown in Figure 13.1. The parts for the assembly drawing have been created as solid models and are included with the datafiles. You will proceed directly to creating the assembly drawing. The purpose of an assembly drawing is to show how the parts go together, not to describe completely the shape and size of each part. Assembly drawings usually do not show dimensions or hidden lines.

Figure 13.1

Attaching Solid Models

In this tutorial you will learn how to use the External Reference commands to attach part drawings to create an assembly drawing. When you use external references to attach a part drawing to the assembly drawing, the AutoCAD software will automatically update the assembly drawing whenever you make a change to the original part drawing. You can use this same method to attach any drawing information into any other drawing as well, for example, to include the outline of a floor plan of a house in a site plan drawing.

You will also learn more about the Insert command and Tool Palettes, which you used to insert the electronic logic symbols. Objects added to a drawing with the Insert command or dragged from a Tool Palette are included in the new drawing, but if you update the original drawing, the AutoCAD software doesn't automatically update the drawing where the copy was inserted.

Objectives

When you have completed this tutorial, you will be able to

1. Create an assembly drawing from solid models.

2. Use external references.

3. Check for interference.

4. Analyze the mass properties of solid models.

5. Create an exploded isometric view.

6. Create leaders with part identification numbers.

7. Create and extract attributes.

8. Create a parts list.

The parts in Figures 13.2 through 13.5 below are provided with the datafiles. Their basepoints points are identified as 0,0 in the figures.

Figure 13.2

Figure 13.3

Figure 13.4

Figure 13.5

Starting

Start the AutoCAD program and begin a new drawing using the drawing template called *proto-iso.dwt* (provided with the datafiles).

Name the drawing *asmb-sol.dwg*.

The drawing editor appears on your screen showing a template drawing for 3D isometric views.

If necessary, switch to paper space and use Zoom All, to fill the graphics area with the layout. Switch back to model space inside the viewport when you are done. Your screen should be similar to Figure 13.6.

Figure 13.6

Check that you are using the **3D Modeling workspace**.

*Click: **the Insert tab** so that it appears uppermost on the ribbon*

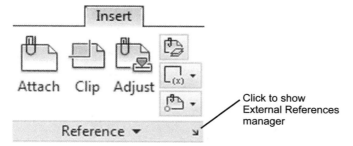

Figure 13.7

Using External References

The External Reference (XREF) command lets you use another drawing without adding it to your current drawing. The advantage of this is that if you make a change to the referenced (original) drawing, any other drawing to which it is attached updates automatically the next time you open that drawing (or when you select to Synchronize the drawing). As with blocks, you can attach external references anywhere in the drawing; you can also scale and rotate them. You can quickly select the External Reference command options from the Reference panel of the ribbon Insert tab. As with any other AutoCAD command, you can also type the command name, -XREF, and select the option you want. You will begin your drawing by attaching the base of the clamp to your assembly drawing as an external reference.

*Click: **the small downward arrow at the lower right of the References panel** to show the Xref Manager as shown in Figure 13.7*

The External Reference Manager appears, as shown in Figure 13.8.

*Click: **Attach icon** from the top left of the External Reference Manager*

The Select Reference File dialog box appears on your screen.

*Click: **base-3d.dwg,** which is in the c:\datafile2012 directory*

*Click: **Open***

The Attach External Reference dialog box appears, similar to Figure 13.9.

Figure 13.8

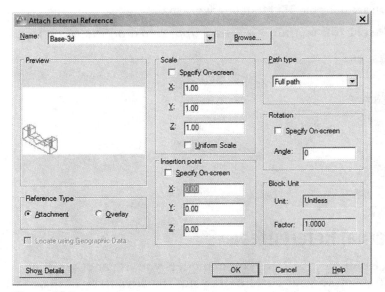

Figure 13.9

Note the options available for Reference Type. Xrefs can be used as an attachment or used as an overlay. If Overlay is selected, when the drawing containing the Xref overlay is inserted into a new drawing, the Xref will NOT be carried along. When Attachment is selected, the Xref-ed file comes along with it.

In the Insertion point area of the dialog box,

> *Deselect: **Specify On-screen** (remove the check)*

The Insertion point of 0,0,0 should no longer be grayed out. If you wanted you could overtype these with new values. The scale will remain as 1 for X, Y, and Z, and the Rotation will remain at angle 0.

> *Click: **OK***

The base part appears in your drawing. You see a message stating that there are "Unreconciled New Layers." Unrecognized layers are often added to a drawing (often through an xref).

> On your own, open the Layer Manager (you can click the link in the message window).

> *Right-click: **on an unreconciled layer** to show the menu*

> *Click: **Reconcile Layer***

> On your own reconcile any remaining layers and close the Layer Manager. Then **close** the External Reference manager for now.

Next you will set the Isolines variable to a larger value to produce more tessellation lines and improve the appearance of the rounded surfaces.

> Command: ***ISOLINES [Enter]***

> Enter new value for ISOLINES <4>: *12 [Enter]*

> Command: ***REGEN [Enter]***

> On your own, set the visual style to **Shaded with Edges**.

> Use **pan** to position the base near the bottom center of the drawing area.

Tip: *The command alias for Regen is RE. You can type this shortcut instead of typing REGEN.*

When you have finished these steps, your screen should be similar to Figure 13.10.

Figure 13.10

Layers and External References

When you attach a drawing to another drawing by using External Reference Attach, all its subordinate features (e.g., layers, linetypes, colors, blocks, and dimensioning styles) are attached with it. You can control the visibility of the layers attached with the referenced drawing, but you cannot modify anything or create any new objects on these layers. The Visretain system variable controls the extent to which you can make changes in the visibility, color, and linetype. If Visretain is set to 0, any changes that you make in the new drawing apply only to the current drawing session and will be discarded when you end it or reload or attach the original drawing. The Refedit command lets you make minor changes to an Xref'd object within the current drawing. Making major changes using Refedit is not advisable as your file size will be significantly larger during in-place editing. You can easily open the referenced drawing in a separate window to edit it to avoid this.

Use Layer Control to pull down the list of available layers.

Scroll to the top of the list, if necessary, to see the result of attaching the base as an external reference.

The list should be similar to that in Figure 13.11.

Note that the layer names attached with the external reference have the name of the external reference drawing in front of them.

Click: *to freeze layer BASE-3D|VISIBLE*

The base externally referenced to the drawing disappears from the screen.

Click: *to thaw layer BASE-3D|VISIBLE*

Figure 13.11

You can also control which portions of an external reference are visible by using the External Reference Clip command. This command creates a paper space viewport that you can use as a window to select the portion of the external reference that you want to be visible in the drawing.

On your own, use the Help command to obtain more information about the Xrefclip command.

Inserting the Solid Part Drawings

Next, you will insert the solid model drawing *cover-3d.dwg* into the assembly drawing as a block. You will use the Insert command, as you did in Tutorial 10 when inserting the electronic logic symbols.

Turn on running mode **Object Snap** for **Endpoint** and **Center**.

Click: **Insert Block icon**

Click: **Browse**

Double-click: **to select cover-3d.dwg from the datafiles directory**

When you have selected the file, you will be able to set the parameters for how the file is inserted. You will use the Specify On-screen option for the Insertion point. Leave the Scale set to the default values of 1 for X, Y, and Z, and the Rotation set to the default of angle 0.

Click: **Specify On-screen** *so that it appears checked in the Insertion point area*

Click: **OK** *to exit the Insert dialog box*

You return to the command prompt for the remaining prompt.

Specify insertion point or [Basepoint/Scale/X/Y/Z/Rotate/PScale/PX/PY/ PZ/PRotate]: *click anywhere in the drawing editor, away from the base part*

The solid model of the clamp cover appears in your drawing, as shown in Figure 13.12.

Figure 13.12

You will now use the Align command to align the edge of the cover with the edge of the base. Refer to Figure 13.12 for the points to select.

Command: ***ALIGN [Enter]***

Select objects: ***select the cover that you just inserted***

Select objects: ***[Enter]***

Specify first source point: ***use Object Snap Endpoint to select point 1***

Specify first destination point: ***use Object Snap Endpoint to select point 2***

Specify second source point: ***use Object Snap Endpoint to select point 3***

Specify second destination point: ***use Object Snap Endpoint to select point 4***

*Specify third source point or <continue>: **[Enter]***

*Scale objects based on alignment points? [Yes/No] <N>: **[Enter]***

Save your drawing.

The solid model of the clamp cover moves to align with the base.

Next you will insert the washers and screws into the assembly. You will select the Attach button from the External Reference dialog box.

Make sure that Snap is off.

*Click: **Model tab** (to disable paper space and switch to viewing only the model)*

Use **Zoom Window** to enlarge the view.

Pan to position it near the center of the screen, if needed.

Your drawing should look similar to Figure 13.13. It is shown here in wireframe mode. Your drawing should still be shaded.

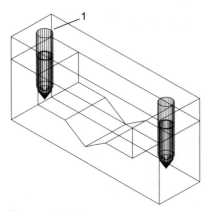

Figure 13.13

*Click: **to show the External Reference manager** (use the small downward arrow from the ribbon Insert tab, Reference panel)*

*Click: **Attach icon***

*Click: **washr-3d.dwg** (being sure to select the drive and directory for your datafiles)*

*Click: **Open***

Tip: *The Align command can also be used with more than one point. For example, you can select additional points to align two points along an edge or three points defining a plane. When you have aligned all of the desired points press [Enter] to have the command take effect.*

The Attach External Reference dialog box appears on your screen. You will now select Specify On-screen for the Insertion point selection. You will leave the Scale and Rotation set to the defaults. Refer to Figure 13.13 for the points to select.

*Click: **Specify On-screen** so it is checked in the Insertion point area*

*Click: **OK** to exit the dialog box*

Specify insertion point or [Scale/X/Y/Z/Rotate/PScale/PX/PY/PZ/PRotate]: ***use Object Snap Center and target the top edge of hole 1***

The washer appears in the drawing as shown in Figure 13.14. To insert the second washer,

*Right-click: **on washr-3d** from the file references list to show the short cut menu*

*Click: **Attach***

*Click: **Specify On-screen** so it is checked in the Insertion point area*

*Click: **OK** to exit the dialog box*

Specify insertion point or [Scale/X/Y/Z/Rotate/PScale/PX/PY/PZ/PRotate]: ***use Object Snap Center and target the top edge of the remaining hole***

Close the External References manager

The second washer appears in the drawing.

Figure 13.14

If you knew that drawing *washr-3d.dwg* had changed and you wanted to update it without having to exit the drawing, you could use the Reload option of the Xref command. Reload is especially useful if you are working on a networked system and sharing files with other members of a design team. At any point you can use the Reload option to update the definition of the referenced objects in your drawing. In this case, you want to insert another copy of the same drawing, so you can just ignore this message. (You could also use the Copy command to create the other washer.)

Next, you will add the two screws to the assembly to finish inserting the parts. You will make a new Tool Palette that has the screw and washer to see another way that you can insert parts.

Click: *Tool Palettes button from the ribbon View, Palettes panel*

Right-click: *on the Tool Palettes*

Click: *New Palette from the pop-up menu*

Type: *3D Parts for the name of the new Tool Palette [Enter]*

Click: *DesignCenter™ button*

Use the Folders list in the DesignCenter on your own to select the **data-file2012** directory and drag and drop **Screw-3d** and **Washr-3d** onto the Tool Palettes as shown in Figure 13.15.

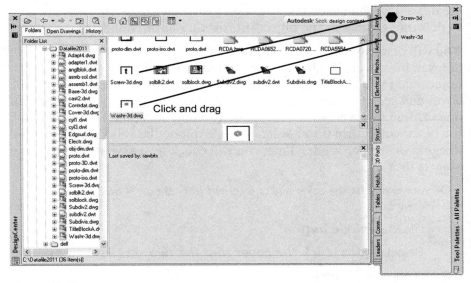

Tip: *You can right-click on the DesignCenter to pop up a context menu of useful options, including changing how the items are viewed. You can right-click the DesignCenter title bar and choose to Auto-hide it.*

Figure 13.15

Click: *to close DesignCenter*

Click/Drag Screw-3d from the Tool Palettes and drop it into the hole location in the washer in your drawing using Object Snap Center.

Repeat this process on your own for the second screw.

Click: *to close Tool Palettes*

Now your drawing should depict the parts in completely assembled form, as shown in Figure 13.16.

Figure 13.16

Checking for Interference

When you are designing a device, you often want to know whether the parts will fit correctly. You can use the AutoCAD software's Interfere command to determine whether two parts overlap. If they do, Interfere creates a new solid showing where they do. You can use this command to determine whether the objects fit together as intended.

You will determine whether the screws in the assembly will fit the holes in the cover. The Interfere command will only analyze solids, but objects that you've inserted in the drawing are now blocks. To return the cover and screws to solids, you will explode them. When you explode an object, doing so removes one level of grouping at a time, so exploding the block will return it to a solid. If you explode the solid, it will become a region or surface model. First, you will check to see what type of objects they are.

On your own, **List** the cover and two screws (they should show as block references).

 Click: **Explode button**

Select objects: *click the cover and the two screws*

Select objects: *[Enter]*

The cover and two screws are now exploded.

List the cover and two screws again on your own (they should now be listed as 3DSOLID objects).

Next you will determine whether the screws interfere with the cover. You can type INTERFERE to run the command or select it from the ribbon Solid tab, Solid Editing panel.

 Click: **Interfere button**

Select first set of solids:

Select objects: *click on the cover*

Select objects: *[Enter]*

Select second set of solids:

Select objects: *click on the two screws*

Select objects: *[Enter]*

Comparing 1 solid against 2 solids.

Solids do not interfere.

Because the solids do not interfere, you know that the screws fit through the cover. If the solids did interfere, you would see a message similar to "Interfering solids: 2 Interfering pairs: 1 Create interference solids? [Yes/N] <N>:" You can type Y [Enter] if you want the AutoCAD software to create a new solid on the current layer from the overlap between the interfering solids.

Determining Mass Properties (MASSPROP)

The software enables you to determine mass properties of solids. One of the advantages of the solid modeler is the accuracy with which volumes and mass properties are calculated. Like Interfere, the Mass Properties command works only on solids, not on external references. To make it easy to select the Region/Mass Properties command, you will turn on the Inquiry toolbar.

Click: **ribbon View tab, Windows panel, Toolbars flyout, AutoCAD, Inquiry** *as shown in Figure 13.17*

Figure 13.17

The Inquiry Toolbar appears on your screen.

 Click: **Region/Mass Properties button** *from the Inquiry toolbar*

Select objects: *click the clamp cover*

Select objects: *[Enter]*

The AutoCAD text window opens displaying the mass property information, as shown in Figure 13.18.

Tip: *If your solids do interfere, your screws may not be assembled properly. If so, erase the screws and use the Insert command to add them. Make sure to use Object Snap Center to place them accurately.*

Scroll through the information in the text window if necessary.

```
AutoCAD Text Window - asmb-sol.dwg                    _ □ X
 Edit
Command: _massprop
Select objects: 1 found

Select objects:

---------------- SOLIDS    ----------------

Mass:                    5.9594
Volume:                  5.9594
Bounding box:       X: -0.6161  --  4.8839
                    Y: 3.5457   --  5.0457
Press ENTER to continue:
                    Z: 2.0000   --  2.7500
Centroid:           X: 2.1339
                    Y: 4.2957
                    Z: 2.3750
Moments of inertia: X: 145.0206
                    Y: 75.4700
                    Z: 152.7023
Products of inertia: XY: 54.6267

Press ENTER to continue: |
```

Figure 13.18

Press ENTER to continue: *[Enter] to close the AutoCAD text window*

You can also write the mass properties information to a file. Once you have closed the text window, you will see the prompt,

Write analysis to a file? [Yes/No] <N>: *[Enter]*

Creating an Exploded Isometric View

Exploded views show the parts removed from their assembled positions yet still aligned, as though the assembly had exploded. You will create an exploded view from your assembly drawing by moving the parts away from each other. Because the exploded parts should be aligned with their assembled positions, you will move them only along one axis. You will use the Move 3D gizmo to move the screws.

Click: the two screws to show their grips and the 3D gizmo

Click on the blue upward pointing arrow and drag the screws up as shown in Figure 13.19.

Figure 13.19

You will continue to use the 3D gizmo to relocate the washers and the clamp cover, keeping them aligned with their present position but three units above, along the Z-axis.

On your own, turn the **grid off**.

Move the washers to align below the screws and then move the **clamp cover** up as shown in Figure 13.20.

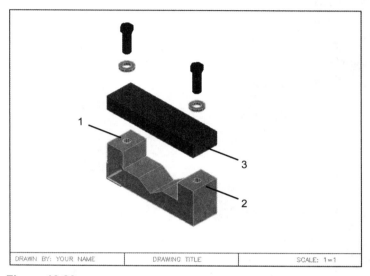

Figure 13.20

When you create an exploded view, you should add thin lines to show how the parts assemble. To create lines in the same plane as the objects' centers, you need to define a UCS that aligns through the middle of the objects. You will make a new layer for the lines. As usual, zoom in if necessary to click the correct locations on the part.

Turn on Object Snap for **Midpoint**.

Create a new layer called **ALIGN** that has color cyan and linetype CONTINUOUS. Set ALIGN as the current layer.

Click: *3 Point from the Home tab, Coordinates panel*

Specify new origin point <0,0,0>: *click the middle of line 1 in Figure 13.20*

Specify point on positive portion of X-axis <1.0000,0.7500,0.0000>: *click the middle of line 2*

Specify point on positive-Y portion of the UCS XY plane <1.0000,0.7500,0.0000>: *click the middle of line 3*

The UCS icon and grid change to align with the plane through the middle of the parts. If they do not, repeat the command and try again.

Draw the lines, showing how the parts align, by clicking points on the Snap or using Object Snap.

Save your drawing before you continue.

When you have finished, your drawing should look like Figure 13.21.

Tip: *Another useful technique in aligning 3D objects in an assembly drawing is to use the Tracking command. You can Attach or move the solids with reference to locations on other solids.*

Figure 13.21

Creating a Dynamic Block for the Ball Tags

Ball tags identify the parts in the assembly. They are made up of the item number in the assembly enclosed in a circle, hence the name ball tags. You can easily add ball tags to the drawing by making a block. You will make a block that has one visible attribute and several invisible attributes. An *attribute* is basically text information that you can associate with a block. It is an effective method of adding information to the drawing. You can also extract attribute information from the drawing and import it into a database or word processing program for other uses.

Dynamic Blocks

D*ynamic blocks* have custom properties that allow you to adjust inserted blocks within your drawing instead of having to redefine them or insert another block. Dynamic blocks must have at least one parameter and one action associated with the parameter. The types of parameters that can be associated with the block are:

Parameter	Control Location	Associated Actions
Point	Defines an X and Y location	Move, Stretch
Linear	Defines a distance between two anchor points	Move, Scale, Stretch, Array
Polar	Defines a distance between two anchor points and an angle value	Move, Scale, Stretch, Polar Stretch, Array
XY	Defines X and Y distances from a base point	Move, Scale, Stretch, Array
Rotation	Defines an angle	Rotate
Flip	Defines a reflection line about which objects can be flipped	Flip

Parameter	Control Location	Associated Actions
Alignment	Defines an X and Y location and an angle which applies to the entire block	No action needs to be associated with this parameter. The alignment parameter allows the block reference to automatically rotate around a point to align with another object in the drawing. An alignment parameter affects the rotation property of the block reference.
Visibility	Controls visibility of objects in the block	No action is assigned, but a list of visibility states for the block is created which can be controlled.
Lookup	Defines a custom property used to look up or evaluate a value from a defined list or table.	Lookup
Base	Defines a base point for the dynamic block	Cannot be associated with any actions, but can belong to an action's selection set.

You will add dynamic properties to your ball tag block so that you can flip the leader to the opposite side of the block and stretch the leader extending from it wherever the block has been inserted. You can create the dynamic block and add its attribute using the Block Editor.

Figure 13.22

Figure 13.22 shows ball tags like the ones you will create. You will use the Block Editor to create the "smart" block for the ball tag.

Click: **TEXT** *as the current drawing layer*

Click: **Block Editor button** *from the Insert tab, Block panel*

The Block Editor Definition dialog box appears on your screen similar to Figure 13.23.

Tip: *You can also use the Block Editor to add dynamic properties and attributes to blocks you have previously created with the block command. Attributes can also be added to blocks using the Attdef command and then selecting the attribute you have defined when you create a block.*

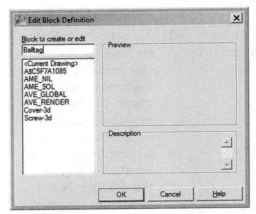

Figure 13.23

Type: ***BALLTAG*** *in the input box for Block to create or edit, as shown in Figure 13.23*

Click: ***OK***

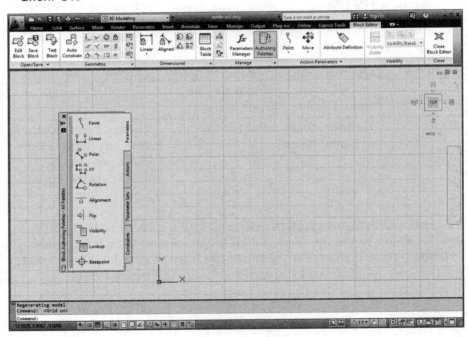

Figure 13.24

Your screen appearance changes to look like Figure 13.24 showing the ribbon and tools for the Block Editor. A new toolbar appears at the top of the screen and the Block Authoring palette is open.

Click: ***Circle button***

On your own, draw a **circle** of diameter 0.25 to the side of the Block Authoring Palettes in the blank area of the drawing editor as shown in Figure 13.25.

Command: ***QLEADER [Enter]***

Use the Quick Leader command to draw a leader with the arrow pointing to the left and connected to the left quadrant of the circle as shown in Figure 13.25. Do not add any text at this time.

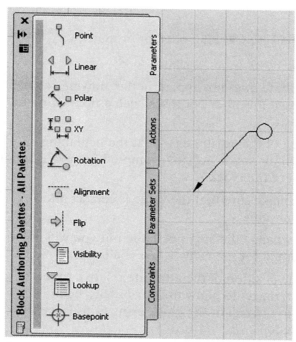

Figure 13.25

Defining Attributes

The Define Attributes command is on the Insert tab, Attributes panel. You can use Define Attributes to create special attribute text objects.

Click: **Define Attributes button** *from the ribbon Insert tab, Attributes panel*

The Attribute Definition dialog box appears on your screen. You will use it to make the selections shown in Figure 13.26.

Figure 13.26

Attribute Modes

Attributes can have the following special modes, or properties.

Mode	Definition
Invisible	The attribute does not appear in the drawing, but can still be used for other purposes, such as extracting to a database.
Constant	The value of the attribute is set at the beginning of its definition, so you are not prompted for a value on insertion of the block.
Verified	You can make sure that the value is correct after typing the value.
Preset	You can change the attribute later, but you will not be prompted for the value when you insert it.
Lock position	Locks the position of the attribute relative to the block reference. To allow the attribute to be moved relative to the rest of the block using grips leave this unchecked.
Multiple lines	Allows the attribute value to contain multiple text lines. You specify a boundary width for the attribute.

You will now use the Attribute Definition dialog box to add the number in the center of the ball tag as a visible attribute. You will also create attributes for the other information commonly shown in the parts list (such as the part name, part number, material, and quantity) as invisible attributes.

Leave each of the Mode boxes unchecked to indicate that you want this attribute to be visible, variable, not verified, and typed in, not preset.

Attribute Tag

The *attribute tag* is a variable name that is replaced with the value that you type when prompted as you insert the attribute block. The tag appears when the block is exploded or before the attribute is made into a block. You will use NUM for the attribute tag.

On your own, type **NUM** in the Tag input box.

Attribute Prompt

The *attribute prompt* is the prompt that appears in the command area when you insert the block into a drawing. Make your prompt descriptive, so it clearly identifies the information to be typed and how it should be typed. For instance, "Enter the date (dd/mm/yy)" is a prompt that specifies not only what to enter—the date—but also the format—numeric two-digit format, with day first, then month and year.

On your own, type **Please type tag number** in the Prompt input box.

Default Attribute Value

Default defines a default value for the attribute. Leaving the box to the right of Value empty results in no default value for the tag. As every tag number will be different, there is no advantage to having a default value for the ball tag attribute. If the prompt would often be answered with a particular response, that response would be a good choice for the default value.

Attribute Text Options

Attributes and regular text use the same types of options. You can center, fit, and align attributes just like any other text.

Select the **Middle** option from the Justification pull-down menu.

Selecting Middle will cause the middle of the text to appear in the center of the ball tag when you type it.

Set the text style to **ROMANS**.

You do not need to change the Text Style setting.

Set the text height to **0.125**.

Leave the rotation set at 0 degrees for this attribute. You do not want the attribute rotated at an angle in the drawing.

Attribute Insertion Point

You can select Specify On-screen in the Insertion Point section to select the insertion point on your screen, or you can type the X-, Y-, and Z-coordinates into the appropriate boxes.

Make sure that Specify On-screen is checked.

Click: **OK**

Check that Object Snap is on with Center selected.

Your drawing returns to the screen. The Block Editor should still be present.

Specify start point: *use Object Snap to click the center of the circle*

The tag NUM is centered in the circle. The circle and the attribute tag should look like Figure 13.27. If the attribute is not in the center of the circle, use the Move command to center it in the circle on your own.

Figure 13.27

Next you will make the attributes for part name (description), part number, material, and quantity. These attributes will be invisible, to avoid making the drawing look crowded, but they can still be extracted for use in a spreadsheet or database.

Command: *[Enter] to restart the ATTDEF command*

Tip: The prompt appears with a colon (:) after it to indicate that some entry is expected. The colon is included automatically; you do not need to type a colon in the dialog box.

Tip: You can create a title block for your drawings that uses attributes. For the drafter's name, you make the attribute prompt "Enter drafter's name".
In the Value text box, you put your own name as the default value.
When you insert the block into a drawing, the default value after the prompt within the AutoCAD default angle brackets will be your own name. To accept the default values press [Enter] instead of having to type in your name each time.

You can also use Fields to display information, such as the current date in the title block.

Tip: Clicking on the Height or Rotation buttons lets you set the height or rotation, either by clicking from the screen or by typing at the command prompt.

The Attribute Definition dialog box appears on your screen. Continue to use it to create an invisible attribute with the following settings.

Select: **Invisible mode** so that a check appears in the box to its left

Tag: **PART**

Prompt: **Please type part description**

Default: (leave the input box empty so that there is no default value)

Justification: **Left**

Text Style: **ROMANS**

Height: **.125**

Rotation: **0**

Make sure that **Specify On-screen** is checked.

When you have entered this information into the dialog box, you are ready to select the location in the drawing for your invisible attribute.

Click: OK

Your drawing returns to the screen.

Specify start point: **click a point to the right of the ball tag circle**

Command: **[Enter]**

The tag PART should appear at the location you selected.

On your own, use this method to create the following three invisible attributes. Choose the box to the left of **Align below previous attribute** to locate each new attribute below the previous attributes.

Select: **Invisible**

Tag: **MATL**

Prompt: **Please type material**

Default: **Cast Iron**

Justification: **Left**

Text Style: **ROMANS**

Height: **.125**

Rotation: **0**

Select: **Invisible**

Tag: **QTY**

Prompt: **Please type quantity required**

Default: (leave blank)

Justification: **Left**

Text Style: **ROMANS**

Height: **.125**

Rotation: **0**

Select: **Invisible**

Tag: **PARTNO**

Prompt: **Please type part number, if any**

Default: (leave blank)

Justification: **Left**

Text Style: **ROMANS**

Height: **.125**

Rotation: **0**

When you have finished, each of the tags should appear in the drawing below the Part tag as shown in Figure 13.28.

Figure 13.28

Defining the Parameters

Now you will add the parameters for the block for the features you will control dynamically.

Click: **Point Parameter** *from the Block Authoring Palette*

Specify parameter location or [Name/Label/Chain/Description/Palette]: **click the endpoint of the leader arrow**

Specify label location: **click a location near the leader arrow** *as shown in Figure 13.29*

The parameter is added to the block definition as in Figure 13.29.

Click: *Flip Parameter from the Block Authoring Palette*

Specify base point of reflection line or [Name/Label/Description/Palette]: **use Object Snap to click the center of the circle**

Specify endpoint of reflection line: **use Ortho or Object Tracking to specify a point directly above the center point you clicked**

Specify label location: **click a point above and to the right of the circle** *as shown in Figure 13.30*

The Flip parameter should appear on screen as in Figure 13.30.

Tip: *The Block Attribute Manager command (Battman) lets you edit a block definition's attributes.*

Figure 13.29

Figure 13.30

Figure 13.31

Defining the Actions

Now that you have the parameters defined, you are ready to add actions to them.

Click: **Actions Tab** *of the Block Authoring palette*

The Actions tab should appear uppermost on the Block Authoring palette as shown in Figure 13.31.

The Actions tab shows the actions that you can add to control blocks dynamically. You will add the stretch action to the point parameter at the end of the leader and the flip action to the flip parameter to allow the leader to flip to the opposite side of the block.

Click: **Stretch Action**

Select parameter: *click on the Point parameter icon that appears as a small square near the end of the leader*

Specify first corner of stretch frame or [CPolygon]: *click below and to the right of the leader*

Specify opposite corner: *click toward the left of the leader at about its midpoint as shown in Figure 13.32 (you only want to stretch this portion)*

Specify objects to stretch: *click the leader line*

Select objects: *[Enter]*

When you have finished, the Stretch action icon will appear on your screen. Moving your cursor over the Stretch action icon shows its features as in Figure 13.32.

Figure 13.32

To add the Flip action,

Click: **Flip Action**

Select parameter: *click on the Flip parameter icon (the square with the arrow)*

Specify selection set for action:
Select objects: *click the leader [Enter]*

The Flip action icon appears as in Figure 13.33.

Figure 13.33

Click: **Parameters tab (from the Block Authoring palette)**

Click: **Base Point Parameter**

Specify parameter location: **click the endpoint of the leader arrow**

A small icon will be added to the dynamic block indicating the base point for the block.

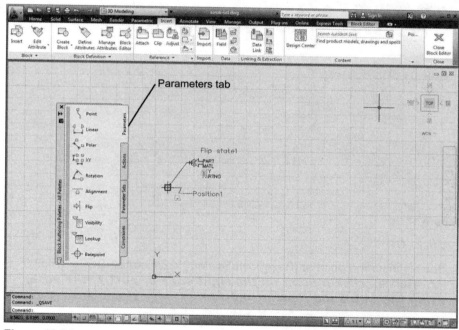

Figure 13.34

Click: **Close Block Editor**

Click: **Save the changes to Balltag** from the Warning message as shown in Figure 13.34

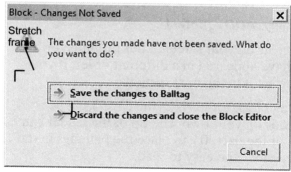

Figure 13.35

Tip: *You may want to use the Write Block command (Wblock) so that the block is available for other drawings. Remember, without Write Block, the block is defined only in the current drawing.*

Inserting the Ball Tags

You will insert the BALLTAG block in paper space. You can use Figure 13.37 as your guide as you insert the ball tags.

Turn **Object Snap Nearest** on.

Make sure Ortho is off.

Double-click outside the viewport to switch to **Paperspace**. Check that you see the paperspace icon.

Click: **Insert Block button**

The Insert dialog box appears on your screen.

Click: **Balltag** *from the pulldown list in the Name area*

The dialog box should look like Figure 13.36. You will specify the location for the block on screen.

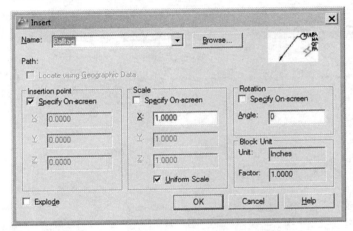

Figure 13.36

Click: **OK**

Specify insertion point or [Basepoint/Scale/X/Y/Z/Rotate/PScale/ PX/PY/ PZ/PRotate]: *click a point on the right edge of part 1, the base, using the AutoSnap Nearest marker*

Enter attribute values

Please type tag number: **1 [Enter]**

Please type part description: **BASE [Enter]**

Please type material <Cast Iron>: **STEEL [Enter]**

Please type quantity required: **1 [Enter]**

Please type part number, if any: **ADD1 [Enter]**

The circle and number 1 appear on your screen. Your prompts for attribute information may have appeared in a different order. If you made a mistake, you can correct it in the next section.

Continue to insert the balltag block for parts 2 (the cover), 3 (the washers), and 4 (the hex head) on your own. The tip of the leader can start anywhere on the edge of the part. Try to place the ball tags in the drawing where they are accessible and easy to read.

Tip: *Remember, the space bar does not act as [Enter] when you are entering text. Because text may include spaces, when you are entering text commands, press [Enter] to end the command.*

Tip: *If the attribute values are not replaced with the text that you typed and do not become invisible, try opening the Block Editor and then resaving the block and closing the Block Editor.*

When adding the ball tags, refer to the following table showing the information for each part.

Item	Name	Mat'l	Q'ty	Number
1	BASE	STEEL	1	ADD1
2	CLAMP TOP	1020ST	1	ADD2
3	.438 X .750 X .125 FLAT WASHER	STOCK	2	ADD3
4	.375-16 UNC X .50 HEX HEAD	STOCK	2	ADD4

When completed, your drawing should look similar to Figure 13.37.

Save your drawing before you continue.

Figure 13.37

Use Zoom Window to enlarge ball tag 1 attached to the base part so that it appears larger on your screen

Click: on the ball tag

The ball tag block become highlighted and icons appear indicating its dynamic properties as shown in Figure 13.38.

Figure 13.38

Now it is time to check out your smart block!

Click: on the Flip arrow

The leader on the ball tag flips to the right side of the block as shown in

Figure 13.39.

Figure 13.39

Click: on the Flip arrow again to return it to the right side

Click: on the Stretch point on the tip of the arrow and stretch it to a new location as shown in Figure 13.40

Figure 13.40

Using these and the other features of dynamic blocks you can make some very useful and sophisticated blocks for use with your drawings.

Changing an Attribute Value

The Edit Attribute command (EATTEDIT) is very useful for changing an attribute value, especially if you mistyped a value or you want to change an existing attribute value.

Click: Edit Attribute (Single) button from the Insert tab, Attribute panel

Click: on balltag 1 block, to edit its attributes

The Enhanced Attribute Editor dialog box appears, as shown in Figure 13.41. Your attributes may appear in a different order.

Tip: *You can start the Enhanced Attribute Editor by double-clicking on a block that has attributes if you have Noun Verb selection turned on in the Options dialog box.*

Tip: *If you have added the datafile base-3d.dwg from a directory where it is "read only" on your network, you will not be able to edit it. Use the Windows Explorer to copy the base-3d. dwg file from the datafile2012 directory to c:\work. Use the XREF command and select the reference for base-3d. Browse to select the file from c:\work (where you should have permission to change files). Select Reload to reload the external reference from this location.*

Figure 13.41

Shown are the block's attributes, prompts, and the values you entered. To change a value, click on an attribute and use the input box at the bottom of the dialog box to change its value. To exit the dialog box,

> *Click: **OK** or click Cancel*

You can also edit multiple attributes at the same time. You might use this if you had created the attribute incorrectly and wanted to change an entire group at once. To do so use Edit Attributes (Multiple) to start the command, –ATTEDIT.

Changing an Externally Referenced Drawing

The primary difference between blocks and externally referenced drawings is that external references are not really added to the current drawing. A pointer is established to the original drawing (external reference) that you attached. If you change the original drawing, the change is also made in any drawing to which it is attached as an external reference. You will try this feature by editing the referenced drawing *base-3d.dwg* in place. You will change the *base-3d.dwg* drawing by filleting its exterior corners.

> *On your own, switch to **model space** so that you can select the parts.*

> *Double-click: **on the Base-3d part** in your drawing to quickly start the Reference Edit command or, click Edit Reference from the ribbon Insert tab, Reference panel*

The Reference Edit dialog box appears as shown in Figure 13.42.

Tip: *If you cannot open base-3D, check to see that your file is not "read-only." Also be sure that the file is not open in another AutoCAD window or session. If it is, you may need to Refclose to close it.*

Figure 13.42

Save Changes | Discard Changes | Add to Working Set | Remove from Working Set

Edit Reference

If the base part is selected as shown,

Click: **OK**

The Edit Reference panel appears on the ribbon along with the message, "Use REFCLOSE or the Refedit toolbar to end reference editing session."

Now the base part is open for editing in place.

Use the commands that you have learned to add a **fillet of radius 0.25** to all four exterior corners of the base so that it looks like Figure 13.43.

DRAWN BY: YOUR NAME | DRAWING TITLE | SCALE: 1∞

Figure 13.43

Click: ***Save Changes from the Edit Reference panel***

Click: ***OK*** *at the message* "All reference edits will be saved."

Open the **base-3d** part you attached as a reference.

Observe that the changes you made in the assembly also have been made to the referenced drawing *base-3d.dwg*. That part now has rounded corners as shown in Figure 13.44.

Figure 13.44

Close base-3d.dwg.

Verify that *asmb-sol.dwg* is your current drawing before continuing.

Its name should appear in the title bar near the top of the screen.

Tip: *You must carefully keep track of your drawings when using external references. If you did not intend to change the assembly but made a change to its externally referenced drawing, the assembly will change. If you want to change an externally referenced drawing but not the assembly, use Save As and save the changed drawing to a new file name. If you move an externally referenced drawing to a different directory, you will have to Reload the external reference and supply the new path in order for the AutoCAD program to find it.*

Creating the Parts List

The next task is to create a parts list for your drawing. The required headings for the *parts list* are Item, Description, Material, Quantity, and Part No. The item number is the number that appears in the ball tag for the part on your assembly drawing. Sometimes a parts list is created on a separate sheet; but often in a small assembly drawing, such as the clamp assembly, it is included in the drawing. This method is preferable because having both in one drawing keeps the parts list from getting separated from the drawing that it should accompany. The parts list is usually positioned near the title block or in the upper right corner of the drawing.

There is no exact standard format for a parts list; each company may have its own standard. You can loosely base dimensions for a parts list on one of the formats recommended in the MIL-15 Technical Drawing Standards or in the ANSI Y14-2M Standards for text sizes and note locations in technical drawings.

On your own, switch to **Layout I** and paper space.

Extracting Attribute Information

You will extract the attribute information that you created to generate the parts list. This data can also be saved to an external file, imported into a spreadsheet or word processing program, and reinserted into your drawing. For this tutorial, you will create a table in the drawing.

Click: **Extract Data button** *from the ribbon Insert tab, Linking & Extraction panel*

The Data Extraction wizard appears. You can start from scratch or use a template previously created using this wizard. Templates allow you to extract data using a format previously established.

Figure 13.45

Click: **the Create a new data extraction** *as shown in Figure 13.45*

Click: **Next**

Use the Save Data Extraction page to name your file *DataOut.dxe*.

The next page of the wizard appears.

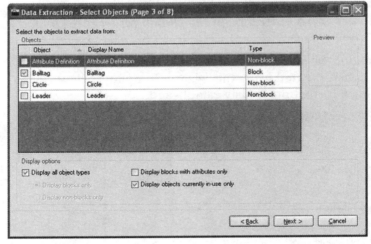

Figure 13.46

Click: ***Select objects in the current drawing*** *as shown in Figure 13.46.*

Click: ***the Select icon from near the center of the dialog box***

Select objects: ***click the four ball tag blocks and press [Enter]***

Click: ***Next***

The Select objects page appears as shown in Figure 13.47.

Figure 13.47

Click: ***so that only balltag is checked from the left column***

Click: ***Next***

The Select Properties page appears as shown in Figure 13.48.

Figure 13.48

Select: **Attribute** *from the Category filter list at the right of the dialog box. It should appear checked. All others should be unchecked.*

Select: **MATL, NUM, PART, PARTNO,** *and* **QTY** *so that they appear checked in the Properties column at the left of the dialog box*

Click: **Next**

Figure 13.49

Click: **to unselect Show count column** *from the lower left of the dialog box, so it appears unchecked*

Right-click: **the Name column** *to show the short-cut menu as shown in* **Figure 13.50**

Click: **Hide**

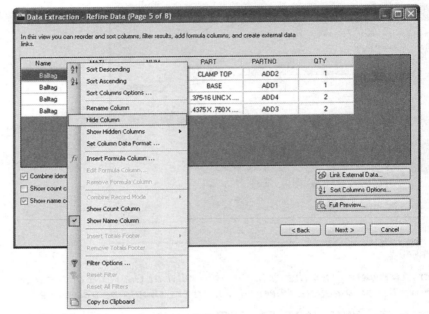

Figure 13.50

On your own, **drag and drop** the columns so that they appear as in Figure 13.51.

Click on the Item column heading to sort the column in ascending order. (Clicking it a second time sorts to descending order.)

Figure 13.51

Click: Next

The Choose Output page of the wizard appears as shown in Figure 13.52.

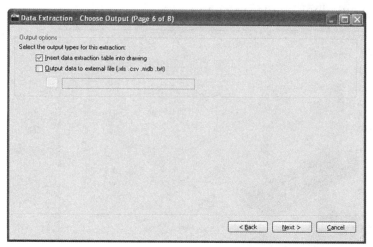

Figure 13.52

Click: **Insert data extraction table into drawing**

Checking Output data to external file, causes the data to be saved to a file format of the types available in the list. For this tutorial, you will create a table in the drawing, so be sure that box is checked.

Click: **Next**

The Table Style page of the wizard appears as shown in Figure 13.53.

Type: **PARTS LIST** *in the title box*

Select: **Use property names as additional column headers**

Tip: *You will usually insert parts lists, notes, and other similar items into the paper space layout, depending on how your drawing is organized.*

Figure 13.53

Click: **Next**

Click: **Finish to extract the data**

The table appears in your drawing attached to the crosshairs.

On your own, position the table near the top of the drawing and click to insert it. Then use the Scale command with a scaling factor of .5 to resize the table. Use Move and locate the parts list in the upper right corner of the drawing. If necessary, switch to model space and pan the parts to a new position on the screen. Switch back to paperspace and move the balltags.

Tip: *If you are going to send a drawing to someone on a disk, you must be sure to send any externally referenced drawings too. Otherwise the recipient will not be able to open the referenced portions of the drawing. A good way to avoid this problem is to use the External Reference command with the Bind option at the command prompt to link the two drawings. Doing so makes the referenced drawing a part of the drawing to which it is attached. Also, it prevents you from unintentionally deleting the original drawing. However, once you have done so, the external reference will no longer update. To use the External Reference Bind option, after you have attached the drawing, pick the External Reference icon, select the referenced objects you want to bind, select the Bind option, and then choose the Bind type (Bind or Insert). One drawback to binding the files is that the file size for the assembly drawing will be larger.*

Your drawing should look similar to Figure 13.54

Figure 13.54

Save your drawing.

Exit the AutoCAD program.

You have completed Tutorial 13.

Key Terms

attribute	attribute tag	dynamic block
attribute prompt	ball tag	parts list

Key Commands

Data Extraction	External Reference	Extract Attributes	Point Parameter
Define Attribute	External Reference Attach	Flip Parameter	Reference Edit
Edit Attribute		Interfere	Zoom Extents
Edit Block Definition	External Reference Clip	Mass Properties	

Exercises

13.1 Clamping Block

Prepare assembly and detail drawings and a parts list based on the following information, using solid modeling techniques. Create solid models of Parts 1 and 2. Join Part 2 to Part 1, using two .500-13UNC 3 2.50 LONG HEX-HEAD BOLTS. Include .500-13UNC NUTS on each bolt. Locate a .625 3 1.250 3 .125 WASHER under the head of each bolt between Parts 1 and 2 and between Part 1 and the NUT. (Each bolt will have three washers and a nut.)

.375-16UNC x 1.50
HEX HEAD SCREW
4 REQD

COVER
MATL = SAE 1020 STEEL

BASE
MATL = SAE 1020 STEEL

GASKET
MATL = .125 NEOPRENE

13.2 Pressure Assembly

Prepare assembly and detail drawings and a parts list of the pressure assembly. Create solid models of the BASE, GASKET, and COVER shown. Use four .375-16UNC 3 1.50 HEX-HEAD SCREWS to join the COVER, GASKET, and BASE. The GASKET assembles between the BASE and COVER.

13.3 Hub Assembly

Create an assembly drawing for the parts shown. Use eight bolts with nuts to assemble the parts.

5.00

2.50

2X ø.6875

8X ø.3125 - EQ SP

ø5.75

ø5.00

ø4.50

22.5°

1   HOUSING
1 REQ

8X ø.3125 - EQ SP

ø5.75

ø5.00

ø4.5025

⌴ ø1.498
⊤ .50

22.5°

.875

.125

2   CAP-2 REQ
RIGHT CAP SHOWN

13.4 Turbine Housing Assembly
Create detail drawings for the two parts shown and save each as a Wblock. Insert each block to form an assembly.

13.5 Geneva Wheel Assembly

Create an assembly drawing for the parts shown, using solid modeling techniques. Experiment with different materials and analyze mass properties.

13.6 Staircase
Use solid modeling to generate this staircase assembly detail.

13.7M Universal Joint

Create an assembly drawing for the parts shown, using solid modeling techniques. Analyze the mass properties of the parts.

SOLID MODELING FOR SECTION AND AUXILIARY VIEWS

14

Introduction

In this tutorial you will learn how to draw section and auxiliary views from 3D solid models. You can generate section and auxiliary views directly from solid models. Refer to Tutorial 9 for review.

Creating Sections from a Solid Model

This time you will start your drawing from a solid model template provided with the datafiles. It is similar to the object that you created in Tutorial 11.

Launch the AutoCAD 2012 software.

Click: *New button*

Use the datafile *solblk2.dwt* as a template for your new drawing.

Save it as *blksect.dwg*.

Select the **3D Modeling** workspace.

A drawing similar to the one you created and modified in Tutorials 11 and 12 appears on your screen, as shown in Figure 14.1.

Figure 14.1

You will use the SOLVIEW command to create a section view that will take the place of front view shown in the lower left viewport. You will erase the lower left viewport by selecting its border. Even though you

Objectives

When you have completed this tutorial, you will be able to

1. Show the internal surfaces of an object, using 3D section views.

2. Section a solid model.

3. Control layer visibility within a viewport.

4. Create an auxiliary view from a 3D model.

Tip: *If necessary, switch to paperspace and use Zoom All to enlarge the layout inside the graphics area.*

can switch between viewports at present, the layer that contains the viewports is frozen. (If the layer on which a viewport resides is frozen or turned off, then you will not be able to erase it.)

On your own, switch to **paperspace**.

Erase the lower left viewport. (Click the magenta viewport border as the object to erase.)

The front view is removed, as in Figure 14.2.

Figure 14.2

Using Solid View (Solview) and Solid Drawing (Soldraw)

The Solview (Solid View) and Soldraw (Solid Drawing) commands are used to generate section and auxiliary views. To create a section view, you specify the cutting plane, the side to view from, the view scaling factor, where to place the section view, and the size of the paper space viewport. Then you use the Soldraw command to view the section hatch. The software automatically generates four new layers for the section view and freezes them where necessary. Use Figure 14.2 to aid in selecting points. You can find the tool on the Home tab Modeling panel.

On your own, verify that running Object Snap for **Endpoint** and **Midpoint** is on.

Make sure that the lower right viewport is active.

 Click: **Solid View button**

Enter an option [UCS/Ortho/Auxiliary/Section]: **S [Enter]**

Specify first point of cutting plane: **use Object Snap Midpoint to select point 1**

Specify second point of cutting plane: **use Object Snap Midpoint to select point 2**

Specify side to view from: *click near point 3*

Enter view scale <0.5000>: *[Enter]*

Specify view center: *click near point 4*

Specify view center <specify viewport>: *[Enter]*

Specify first corner of viewport: *click A, targeting the viewport Endpoint*

Specify opposite corner of viewport: *click B, targeting the viewport Endpoint*

Enter view name: *SECTION [Enter]*

Enter an option [UCS/Ortho/Auxiliary/Section]: *[Enter]*

Your screen should be similar to Figure 14.3.

Tip: *If you want to select in a viewport that is not active, press [Ctrl]-R to toggle the active viewport during commands.*

Figure 14.3

Note that the section hatch pattern is not shown in the front view. You will use Soldraw to show the hatch.

 Click: *Solid Drawing*

Select viewports to draw...

Select objects: *click the border of the lower left viewport*

Select objects: *[Enter]*

One solid selected.

The section hatch should have appeared in the lower left viewport on the screen, similar to Figure 14.4.

If you look at the Layer Control pull-down list, you will see that the Solview command has created a number of new layers with the proper visibilities set for each viewport.

On your own, change the color for layer **SECTION-HAT** to **Red** and set its lineweight to **0.30 mm**. Change the lineweight for layer **SECTION-VIS** to **0.60 mm**.

Figure 14.4

Setup Profile

As you learned in Tutorial 12, Setup Profile, or the Solprof command, eliminates lines on the back surfaces of the object from the screen and inserts hidden lines where necessary in the drawing. Next, you will use the Solprof command to generate 2D profiles in the upper left and lower right viewports.

On your own, switch to model space if needed and activate the upper left viewport.

Click: **Solid Profile**

Select objects: **click on an edge of the object in the upper left viewport**

Select objects: **[Enter]**

Display hidden profile lines on a separate layer? <Y>: **[Enter]**

Project profile lines onto a plane? <Y>: **[Enter]**

Delete tangential edges? <Y>: **[Enter]**

One solid selected.

Click: **the lower right viewport to make it active**

Command: **[Enter]** to restart the Solprof command

Select objects: **click on an edge of the object in the lower right viewport**

Select objects: **[Enter]**

Tip: *Don't forget you can switch to model space and activate a viewport at the same time by double-clicking inside a viewport.*

Display hidden profile lines on a separate layer? <Y>: *[Enter]*

Project profile lines onto a plane? <Y>: *[Enter]*

Delete tangential edges? <Y>: *[Enter]*

One solid selected.

On your own, change the linetype and color of the PH- layers to hidden and blue with lineweight 0.30 mm. Set the lineweight for the PV- layers to 0.60 mm.

Using techniques used earlier in this manual, **freeze layer MYMODEL in the upper left and lower right viewports only**. (Remember to use the Current VP Freeze selection in the Layer Control.)

Black visible lines created by the Solprof command should be visible, with blue hidden lines as shown in Figure 14.5.

Add a cutting plane line to the top view if you want. (It is optional because it is clear where the section was created.)

Adjust the scale and angle of the hatching using the techniques you learned in Tutorial 9.

Add centerlines on your own, remembering to control layer visibility in other viewports.

Save and **close** your drawing before continuing.

Tip: *Remember that you can use Draworder to locate the hatch behind or in front of the object outline.*

Figure 14.5

Next you will use Live Section to create a section through the solid model. This method is useful during modeling and for visualization. You can also use these methods to create drawing views similar to the Solview method you just used. For these tutorials, use the method described. When you are creating your own drawings, use the method that works best for you and fits the needs of your drawing.

You will start a new drawing, using the same prototype previously used.

On your own, use the datafile drawing *solblk2.dwt* as a template to create a new drawing. Save your drawing as **blksect2.dwg**.

A drawing similar to the one you just used appears on your screen as shown in Figure 14.6.

Figure 14.6

You will use the Midpoint running object snap to create a UCS through the center of the part. You will type the UCS command at the prompt. Refer to Figure 14.6 to make your selections.

Turn on running Object Snap for **Midpoint**.

Click: **the upper left viewport to make it active**

Using Section Plane

The Sectionplane command is used to create a section plane object, which represents a cutting plane. The section plane object can be used with the Livesection command to slice the part for visualization or with the Sectionplanetoblock command to generate blocks which can be placed to use as drawing views. Sectionplane can be used with 3D solids, surfaces, and meshes. When you are in the 3D Modeling workspace, Section Plane is available both from the ribbon Home tab, Section panel and from the Solid tab, Section panel. You will use the Solids tab to select it.

Click: **Section Plane button** *from the ribbon Solid tab, Section panel*

Select face or any point to locate section line or [Draw section/Orthographic]: **O [Enter]**

Align section to: [Front/bAck/Top/Bottom/Left/Right] <Top>: **F [Enter]**

The cutting plane object appears parallel to the front view as shown in Figure 14.7. Live sectioning turns on automatically so the object appears cut in half.

In addition to the aligning to an Orthographic orientation relative to a UCS as you just did, you can also specify the cutting plane by choosing:

a *face* -aligns the cutting plane with any surface you select.

a *point* -select any point that is not on a face, then give a through point to define the plane of the section object.

Draw -prompts you for points through which the cutting plane passes. You can draw more than two points that are not in a line to create aligned and offset cutting planes.

Figure 14.7

Using Live Section

Live section generates cross sections of 3D objects intersected by a section plane object. In the last step, the live section was generated in the same step as the Sectionplane. Next you will use Live Section to return the normal appearance of the object. This command also works the other way, to show the cut view.

Click: **Live Section button**

Select section object: **click on the gray section plane object**

The cut portion is restored to the view as shown in Figure 14.8.

Tip: *You can use Solprof to generate the correct 2D top and side views before you section the model.*

Figure 14.8

Section Settings

The Section Settings dialog box lets you control the appearance of 2D section blocks, 3D section blocks, and Live Sections.

To show the Section Settings dialog box,

> *Click: on the small downward arrow at the lower right of the Sections panel*

The dialog box appears on your screen.

> *Click: Select section plane button from the top of the dialog box.*
>
> *Click: on the cutting plane object from your drawing*
>
> Select: *Live Section settings from the radio buttons near the top of the dialog box*

In the Intersection Fill area, make the following selections:

> Face Hatch: *Predefined ANSI31*
>
> Hatch Scale: *2.0000*
>
> Color: *Red*
>
> Lineweight: *0.30 mm*

Leave the other selections set to the defaults.

From the bottom of the dialog box,

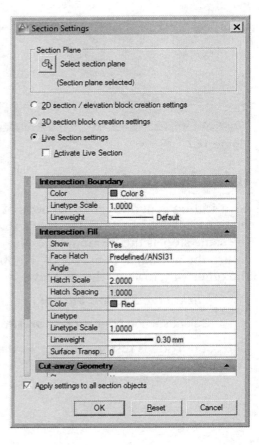

> *Select:* **Apply settings to all section objects, so that it appears checked**
>
> *Click:* **OK to exit the dialog box.**

The settings are applied to the section in your drawing. To see them,

> *Click:* **Live Section button**
>
> Select cutting plane object: **click on the cutting plane**

Notice that now the hatching is shown in red using the angled ANSI31 pattern.

Generate Section

The Sectionplanetoblock command creates block from the section. You can insert the block to create section drawing views. Experiment with this feature on your own.

> **Save** and **close** your drawing.

Creating an Auxiliary View from a 3D Model

You can easily create auxiliary views of 3D solid models by changing the viewpoint in any viewport to show the desired view. You can view the model from any direction inside any viewport. However, good engineering drawing practice requires that adjacent views align; otherwise, interpreting the drawing can be difficult or impossible. In general, you should show at least two principal orthographic views of the object. Additional views are sometimes placed in other locations on the drawing sheet or on a separate sheet. If you use a separate sheet, you should clearly label on the original sheet the view that is located elsewhere. When placing auxiliary views in other locations, you should show a viewing plane line, similar to a cutting plane line, that indicates the direction of sight for the auxiliary view. A viewing direction arrow can also be used to specify the viewing direction. You should clearly label the auxiliary view and preserve its correct orientation, rather than rotate it to a different alignment.

> On your own, start a new drawing.
>
> Use the drawing *anglblok.dwt* provided with the data files as the template.
>
> Name the new drawing *aux3d.dwg*.
>
> If necessary, switch to paperspace and use Zoom All so that the drawing fills the available viewing area.

The solid model shown in Figure 14.9 appears on your screen. You will continue working with this drawing, creating an auxiliary view that shows the true size of the inclined surface.

You will use hot grips to stretch the viewports to different sizes in order to make room for the auxiliary view. Layer VPORT should be turned on. You should see the viewport borders in your drawing.

Figure 14.9

Viewports are paper space objects. Like any other object, you can modify them using Scale, Rotate, Stretch, and Copy, among other commands. To do so, you must be in paper space.

On your own, **switch to paper space**

You should see the paper space icon in the lower left of the screen. Next you will select the viewports so that you can stretch them.

*Click: **on each of the viewport borders** so that their grips appear as shown in Figure 14.9*

*Click: **the grip in the center of the four viewports** as the base grip*

On your own, use Ortho and stretch the viewports to the right so that the final result on the screen looks like Figure 14.10.

Tip: *To activate the grip for each of the four viewports, make an implied Crossing box where the viewports come together at the center of the screen.*

Figure 14.10

Next you will switch to model space to do the following steps.

Command: *MS [Enter]*

Click: *the top right view to make it active*

Command: *Z [Enter]*

Specify corner of window, enter a scale factor (nX or nXP), or [All/Center/ Dynamic/Extents/Previous/Scale/Window/Object] <real time>: *.6X [Enter]*

Now the pictorial view should be shown at 6/10 of its previous size.

> On your own, pan the view of the angled block until it is centered in the upper right viewport.

> Then use Pan Realtime while holding down [Shift] to position the views in the lower right and upper left viewports to make room for a new viewport and realign them with the lower left viewport. Pressing [Shift] while panning constrains the movement to horizontal or vertical, which retains the original alignment.

You will now create your new viewport, using the View menu.

> Check to ensure that VPORT is the current layer.

> Make the upper right viewport active.

Click: *Rectangular from the View tab, Viewports panel*

Specify corner of viewport or [ON/OFF/Fit/Shadeplot/Lock/Object/ Polygonal/Restore/2/3/4] <Fit>: *click point A (Figure 14.11)*

Specify opposite corner: *click point B*

The new viewport appears, as shown in Figure 14.11. The overlapping viewport borders do not matter because you will turn their layers off before plotting your drawing. Depending on which viewport was active when you switched to paper space, you may see a different view in the viewport. This is okay. You will create the auxiliary view in the viewport after a few more steps.

Figure 14.11

Orienting the View

You will reorient the view in the new center viewport so that you can see the angled face clearly.

> Switch to **model space** inside the center viewport. If the viewport is difficult to select, click in any viewport and press [CTRL]+R until the center viewport is selected.

> Use the **maximize viewport** button from the status bar to show only the center viewport.

> If necessary, use the **Steering wheel** to rotate the view of the angled face so that it is clearly visible.

Next you will align the UCS with the angled surface and then use the Plan command inside the new viewport to show the view looking straight toward the UCS. The points you will select are shown in Figure 14.12.

Figure 14.12

3 Point UCS

The 3 Point option of the UCS command creates a User Coordinate System that aligns with the three points you specify. You are prompted to click the origin, a point in the positive X-direction, and a point in the positive Y-direction. Refer to Figure 14.17 for the points to select.

First make sure the UCS icon is displayed at the origin of the coordinate system.

> Command: **UCSICON [Enter]**

> Enter an option [ON/OFF/All/Noorigin/ORigin/Properties] <ON>: **OR [Enter]**

> On your own, be sure that Object Snap is active with **Endpoint** and **Quadrant** selected.

> Click: **3 Point UCS button** from the View tab, Coordinates panel

> Specify new origin point <0,0,0>: **click Endpoint 1**

> Specify point on positive portion of the X-axis <14.000,4.5000,0.5000>: **click Endpoint 2**

> Specify point on positive-Y portion of the UCS XY plane <12.0000,4.5000,0.5000>: **click on the upper curved line at point 3, using Object Snap to Quadrant**

Tip: *You can click and drag the UCSicon to align it to the angled face.*

The UCS icon should appear at the origin and aligned with the angled face. The UCS icon is important because it tells you that the User Coordinate System is correctly aligned with the angled surface. Make sure that the coordinate system appears parallel to the angled face as shown in Figure 14.13.

Figure 14.13

Using Plan

The Plan command aligns the viewpoint in the active viewport so that you are viewing the current UCS, a named UCS, or the WCS straight on. You will accept the default, the current UCS, to show the true size view of the angled surface, with which you have already aligned the coordinate system. You will type the Plan command at the command prompt.

On your own, change the visual style for the viewport to **Wireframe**.

Command: *PLAN [Enter]*

Enter an option [Current ucs/Ucs/World] <Current>: *[Enter]*

The view in the center viewport changes so that you are looking straight at the angled surface as shown in Figure 14.14. Next you will name and save this view so it can easily be restored.

Figure 14.14

Tip: *If you have trouble clicking inside a viewport because it overlaps other viewports, type [Ctrl]-R to toggle the viewport.*

Tip: *When viewports overlap you may notice some viewing issues in the software.*

Tip: *If your viewport is not large enough to show the entire view zoomed to half size, switch back to paper space and use hot grips to stretch the viewport so that it is slightly larger than before. Switch back to model space when you are finished and use Pan once again to position the view.*

Tip: *You can set the Ucsfollow variable to generate the plan view of the current UCS automatically. Pick in a viewport to make it active and then set Ucsfollow to 1. The AutoCAD software automatically generates a plan view of the current UCS in that viewport whenever you change the UCS.*

Command: *VIEW [Enter]*

On your own, select New and name the new view PlaneTrueSize. When you have finished, exit the dialog box.

Now you are ready to return to the layout.

*Click: **Minimize viewport button***

*Double-click: **outside of the viewports to switch to paperspace***

The layout with five viewports return to the screen.

On your own, make the center viewport active and restore the view named PlaneTrueSize. You can use the Viewport control to select the Custom view.

Figure 14.15

Next set the Viewport Scale to half size for the new view. The original views were at half size in the data file.

*Click: **the center viewport** to select it in paperspace*

*Click: **6"=1' from the Viewport Scale list on the status bar***

Switch to model space inside the center viewport. Use the **Pan** to center the view inside the viewport on your own. If the contents of the center viewport don't display correctly, switch to paperspace briefly, then return to model space and resume panning..

When you have finished these steps, your screen should look like Figure 14.16. The view showing the true size of the angled surface is not aligned in projection with the front view.

Figure 14.16

Using 3D Dynamic View

The 3D Dynamic View command uses the metaphor of a camera and a target, where your viewing direction is the line between the camera and the target. It is called 3D Dynamic View because while you are in the command, you can see the view of the selected objects change dynamically on the screen when you move your pointing device. If you do not select any objects for use with the command, you see a special block shaped like a 3D house instead. Use AutoCAD Help to discover more information about the options of the 3D Dynamic View command.

In the next steps you will use the 3D Dynamic View command with the Twist option to twist the viewing angle. You will type DVIEW at the command prompt. The angled surface is at 60° in the front view. You will type 30 for the twist angle, which will produce a view that is aligned 90° to the front view.

On your own, verify that the center viewport is active.

Command: *DVIEW [Enter]*

Select objects or <use DVIEWBLOCK>: *click the 3D model [Enter]*

Enter option [CAmera/TArget/Distance/POints/PAn/Zoom/TWist/ CLip/Hide/Off/Undo]: *TW [Enter]*

Specify view twist angle <0.00>: *30 [Enter]*

CAmera/TArget/Distance/POints/PAn/Zoom/TWist/CLip/Hide/ Off/Undo/<exit>: *[Enter]*

The view is twisted 30° to align with the edge view of the angled surface. Your screen should look like Figure 14.17.

Figure 14.17

On your own, return to paper space and use hot grips to **stretch** the center viewport so that it is large enough to show the entire object.

When you have it sized as you want, set layer **MYMODEL** as the current layer.

Freeze layer VPORT.

When you have finished, your screen should be similar to Figure 14.18.

Figure 14.18

Save your drawing.

Use Save As to save the drawing with the new name *aux3D-2.dwg.*

On your own, thaw layer **VPORT and make it current**.

Switch to **paperspace**.

Erase the center viewport showing the auxiliary view.

Using Solview

This time you will use Solview to create your Auxiliary view. After performing the previous tasks, your screen should look like Figure 14.19.

Figure 14.19

Command: *SOLVIEW [Enter]*

Enter an option [Ucs/Ortho/Auxiliary/Section]: *A [Enter]*

Specify first point of inclined plane: *select point 1 using Object Snap Endpoint*

Specify second point of inclined plane: *select point 2 using Object Snap Quadrant*

Specify side to view from: *click point 3*

Specify view center: *click near point 4*

Specify view center <specify viewport>: *[Enter]*

Specify first corner of viewport: *select point A*

Specify opposite corner of viewport: *select point B*

Enter view name: *AUXILIARY [Enter]*

Enter an option [Ucs/Ortho/Auxiliary/Section]: *[Enter]*

On your own, make layer MYMODEL current.

Freeze layer VPORT and layer VPORTS created by the Solview command.

Your drawing should appear on the screen as shown in Figure 14.20.

Figure 14.20

You have completed Tutorial 14. You can use the techniques you learned previously to project 2D views from the solid with hidden lines shown correctly. Dimensions can be added in paper space to complete the drawing.

Key Terms

cutting plane line	pictorial full section	section view

Key Commands

3 Point UCS	Hide	Sectionplane	Soldraw
3D Dynamic View (Dview)	Livesection	Sectionplanetoblock	Solview
	Object UCS	Setup Drawing	Setup View (Solview)

Exercises

Use solid modeling to create the parts shown. Section the part along the vertical centerline in the front view. The letter M after an exercise means that the given dimensions are in millimeters.

14.1 High-Pressure Seal

14.2 Valve Cover

14.3M Pulley

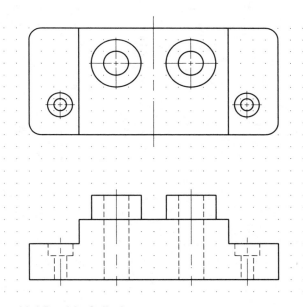

14.4 Double Cylinder

Use solid modeling to draw this object; the grid shown is 0.25 inch. Show the front view as a half section and show the corresponding cutting plane in the top view. On the same views, completely dimension the object to the nearest 0.01 inch. Include any notes that are necessary.

14.5 Plate

Use solid modeling to construct the top view with the cutting plane shown and show the front view in section.

14.6 Support Bracket

Create a solid model of the object shown, then produce a plan view and full section front view. Note the alternate units in brackets; these are the dimensions in millimeters for the part.

14.7 Shaft Support

Generate the given front view from your solid model and create a section view. Assume that the vertical centerline of the shaft in the front view is the cutting plane line for the section view.

14.8 Wedge

Make a solid model based on the given views, then produce a plan view and a full-section front view. Align the sectioned front view with the plan view. Hidden lines and/or cutting planes are not needed in the plan view.

14.9M Pulley Arm

Use solid modeling to create a pictorial view like the one shown.

Use the 2D or solid modeling techniques you have learned in the tutorial to create an auxiliary view of the slanted surfaces for the objects below. The letter M after an exercise number means that the given dimensions are in millimeters.

14.10 Stop Block

14.11 Bearing

14.12 Level

14.13M Tooling Support

RENDERING

Introduction

The *Render* command allows the creation of rendered images of Auto-CAD objects that have surfaces. Rendering is the process of calculating the lighting effects, color, and shape of an object to produce a single view. A rendered view adds greatly to the appearance of the drawing. It makes the object appear more real and aids in interpretation of the object's shape, especially for those unfamiliar with engineering drawings. Rendered drawings can be used very effectively in creating presentations.

AutoCAD objects that have surfaces can be rendered. Objects that have surfaces include solid models, regions, and objects created with the AutoCAD surface modeling commands.

Rendering is a mathematically complex process. When you are rendering, the capabilities of your hardware, such as speed, amount of memory, and the resolution of the display, are particularly noticeable. The complex rendering calculations demand more of your hardware than just running the AutoCAD program, so you may notice that your system seems slower. Resolution affects not only the speed with which objects are rendered, but also the quality of the rendered appearance. Better appearance can be gained by rendering to a higher resolution and more colors; however, increased resolution and more colors take longer to render.

In this tutorial you will learn to apply materials, surface maps, and lighting to your drawing and to render views of an object. Applying a material to a surface in your drawing gives the surface its color and shininess; it is similar to painting the surface. Materials can also reflect light like a mirror or be transparent like glass. Adding a surface map is similar to adding wallpaper; surface maps are patterns or pictures that you can apply to the surface of an object. Lighting illuminates the surfaces. Lighting is a very important factor in creating the desired effect in your rendered drawing.

In addition to single views, views can be rendered sequentially to produce the sense of motion, similar to the way a flip book works. You can use this to create animations for presentations and snapshot views for navigating through a complex drawing.

Starting

In this tutorial you will use Render to shade a solid model.

Launch the AutoCAD 2012 program.

Start a new drawing from the template drawing *GuidePart.dwg* provided with the datafiles.

Save your drawing as *GuideRender.dwg*.

15

Objectives

When you have completed this tutorial, you will be able to

1. Realistically shade a solid model or surface mesh-modeled drawing.

2. Set up and use lighting effects.

3. Apply materials.

4. Save rendered files for use with other programs.

The drawing appears on your screen, as shown in Figure 15.1.

Render has its own ribbon tab.

Click: **Render tab**

Tip: *Turn off the grid before you render if you do not like its appearance.*

Figure 15.1

The render tab has four main panels: Lights, Sun and Location, Materials, and Render (Figure 15.2). Each of these panels provides settings that control the resulting image when you render your model. For the beginner many of the settings can be left set at the defaults. In general, when you have a number of settings, it is best to make small changes and view the result, rather than making a number of changes at once.

Figure 15.2

The Render Panel

Render Preset List/Select Render Preset

At the top of the Render panel is a list of standard render presets ranging from lowest to highest quality, and up to four custom render presets. It also allows access to the Render Presets Manager.

Click: **Medium** *to expand the Render Preset list*

The rendering presets that control the quality of the output image are: Draft, Low, Medium, High, and Presentation.

Draft -used for quick test renderings. Quality is poor because *anti-aliasing* is bypassed and *sample filtering* is very low. This render preset produces very low quality rendering but renders quickly.

Low - provides better quality than the Draft preset. Anti-aliasing is bypassed but sample filtering is improved. Raytracing is also active, by default, so better quality shading occurs. This preset is best used for test rendering that requires better quality than Draft.

Medium - uses better sample filtering, and anti-aliasing is active. Ray-tracing is active with increased reflection depth settings when compared to the Low render preset. This preset offers a good balance between quality and render speed.

High - matches the Medium preset settings with regards to antialiasing, but sample filtering and raytracing is improved. Due to the improved sample filtering and raytracing, rendered images take longer to process, but the image quality is much better.

Presentation - used for high-quality, photo-realistic rendered images. This takes the longest to process. Sample filtering and raytracing are further improved. Since this preset is used for final renderings, global illumination settings are commonly used in conjunction.

When you are rendering, the best approach often is to start with the least complex method and progress to more complex renderings. This way, while you are working out the details of how to set up the lighting and surfaces for a realistic appearance, you do not have to wait a long time for a complex rendering. For this tutorial, you will use the Medium preset setting.

There are many settings that are adjusted when you select a preset. To see what settings are available, enter Renderpresets on the command line.

    Command: ***RENDERPRESETS [Enter]***

The Render Presets Manager appears on your screen as shown in Figure 15.3. You can add your own custom presets or review and change the standard ones.

    On your own, click on the various presets on the left of the dialog box and observe the changing settings on the right. Close the Render Presets Manager dialog box when you are done reviewing.

Figure 15.3

Tip: *If prompted whether to install the medium images library, do so.*

Render

The Render button generates a realistically shaded image of the model. You see the results quickly which is useful when you are testing your render settings. Producing the best appearance often takes a sequence of changing settings, lighting, and materials a bit at a time.

Click: ***Render***

The render window appears on your screen with the generated rendering of the object similar to Figure 15.4. The rendered image looks very similar to your original drawing. This is because there are no lights or material added. You will add those later in this tutorial.

Examine the Image Information listed alongside the rendered view. These are current settings used for this rendering. The more complex the calculations, the more time it will take to render. Starting with lower quality and working toward higher quality is more efficient.

Figure 15.4

Close the Render window.

Render Progress Shows a visual bar representing the percentage complete for the rendering. This allows you to estimate how much longer the rendering will take.

Render Output Files

Render Output File This button is a toggle. When the button is not highlighted (off) the render command output is shown in the Render Window.

When the button is highlighted, the rendered image is written to a file in the location and filename you specify in the input box area. You can browse to select using the ellipsis (...) selection at the right, when the Render Output File button is toggled on.

Click: **Render Output File button** to toggle it on

Click: **ellipsis (...)** to show the Render Output File Browser

Click: **to expand the Files of Type list** as shown in Figure 15.5

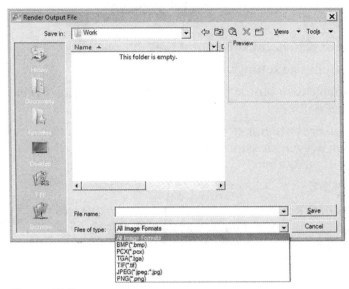

Figure 15.5

The File Type list shows the following formats:

- **BMP (*.bmp)** Still-image bitmap file in the Windows bitmap (*.bmp*) format.

- **PCX (*.pcx)** Simple format that provides minimum file compression.

- **TGA (*.tga)** File format that supports 32-bit true color; (24-bit color plus an alpha channel). It is typically used as a true color format.

- **TIF (*.tif)** Multiplatform bitmap format.

- **JPEG (*.jpg)** Popular format for posting image files on the Internet for minimum file size and minimum download time.

- **PNG (*.png)** Still-image file format developed for use with the Internet and World Wide Web.

Close the Render Output dialog box

Click: **to toggle the Render Output File button off**

Click: **to expand the Render panel** by clicking its title bar where you see the small downward arrow

Click: **to pin the Render panel**

The expanded Render panel shows options and controls.

The **Render Quality Slider** adjusts the sampling to produce poorer quality, but quicker renders, or higher quality and slower renders.

Render Output Size

Render Output Size shows the current output resolution setting for the rendered image. The default is 640 x 480 pixels. A higher number of pixels produces a smoother appearing image. Opening the Output Size list displays the following:

- Four of the most commonly used output resolutions.
- Up to four custom size settings.
- The Specify Image Size button used to show the dialog box to set any desired size.

Note: Custom output sizes are not stored with the drawing and they are not retained between drawing sessions.

Adjust Render Exposure

 Click: ***the Adjust Render Exposure button*** *to display the Adjust Render Exposure dialog box shown in Figure 15.6*

Figure 15.6

Brightness Controls the viewport's brightness level for photometric lighting. Sets the LOGEXPBRIGHTNESS system variable.

Contrast controls the viewport's contrast for photometric lighting.

Mid tones controls the viewport's mid tones level for photometric lighting.

Exterior Daylight controls whether the exterior daylight is enabled when using photometric lighting.

Process Background controls whether the background should be processed using exposure control during the rendering process.

Click: ***Cancel*** *to exit the dialog box without making any changes*

Render Environment

You can use environmental features to set up atmospheric effects or background images. You can enhance a rendered image by means of atmospheric effects like fog and depth cuing or by adding a bitmap image as a background.

 *Click: **Render Environment button***

The Render Environment dialog box appears similar to Figure 15.7.

Figure 15.7

Fog and depth cuing are very similar atmospheric effects that cause objects to appear to fade as they increase in distance from the camera. Fog uses a white color while depth cuing uses black.

*Click: **OK** to exit the dialog box*

Render Window

This button Redisplays the contents of the render window.

Advanced Render Settings

*Click: **the small downward arrow at the right of the Render Palette title bar** to display the Advanced Render Settings palette as shown in Figure 15.8*

Render Context

Rendering Procedure Controls the model content that gets processed during rendering. The render procedure has three settings: View, Crop, and Selected.

- **View** renders the current view without displaying the Render dialog box.
- **Crop** prompts to specify an area to render. This option is only available when Viewport is selected as the Destination.
- **Selected** prompts to select objects during the render operation.

Destination specifies whether to send the rendered result to the Render Window or to a viewport.

Output File Name allows you to specify a file name and location where the rendered image will be stored.

Figure 15.8

Output Size specifies the output resolution for the rendered image.

Exposure Type controls the tone operator setting. This does not need to be stored in the named render preset. Rather it can be stored per drawing in the render context.

- **Automatic** specifies that the tone operator used should be chosen to match the current viewport tone operator strategy.

- **Logarithmic** specifies to use the log exposure control.

Physical Scale specifies the physical scale. The default is 1500. If you have very small or very large objects to render, you may want to adjust this value.

Medium	
General	
Render Context	
Procedure	View
Destination	Window
Output file n...	
Output size	640 x 480
Exposure Type	Automatic
Physical Scale	1500.0000
Materials	
Apply materi...	On
Texture filter...	On
Force 2-sided	On
Sampling	
Min samples	1
Max samples	4
Filter type	Gauss
Filter width	3.0000
Filter height	3.0000
Contrast color	0.0500, 0.0500, 0.0500, 0.0500
Contrast red	0.0500
Contrast blue	0.0500
Contrast gre...	0.0500
Contrast alpha	0.0500
Shadows	
Mode	Simple
Shadow map	Off
Sampling M...	1/2
Ray Tracing	
Indirect Illumination	
Global Illumination	
Final Gather	
Light Properties	
Diagnostic	
Processing	

Advanced Render Settings

Materials

Toggles which control how materials are handled by the renderer.

Apply Materials applies the surface materials that you defined and attached to the objects in the drawing. If Apply Materials is not on, all objects in the drawing assume the values defined for the GLOBAL material.

Texture Filtering specifies filtering for texture maps.

Force 2-Sided controls whether both sides of faces are rendered.

Sampling

Min Samples sets the minimum sample rate. The value represents the number of samples per pixel. A value greater than or equal to 1 indicates that one or more samples are computed per pixel. A fractional value indicates that one sample is computed for every N pixels (for example, 1/16 computes a minimum of one sample for every sixteen pixels).

Max Samples sets the maximum sample rate. If neighboring samples find a difference in contrast that exceeds the contrast limit, the area containing the contrast is subdivided to the depth specified by Maximum.

The values of the Min Samples and Max Samples lists are "locked" together so that the value of Min Samples can't exceed the value of Max Samples.

Filter Type Determines how multiple samples are combined into a single pixel value. The filter types are:

- **Box** sums all samples in the filter area with equal weight. This is the quickest sampling method.

- **Gauss** weights the samples using a bell curve centered on the pixel.

- **Triangle** weights the samples using a pyramid centered on the pixel.

- **Mitchell** weights the samples using a curve (steeper than Gauss) centered on the pixel.

- **Lanczos** weights the samples using a curve (steeper than Gauss) centered on the pixel, diminishing the effect of samples at the edge of the filter area.

Filter Width and Filter Height specifies the size of the filtered area. Increasing the value of Filter Width and Filter Height can soften the image; however, it will increase rendering time.

Contrast Color opens the Select Color dialog box where you interactively specify the R,G,B threshold values.

Contrast Red, Blue, Green specifies the threshold values for the red, blue, and green components of samples. These values are normalized, and range from 0.0 to 1.0, where 0.0 indicates the color component is fully unsaturated (black, or 0 in eight-bit encoding) and 1.0 indicates the color component is fully saturated (white, or 255 in eight-bit encoding).

Contrast Alpha specifies the threshold value for the alpha component of samples. This value is normalized and ranges from 0.0 (fully transparent, or 0 in eight-bit encoding) to 1.0 (fully opaque, or 255 in eight-bit encoding).

580 Tutorial 15 RENDERING

Shadows

Shadows affect how shadows appear in the rendered image.

Enable specifies if shadows are computed during rendering.

Mode allows Simple, Sort, or Segments.

- **Simple** generates shadow shaders in a random order.
- **Sort** generates shadow shaders in order, from the object to the light.
- **Segments** generates shadow shaders in order along the light ray from the volume shaders to the segments of the light ray between the object and the light.

Shadow Map controls if shadow mapping is used to render shadows. When on, the renderer renders shadow-mapped shadows. When off, all shadows are ray-traced.

Sampling Multiplier limits shadow sampling for area lights. Allows draft and low-quality presets to reduce area light sampling.

Ray Tracing

This contains settings that affect the shading of a rendered image.

Enable specifies if ray tracing should be performed when shading.

Max Depth limits the combination of reflection and refraction. Tracing of a ray stops when the total number of reflections and refractions reaches the maximum depth. For example, if Max Depth equals 3 and the two trace depths each equal the default value of 2, a ray can be reflected twice and refracted once, or vice versa, but it cannot be reflected and refracted four times.

Max Reflections sets the number of times a ray can be reflected. At 0, no reflection occurs. At 1, the ray can be reflected once only. At 2, the ray can be reflected twice, and so on.

Max Refractions sets the number of times a ray can be refracted. At 0, no refraction occurs. At 1, the ray can be refracted once only. At 2, the ray can be refracted twice, and so on.

Global Illumination

Global Illumination affects how your scene is illuminated.

Enable specifies if lights should cast indirect light into the scene.

Photons/Samples sets how many photons are used to compute the intensity of the global illumination. Increasing this value makes global illumination less noisy but also more blurry. Decreasing this value makes global illumination more noisy but less blurry. The larger the Samples value, the greater the rendering time.

Use Radius determines the size of photons. When on, the spinner value sets the size of photons. When off, each photon is calculated to be 1/10 of the radius of the full scene.

Radius specifies the area within which photons will be used when illuminance is computed.

Max Depth limits the combination of reflection and refraction. Reflection and refraction of a photon stop when the total number of both equals the Max Depth setting. For example, if Max Depth equals 3 and the trace depths each equal 2, a photon can be reflected twice and refracted once, or vice versa, but it can't be reflected and refracted four times.

Max Reflections sets the number of times a photon can be reflected. At 0, no reflection occurs. At 1, the photon can be reflected once only. At 2, the photon can be reflected twice, and so on.

Max Refractions sets the number of times a photon can be refracted. At 0, no refraction occurs. At 1, the photon can be refracted once only. At 2, the photon can be refracted twice, and so on.

Final Gather

Final Gather calculates global illumination.

Mode controls the final gathering dynamic settings.

- **On** turns on the global illumination in final gather.
- **Off** turns off the calculation of global illumination in final gather.
- **Auto** indicates that the final gather should be dynamically enabled or disabled at render time based on the skylight status.

Rays sets how many rays are used to compute indirect illumination in a final gather. Increasing this value makes global illumination less noisy, but also increases rendering time.

Radius Mode specifies the radius mode for final gather processing.

- **On** specifies that the setting means the Max Radius setting is used for final gather processing. The radius is specified in world units, and defaults to 10 percent of the maximum circumference of the model.
- **Off** specifies the maximum radius is the default value of 10 percent of the maximum model radius, in world units.
- **View** specifies the Max Radius setting in pixels instead of world units and is used for final gather processing.

Max Radius sets the maximum radius within which final gathering is processed. Reducing this value can improve quality at a cost of increased rendering time.

Use Min controls whether the Min Radius setting is used during final gather processing. When on, the minimum radius setting is used for final gather processing. When off, the minimum radius is not used.

Min Radius sets the minimum radius within which final gathering is processed. Increasing this value can improve quality but increase rendering time.

Light Properties

Light Properties affects how lights behave when calculating indirect illumination. By default, the energy and photon settings apply to all lights in a scene.

Photons/Light sets the number of photons emitted by each light for use in global illumination. Increasing this value increases the accuracy of global illumination, but also increases the amount of memory used and the length of render time. Decreasing this value improves memory usage and render time, and can be useful for previewing global-illumination effects.

Energy Multiplier multiplies the global illumination, and indirect light, intensity of the rendered image.

Visual

Visual helps you understand why the renderer is behaving in a certain way.

Grid renders an image that shows the coordinate space of objects, the world, or camera.

- **Object** shows local coordinates (UVW). Each object has its own coordinate space.
- **World** shows world coordinates (XYZ). The same coordinate system applies to all objects.
- **Camera** shows camera coordinates, which appear as a rectangular grid superimposed on the view.

Grid Size sets the size of the grid.

Photon renders the effect of a photon map. This requires that a photon map be present. If no photon map is present, the Photon rendering looks just like the nondiagnostic rendering of the scene: the renderer first renders the shaded scene, then replaces it with the pseudocolor image.

- **Density** renders the photon map as it is projected into the scene. High density is displayed in red, and lower values render in increasingly cooler colors.
- **Irradiance** is similar to Density rendering, but shades the photons based on their irradiance. The maximum irradiance is rendered in red, and lower values render in increasingly cooler colors.

BSP renders a visualization of the parameters used by the tree in the BSP ray-trace acceleration method. If a message from the renderer reports excessively large depth or size values, or if rendering seems unusually slow, this can help you locate the problem.

- **Depth** shows the depth of the tree, with top faces in bright red, and increasingly deep faces in increasingly cool colors.
- **Size** shows the size of leaves in the tree, with differently sized leaves indicated by different colors.

Processing

Tile Size determines the tile size for rendering. To render a scene, the image is subdivided into tiles. The smaller the tile size, the more image updates are generated during rendering. When the tile size is reduced, the number of image updates increases, meaning that a rendering takes longer to complete. If the tile size is increased, fewer image updates occur and the rendering takes less time to complete.

Tile Order specifies the render order for image tiles. This determines how the tile order appears as the image is rendered in the Render Window.

- **Hilbert** causes the next tile to be rendered to be based on the "cost" of switching to the next one.
- **Spiral** renders tiles beginning at the center of the image, and spiral outward.
- **Left to Right** renders tiles in columns, from bottom to top, left to right.
- **Right to Left** renders tiles in columns, from bottom to top, right to left.
- **Top to Bottom** renders tiles in rows, from right to left, top to bottom.
- **Bottom to Top** renders tiles in rows, from right to left, bottom to top.

Memory Limit determines the memory limit for rendering. If the memory limit is reached, the geometry for some objects is discarded in order to allocate memory for other objects.

On your own, close the Advanced Render Settings palette.

Adding Lights

When there are no lights in a scene, the scene is shaded or rendered with default lighting. Default lighting is derived from two distant sources that follow the viewpoint as you move around the model. All faces in the model are illuminated so that they are visually discernible. To turn the default lighting on or off use the DEFAULTLIGHTING system variable.

Once you have added lights you can control the overall brightness of the rendering by adjusting the render exposure, which is used to simulate ambient light. If you want to adjust the exposure/ambient light, enter RENDEREXPOSURE on the command line or adjust it using the ribbon Render tab, expand the Render panel and select Adjust Render Exposure.

Ambient lighting illuminates every surface equally, so distinguishing one surface on the object from the next may be difficult. The best use for ambient lighting is to add some light to back surfaces of the object so that they do not appear entirely dark. You can improve the look of your rendered drawing by adding additional lights. Lighting is very important in achieving good-looking rendering results.

In addition to ambient light, three different types of lights are available. A *point light* is like a bare lightbulb that casts light in every direction (i.e., it is omnidirectional). A *distant light* is like sunlight. It illuminates with equal brightness all the surfaces on which it shines. A *spotlight* highlights certain key areas and casts light only toward the selected target. Point lights and spotlights create indoor lighting effects.

Click: **Create Lights button** *to expand the lighting choices*

Click: **Point** *from the list*

A warning may display as shown in Figure 15.9 telling you that the default lighting will be turned off when you use custom lighting.

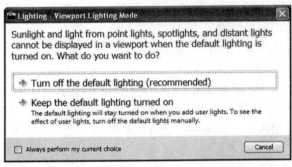

Figure 15.9

Click: **Turn off the default lighting (recommended)**

You are now prompted to enter the location of the light source. You can position the light by clicking a location from the screen; however, for this example you will type in the coordinates for the light. Positioning the light by clicking from the screen is difficult because you are selecting only the X- and Y-coordinates. (You can use point filters and then set the Z-location if you want. Use Help to find out more about point filters.) When specifying the coordinates for the light position, do not position it too close to the object.

Specify source location <0,0,0>: *0,-2,5 [Enter]*

You will enter the name of the new light and features that determine its appearance such as intensity (brightness).

Enter an option to change [Name/Intensity/Status/shadoW/Attenuation/Color/eXit] <eXit>: *N [Enter]*

Enter light name <Pointlight1>: *FILL [Enter]*

Enter an option to change [Name/Intensity/Status/shadoW/Attenuation/Color/eXit] <eXit>: *I [Enter]*

Enter intensity (0.00 - max float) <1.0000>: *.5 [Enter]*

Enter an option to change [Name/Intensity/Status/shadoW/Attenuation/Color/eXit] <eXit>: *[Enter]*

On your own, use **Zoom Extents** to see the point light *glyph* (light symbol).

The light is represented with a symbol called a glyph. It appears like a circle with a cross at the center as shown in Figure 15.10.

Light glyph

Figure 15.10

Whenever you make changes that affect the rendered appearance of your object, check the result by rendering your drawing.

*Click: **Render button***

The Render window appears.

> Use your task bar to show the Render Window if it is behind another window. You may have to use the Render Window Tools menu and select Zoom + to get a closer look at the rendering. Notice the image now has directed light and the addition of shadows. Close the Render Window on your own.

The new light is too close to the object, causing it to appear washed out near the light. Next you will move it up using the 3D gizmo.

*Click: **on the point light glyph** to show the 3D gizmo (Figure 15.11).*

Use 3D gizmo
to drag the light
glyph upward

Figure 15.11

*Click: **the blue arrow and drag the light glyph upward** in the z-direction to a location of about 0,-2,22*

When you quit dragging, you will notice the lighting on the screen view of the object changing to reflect the new position of the light.

*Click: **Render button***

The Render Window shows the new appearance.

Figure 15.12

*Click: **to close the Render Window***

*Click: **the light glyph***

*Press: **[Ctrl]–1 to show the Properties palette***

The Properties palette appears as shown in Figure 15.13.

Figure 15.13

Review the properties of the Light. Notice the Name, Type, Intensity factor, and position values that you entered earlier. You can make changes to these at any time. For now, do not make any changes.

Close the Properties palette.

Press [ESC] twice to unselect the light glyph

Change the Visual Style to Realistic on your own.

Next, you will add a spotlight behind the object to light the right surface and provide highlights in the drawing.

Click: **the Lights button to expand the lighting choices**

Click: **Spotlight**

You are now prompted to enter the location of the light source followed by the target that the light will point at. You will also name the light "Accent" and set the intensity.

Specify source location <0,0,0>: *0,–60,50 [Enter]*

Specify target location <0,0,0>: *use Object Snap Endpoint to select the right corner of the rounded arc identified as A in Figure 15.13*

[Name/Intensity/Status/Hotspot/Falloff/shadoW/Attenuation/Color/eXit] <eXit>: *N [Enter]*

Enter light name <Spotlight1>: *ACCENT [Enter]*

[Name/Intensity/Status/Hotspot/Falloff/shadoW/Attenuation/Color/eXit] <eXit>: *I [Enter]*

Enter intensity (0.00 - max float) <1.0000>: *0.75 [Enter]*

Next, you will set the falloff and hotspot for the spotlight. *Falloff* is the angle of the cone of light from the spotlight. *Hotspot* is the angle of the cone of light for the brightest area of the beam. The angles for the falloff and hotspot must be between 0° and 160°. You can not set Hotspot to a greater value than Falloff.

Enter an option to change

[Name/Intensity/Status/Hotspot/Falloff/shadoW/Attenuation/Color/eXit] <eXit>: *H [Enter]*

Enter hotspot angle (0.00-160.00) <45.0000>: *15 [Enter]*

[Name/Intensity/Status/Hotspot/Falloff/shadoW/Attenuation/Color/eXit] <eXit>: *F [Enter]*

Enter falloff angle (0.00-160.00) <50>: *30 [Enter]*

[Name/Intensity/Status/Hotspot/Falloff/shadoW/Attenuation/Color/eXit] <eXit>: *[Enter]*

Click: **Render button**

The model is rendered to the render window. Notice that the right side of the model is lit more.

Choosing Materials

You can also improve your rendered drawing by selecting or creating realistic-looking *materials* for the objects in it. You can either use the materials that are provided in the Materials Library or create your own materials with Render.

Click: **Materials Browser button**

Click: **Autodesk Library** *from the list at left (if it does not show, click the icon identified in Figure 15.14)*

On your own, click and drag on the right edge of the browser window to make the browser window wider.

Click the **Swatch Size slider** and drag it smaller to fit more samples (or swatches) in the browser area as shown in Figure 15.14.

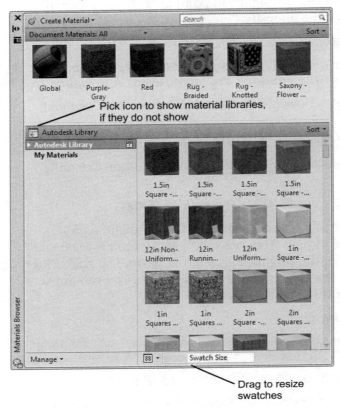

Figure 15.14

A single solid object in the drawing can have only one material assigned. This limitation usually isn't a problem in engineering drawings because you will typically make each part in an assembly a separate object in the drawing. Do not use Boolean operators to join parts to which you want to assign different materials.

To select from the library of premade materials,

Click: **Autodesk Library** *so the small arrow points downward, indicating it is expanded*

The categories of materials in that library show in the left pane of the dialog box.

Click: **Metal - Aluminum** *from the left pane of the dialog box*

Drag and drop Anodized - Red on to your drawing object.

Once the material is used in the drawing it is added to the Document Materials shown at the top row of the Materials Browser. Your screen should look similar to Figure 15.15.

Figure 15.15

The object in the viewport now appears as though it is made of red annodized aluminum..

Creating a New Material

You can create your own materials. Next, you will create a material that looks like copper. Make sure that the Materials palette is still open.

Click: **Create New Material** *from the upper left of the Material Browser*

Click: **Ceramic** *from the drop down list as shown in Figure 15.16*

Figure 15.16

The Materials Editor appears as shown in Figure 15.17.

Tip: *An extensive material and texture library is included with AutoCAD 2012.*
Make sure to install the Materials Library. The library can be accessed through the Configuration button on Add/Remove features in the installer. By default, the materials are installed in the File Locations path specified on the Files tab of the Options dialog box. (See Texture Maps Search Path on the Files tab for the location of texture maps.)

Note: *The materials library components are always installed to the default location. If you change the paths before you install the materials library, the new materials may not display on the Material Browser and the texture maps may not be referenced by the materials. Either copy the newly installed files to the location you want, or change the path to the correct location.*

Warning: *If you don't see the list of materials shown in Figure 15.14, you may not have the path set correctly to tell the AutoCAD software where to look for texture files. To change the path, pick Tools, Options. Use the Files tab of the dialog box to set the path to where your texture files are stored. Make sure that you have loaded the materials files.*

Type: **MyCeramic** *in the Name box in place of Default Ceramic*

Click: **to expand the color and texture options** *(the small arrow to the right of the Color input)*

Click: **Speckle**

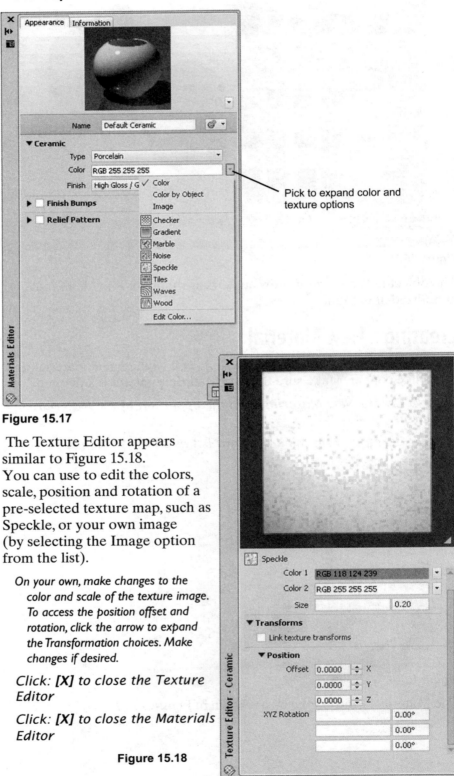

Pick to expand color and texture options

Figure 15.17

The Texture Editor appears similar to Figure 15.18. You can use to edit the colors, scale, position and rotation of a pre-selected texture map, such as Speckle, or your own image (by selecting the Image option from the list).

On your own, make changes to the color and scale of the texture image. To access the position offset and rotation, click the arrow to expand the Transformation choices. Make changes if desired.

Click: **[X]** *to close the Texture Editor*

Click: **[X]** *to close the Materials Editor*

Figure 15.18

The new MyCeramic material now shows in the Materials Browser preview box. To save the materials to your custom library,

> Right-click: *on the desired material,*
>
> Click: **Add to**
>
> Click: **My Materials, then select your library**

Figure 15.19

To apply the new material to the object it is best to remove the old material first.

> Drag and drop: **Global material** *onto your object*

The object will return to its original color. Now add the new material.

> Drag and Drop: **MyCeramic** *onto your object*
>
> Click: **Render button** *to see the results of the new material*

Next you will use a noticeably patterned material so that you can easily see the results in the next steps.

> On your own, drag and drop the Flooring - Vinyl, Checker Black - White material onto your object. Render the result in the render window with the default lighting. The result should look similar to Figure 15.20.
>
> Close the Material Browser.

Figure 15.20

Warning: *The AutoCAD software keeps track of the location (path) for the textures and bitmapped materials. If your options do not show this location correctly for where your files are stored, you will not be able to see materials that contain textures (bitmaps) correctly.*

Adjusting Mapping

When bitmaps or materials that use bitmapped patterns are applied to surfaces in your drawing, you can control the type of mapping, coordinates, scale, repeat, and other aspects of the maps' appearance. There are several types of mapping.

Planar Mapping

This maps the image onto the object as if you were projecting it from a slide projector onto a 2D surface. The image is not distorted, but the image is scaled to fit the object. This mapping is most commonly used for faces.

Box Mapping

This maps an image onto a boxlike solid. The image is repeated on each side of the object.

Spherical Mapping

Warps the image both horizontally and vertically. The top edge of the map is compressed to a point at the "north pole" of the sphere, as is the bottom edge at the "south pole."

Cylindrical Mapping

This maps an image onto a cylindrical object; the horizontal edges are wrapped together but not the top and bottom edges. The height of the image is scaled along the cylinder's axis.

Click: *to expand the Mapping drop-down list from the Render tab, Materials panel*

Click: *Box button*

Select faces or objects: *click anywhere on the model [Enter]*

Accept the mapping or [Move/Rotate/reseT/sWitch mapping mode]: *click and drag on a triangular grip or use the axes of the 3D gizmo to move the pattern (Figure 15.21)*

Figure 15.21

Right-click on the 3D gizmo and use the rotation orbits to rotate the pattern. When you have finished experimenting with the rotation, right-click on the 3D gizmo and click **Reset**. (Notice you can type the option letters also.)

Accept the mapping or [Move/Rotate/reseT/sWitch mapping mode]: *[Enter] to end the command*

Using mapped materials is a good way to add detail to your rendered drawing without creating complex models. For example, you could model every brick in a wall as a separate solid and create a different solid for the mortar between them. Doing so would create a very complex solid model with a lot of vertices.

Instead, you can create the entire wall as a single flat surface and then apply the appearance of brick to it as a bitmapped pattern. The drawing will look very detailed but will have far fewer vertices and take less file space than the previous example. You can combine bitmaps and bump maps to give a raised appearance to parts of the material.

Adding Backgrounds

You can add a background to your rendering by using the Named Views button on the View toolbar. Backgrounds can be solid colors, gradient colors (which blend one to three colors), images (bitmaps), or the current AutoCAD image (selected using Merge).

Click: **View Manager button** *from the ribbon View tab, Views panel*

The View Manager dialog box appears as shown in Figure 15.22.

Click: **New button**

The New View dialog box appears, similar to Figure 15.22 at right.

Figure 15.22

Type: **RenderWithBackground** *for the View name*

On your own, use the Background drop-down list from the bottom of the dialog box to set a solid background. Select a color for the background (setting R, B, and G for red, blue, and green each to 255). (Notice that you can also use a gradient or an image for the background.)

Click: **OK** *to exit the Background dialog box*

Click: **the RenderWithBackground** *view name to highlight it*

Click: **Set Current button**

Click: **OK** *to exit the View dialog box*

Click: **Render button**

The drawing in the Render Window, now appears with a solid colored background as shown in Figure 15.23.

Figure 15.23

Rendering to a File

Rendering your drawing to a file allows you to use it in other programs. For example, you can render your drawing to a Windows metafile format and paste it into various Windows applications.

Click: **Render Output File button** *(toggle it to on)*

Click: **...** *(ellipsis) at right of Render Output File button*

On your own, use the dialog box to enter a file name. Click *.tif* as the type of rendered file. Click the Save button to continue.

The TIFF Image Options dialog box appears.

Set the options for the resolution and color depth for your file.

Click: **Render button**

The Render window will appear and the rendering will take place and the file will be written to your desired location. You can use Windows Explorer to locate the file and preview it.

On your own, **save** and **close** your *GuideRender.dwg* file.

Using Sun Properties

Sun properties is a particularly useful feature for creating lighting and doing lighting studies in architectural drawings. You can use it to show

Render Output   Ellipsis
File button

the different effects that sunlight has on the rendered view at different times of the day and year. The Sun Properties feature provides this lighting information without laborious information look up from tables. You can even set the geographic location by clicking from the map.

The rays of the sun are parallel and have the same intensity at any distance. Shadows can be on or off. To improve performance, turn off shadows when you don't need them. All settings for the sun except geographic location are saved per viewport, not per drawing. Geographic location is saved per drawing.

> Start a new drawing from the *house3d.dwg* provided with the data files. Save your drawing as **housesun.dwg**. Change the Visual Style to Realistic.

The drawing should look similar to Figure 15.24.

Figure 15.24

Geographic Location

The angle of the sun depends on the geographic location as well as the date and time. To set the location for your model,

> Click: **Set Location** *from the ribbon Render tab, Sun and Location panel*

The message show in Figure 15.25 appears. As you can see from the message, you have the options to:

- import *.kml* and *.kmz* files, which are types associated with Google Earth
- open Google Earth to retrieve a current location
- enter location values using the Geographic Location dialog box.

A message box appears on your screen.

*Click: **Enter the location values***

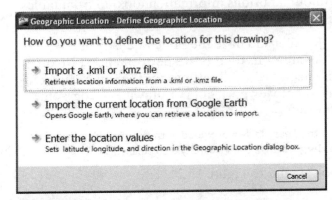

Figure 15.25

The Geographic Location dialog box appears on the screen.

*Click: **Use Map button** from the upper right of the dialog box*

The Location Picker appears so that you can select your location.

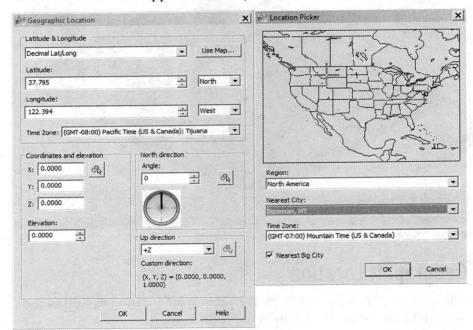

Figure 15.26

Move your cursor over the map until it is positioned as shown and click.

Note that Bozeman, MT (cultural center of the universe) appears as the Nearest City in the list as shown in Figure 15.26.

You can also scroll down the list of cities to make a selection. Note the words North America at the upper left of the map area.

*Click: **North America** from the Region list to expand the choices*

The major cities of other continents are stored in the database, and you can select them by clicking from the map or by scrolling down the list of cities.

Do not change the continent selection at this time. Leave it set to North America.

*Click: **OK** to exit the Location Picker*

*Type: **4950** into the Elevation input box*

*Click: **OK** to exit the Geographic Location dialog box*

You should see a Geo-Marker appear in your drawing storing the location.

*Click: **Sun Status button** (see Figure 15.28)*

If default lighting is turned on, you will see the message shown in Figure 15.27. If so,

*Click: **Turn off the default lighting (recommended)***

Tip: *You may see a message regarding updated time zones. If so, accept the updated time zone.*

Figure 15.27

The Sun Status button is a toggle. It switches on and off the use of the Sun lighting feature. Once it is turned on, you should notice that the lighting in your model is set to reflect how it would appear if lit by the sun on the date and time listed in the Sun and Location panel.

Drag the date and time sliders to see the result of changing the sun angle on your model shading as shown in Figure 15.28.

Use Render to show a realistically shaded view in the Render Window on your own.

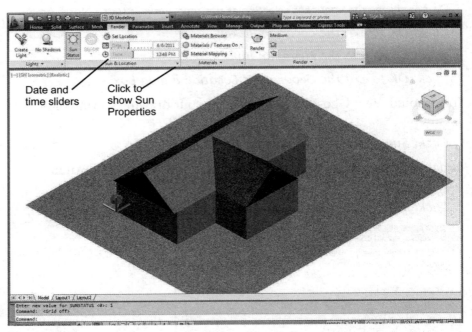

Figure 15.28

Click: on the small arrow at the right of the Sun and Location panel to show the Sun Properties (Figure 15.29)

Figure 15.29

On your own, click and drag the lower corner of the dialog box to expand it so that you can see all of the inputs. Drag the panel between the Sun properties and the Geographic location so that you can see all of them.

The Sun Properties dialog box provides the following inputs:

General

Status turns the sun lighting on and off. If lighting is not enabled in the drawing, this setting has no effect.

Intensity Factor sets the intensity or brightness of the sun. The higher the number, the brighter the light.

Color controls the color of the light.

Shadows turns display and calculation of shadows for the sun on and off. Turning shadows off improves performance.

Sky Properties

Status On makes the sky illumination available for the rendering computation. This has no impact on the viewport illumination or the background.

Intensity Factor magnifies the effect of the skylight.

Haze determines the magnitude of scattering effects appearing like haze in the atmosphere.

Horizon

Height determines the height of the ground plane above WCS zero, formatted in the current length units.

Blur specifies the blurring between ground plane and sky.

Ground Color specifies the color of the ground plane.

Advanced Category

Night Color specifies the color of the night sky.

Aerial Perspective turns On/Off aerial perspective.

Visibility Distance specifies the distance for 10% haze occlusion.

Sun Angle Calculator

Date shows the current date setting.

Time shows the current time setting.

Daylight Saving shows the current setting for daylight saving time.

Azimuth shows the azimuth, the angle of the sun along the horizon clockwise from due north. This setting is read-only.

Altitude shows the altitude, the angle of the sun vertically from the horizon. The maximum is 90 degrees, or directly overhead.

Source Vector displays the coordinates of the direction of the sun.

Rendered Shadow Details

Type displays the setting for shadow type. The selections are Sharp, Soft (mapped), which displays the Map size option, and Soft (area), which displays the Samples option. Soft (area) is the only option for the sun in photometric workflow.

Map Size (Standard Lighting Workflow Only) displays the size of the shadow map.

Samples specifies the number of samples to take on the solar disk.

Softness displays the setting for shadow edge appearance.

When you are finished examining the Sun properties, close the dialog box on your own.

Save your file.

Exporting AutoCAD Files

You can export your AutoCAD drawings for use with other software.

Click: ***Application icon, Export***

Click: ***Other Formats*** *from the bottom of the list*

Figure 15.30

The Export Data dialog box appears on your screen, as shown in Figure 15.30. You will find these file types:

3D dwf	*.dwf
3D dwfx	*.dwfx
FBX	*.fbx
Metafile	*.wmf
ACIS	*.sat
Lithography	*.stl
Encapsulated PS	*.eps
DXX Extract	*.dxx
Bitmap	*.bmp
Block	*.dwg
MicroStation® V8 DGN	*.dgn
MicroStation® V7 DGN	*.dgn
IGES	*.iges
IGS	*.igs

Tip: *You can use SaveAs and change the Save As Type area to save your drawing files back to previous AutoCAD versions.*

Tip: *You can create electronic drawing sets using the Publish command found by clicking the Application icon. Other people, such as your clients, can view the published set of drawings using a free download of Autodesk Express Viewer available at www.Autodesk.com.*

You *can also use the Publish to Web menu selection to create a web page to display images from one or more drawing files.*

Key Terms

ambient	falloff	point light	spotlight
ambient lighting	hotspot	reflection	surface map
back faces	intensity	refraction	transparency
bump map	materials	resolution	
distant light	normal	scene	

Key Commands

Background	Mapping	Publish	Sunproperties
Lights	Materials	Render	

Click: Cancel

Drawing Web Format

The Drawing Web Format allows you to convert an AutoCAD drawing so that it can be viewed on the Web. You can also plot to a 2D dwf file. To do this, select the *DWF ePlot.pc3* file as the output device for the plot command. A DWF file will be created in your default directory. You can publish this file to the Web for others to view. They must have installed the WHIP!® plug-in version 4.0 or later on their system to view DWF files with a browser such as Firefox or Microsoft Internet Explorer.

On your own, save and close the file.

Exit the AutoCAD program.

You have completed Tutorial 15 and this tutorial guide! Use what you have learned from these tutorials along with the AutoCAD software's Help files to continue exploring and learning to communicate your designs and ideas. There is still so much more to learn.

Exercises

Use solid modeling to create the objects shown below or retrieve your files from the exercises you did earlier. Produce three different renderings of the object, varying the type, location, intensity, and color of the light. Experiment with different materials and backgrounds.

15.1 Clamping Block

.375-16UNC x 1.50
HEX HEAD SCREW
4 REQD

2X ø1.00

1.00

2.00

1.00

.75

ø1.50

4X ø.40

2.00

.38

.50

2.00

3.62

4.00

.38

1.50

2.62

4.00

COVER
MATL = SAE 1020 STEEL

4X ø.375 - 16UNC x 1.50 DEEP

8X .38
ALL FOUR CORNERS

.50 DEEP

ø1.000 CENTERED
ON RECESSED SURFACED

.75

2.50

2.50

.75

1.50

3.00

4.00

BASE
MATL = SAE 1020 STEEL

8X ø.38
ALL FOUR CORNERS

4X ø.40

2.50

4.00

.75

.75

1.50

3.00

GASKET
MATL = .125 NEOPRENE

15.2 Pressure Assembly

ø1.20

ø.75 THRU

R.06

1.66

.25

8X ø.25
EQ SPACED

ø.75 THRU

ø2.50

.25

8X ø.25
EQ SPACED

ø1.75

15.3 Hub Assembly

5.00

2.50

2X ø.6875

8X ø.3125 - EQ SP

ø5.75

ø5.00

ø4.50

22.5°

1 HOUSING
   1 REQ

8X ø.3125 - EQ SP

ø5.75

ø5.00

ø4.5025

⌴ ø1.498
↧ .50

22.5°

.875

.125

2 CAP-2 REQ
   RIGHT CAP SHOWN

15.4 Turbine Housing Assembly

ø2.40
.10 X .06 KEYWAY
R.23
45°
45°
.24
R.97
R1.70
ø1.00
.25
ø.36
45°
ø.22
R1.33
ø2.32
.10 X .06 KEYWAY
R.94
R.94
ø.38
.25
.50

15.5 Geneva Wheel Assembly

15.6M Universal Joint

15.7 Staircase

Create the staircase or retrieve your file from Tutorial 13 exercise.
Render the stairs using wood materials.

GLOSSARY

absolute coordinates	The exact location of a specific point in terms of x, y, and z from the fixed point of origin.
absolute value	The numerical value or magnitude of the quantity, without regard to its positive or negative sign.
alias	A short name that can be used to activate a command; you can customize command aliases by editing the file *acad.pgp*.
ambient	The overall amount of light that exists in the environment of a rendered scene.
And gate	An electronic logic symbol; if either input is zero, the output is zero.
angle brackets	A value that appears in angle brackets < > is the default option for that command, which will be executed unless it is changed.
aperture	A type of cursor resembling a small box placed on top of the cross-hairs; used to select in the object snap mode.
architectural units	Drawings made with these units are drawn in feet and fractional inches.
aspect ratio	The relationship of two dimensions to each other.
associative dimensioning	Dimensioning where each dimension is inserted as a group of drawing objects relative to the points selected in the drawing. If the drawing is scaled or stretched, the dimension values automatically update.
associative hatching	The practice of filling an area with a pattern w' updates when the boundary is modified.
attribute	Text information associated with a bl
attribute prompt	The prompt, which you define, t' when you insert the block into
attribute tag	A variable name that is rep' prompted as you insert th
AutoSnap™	A feature which displa object snap location

auxiliary view	An orthographic view of an object using a direction of sight other than one of the six basic views (front, top, right side, rear, bottom, left side).
ball tag	A circled number identifying each part shown in an assembly drawing; also called a balloon number.
base feature	In a feature-based model, the main feature from which other features are defined based on the constraints put on the model.
base grip	The selected grip, used as the base point for hot grip commands.
baseline dimensioning	A dimensioning method in which each successive dimension is measured from one extension line or baseline.
basic dimension	A theoretically exact dimension to which no tolerance is applied.
basic view	One of the six standard views of an object: front, top, right side, rear, bottom, or left side.
bearing	The angle to turn from the first direction stated toward the second direction stated.
bicubic surface	A sculptured plane, mathematically describing a sculptured surface between three- dimensional curves.
bidirectional associativity	Describes the link between the drawing and the model. If a change is made to the model, the drawing is automatically updated to reflect the change; if a change is made to the parametric dimensions in the drawing, both the drawing and the model update automatically.
bilateral tolerances	Tolerances specified by defining a nominal dimension and the allowable range of deviation from that dimension, both plus and minus.

crosses that appear on the screen, indicating where a location
ed.

cts that have been grouped together to act as one, and
nd used in the current drawing and in other drawings.

lar named group of objects.

of a block into a drawing (blocks can be

erence (subtraction), and intersection
sets.

bump map	Converts color intensity or grayscale information to heights to give the appearance that features are raised above the surface, like embossed letters.
buttons	A method of selecting options by picking in a defined area of the screen resembling a box or push button.
Cartesian coordinate system	A rectangular coordinate system created by three mutually perpendicular coordinate axes, commonly labeled x, y, and z.
chained (continued)	A dimensioning method in which each successive dimension is measured
dimensioning	from the last extension line of the previous dimension.
chamfer	A straight line segment connecting two otherwise intersecting surfaces.
chord length	The straight line distance between the start point and the endpoint of an arc.
circular view	A view of a cylinder in which it appears as a circle (looking into the hole).
circumscribed	Drawn around the outside of a base circle.
clearance fit	The space available between two mating parts, where the greatest shaft size always is smaller than the smallest hole size, thus producing an open space.
colinear constraint	Lying on the same straight line.
command aliasing	The creation and use of alternative short names for commands, such as LA for Layer.
command prompt	The word or words in the command window that ask for the next piece of information.
command window	The lines of text below the graphics window that indicate the status of commands and prompt for user input.
construction plane	A plane that is temp orarily defined during commands for creating new drawing objects.
context sensitive	Recognizes when you are in a command, and displays information for that command.
Coons patch	A bicubic surface interpolated between four edges.

coordinate system locator	An icon to help you visually refer to the current coordinate system.
coordinate values	Used to identify the location of a point, using the Cartesian coordinate system; x represents the horizontal position on the X axis, and y represents the vertical position on the Y axis. In a three-dimensional drawing, z represents the depth position on the Z axis.
crosshatching	The practice of filling an area with a pattern to differentiate it from other components of a drawing.
current layer	The layer you are working on. New drawing objects are always created on the layer that is current.
cursor (crosshairs)	A mark that shows the location of the pointing device in the graphics window of the screen; used to draw, select, or pick icons, menu items, or objects. The appearance of the cursor may change, depending on the command or option selected.
custom hatch pattern	A design that you have previously created and stored in the file *acad.pat* or another *.pat* file of your own making to use to fill an area.
customize	To change the toolbars, menus, and other aspects of the program to show those commands and functions that you want to use.
cutting edges	Objects used to define the portions to be removed when trimming an object.
cutting plane line	Defines the location on the object where the sectional view is taken.
datum surface	A theoretically exact geometric reference used to establish the tolerance zone for a feature.
default	The value that AutoCAD will use unless you specify otherwise; appears in angle brackets < > after a prompt.
default directory	The directory to which AutoCAD will save all drawing files unless instructed otherwise.
delta angle	The included angular value from the start point to the endpoint.
diameter symbol Ø	Indicates that the value is a diameter.
difference	The area formed by subtracting one region or solid from another.
dimension line	Drawn between extension lines with an arrowhead at each end; indicates how the stated dimension relates to the feature on the object.
dimension style	A group of dimension features saved as a set.

dimension value	The value of the dimension being described (how long, how far across, etc.); placed near the midpoint of the dimension line.
dimension variables	Features of dimensions that can be altered by the user; you control the features by setting the variables using the Dimension Style dialog box.
dimension	Describes the size and location of a part or object so that it can be manufactured.
distance across the flats	A measurement of the size of a hexagon from one flat side to the side opposite it.
docked	Attached to any edge of the graphics window, as a toolbar can be.
draft angle	The taper on a molded part that makes it possible to easily remove the part from the mold.
drag	To move an object on the screen and see it at the same time, in order to specify the new size or location.
edge view	A line representing a plane surface shown on its end.
elements	Parts of a multiline, which can be made up of up to 16 lines.
engineering units	Drawings made with these units are drawn in feet and decimal inches.
export	To save a file from one application as a different file type for use by another application.
extension line	Relates a dimension to the feature it refers to.
extension line offset	Specifies a distance for the gap between the end of the extension line and the point that defines the dimension.
extrusion	Creates a long three-dimensional strip with the shape of a closed two-dimensional shape, as if material had been forced through a shaped opening.
falloff	The angle of the cone of light from a spotlight.
feature	Any definable aspect of an object—a hole, a surface, etc.
feature control frame	Geometric dimensioning and tolerancing specification that uses rectangular boxes with symbols to specify allowable variations in the manufactured part.
file extension	The part of a file name that is composed of a period, followed by one to three characters, and that helps you to identify the file type.

fillet	An arc of specified radius that connects two lines, arcs, or circles, or a rounded interior corner on a machined part.
floating	Refers to the toolbar's or command window's ability to be moved to any location on the screen.
floating viewport	A window, created in paper space, through which you can see your model space drawing; very useful for plotting the drawing, adding drawing details, showing an enlarged view of the object, or showing multiple views of the object.
flyout	A sub-toolbar that becomes visible when its representative icon on the main toolbar is chosen.
font	A character pattern defined by the text style.
foreshortened	Appears smaller than actual size, due to being tipped away from the viewing plane.
fractional units	Drawings made with these units express lengths less than 1 as fractions (e.g., 15 1/4).
freeze	Make a layer invisible and exclude it from regeneration and plotting.
G2 continuity	The position, tangency, and curvature between the surfaces match.
generated layer	A layer created automatically (instead of by the user) during commands such as SOLPROF.
geometric characteristic symbol	Form, orientation, profile, runout, and locational symbols used to specify allowable variations in the manufactured part.
geometric tolerance	Specialized tolerance symbols based on geometric form.
global linetype scaling factor	The factor of the original size at which all lines in the drawing are displayed.
globe	Used to select the direction for viewing a three-dimensional model.
graphics window	The central part of the screen, which is used to create and display drawings.
grid	Regularly spaced dots covering an area of the graphics window to aid in drawing.
group	A named selection set of objects.
handle number	A unique identifier assigned to each AutoCAD drawing object, including viewports.

heads-up	Entering a command while looking at the screen; by picking an icon, for example, you do not need to look down to the keyboard to enter the command.
hidden line	A line that represents an edge that is not directly visible because it is behind or beneath another surface.
highlight	A change of color around a particular command or object, indicating that it has been selected and is ready to be executed or worked on in some way.
hot grips	A method for editing an already drawn object using only the pointing device, without needing to use the menus, toolbars, or keyboard.
hotspot	The angle of the cone of light for the brightest area of the beam of a spotlight.
image tile	An active picture which displays dialog box choices as graphic images rather than words.
implied Crossing mode	When this mode is activated, the first corner of a box is started when you select a point on the screen that is not on an object in the drawing. If the box is drawn from right to left, everything that partially crosses as well as items fully enclosed by the box are selected.
implied Windowing mode	When this mode is activated, the first corner of a box is started when you select a point on the screen that is not on an object in the drawing. If the box is drawn from the left to right, a window is formed that selects everything that is entirely enclosed in the box.
import	To open and use a file created by a different application than the one being used.
inclined surface	Slanted at an angle, a surface that is perpendicular to one of the three principal views and tipped away from the other principal views.
included angle	The angular measurement along a circular path.
inscribed	Drawn inside a base circle.
inspection	The act of examining the part against its specifications.
instance	Each single action of a command.
intensity	The brightness level of a light source.
intersection	The point where two lines or surfaces meet, or the area shared by overlapping regions or solid models.

Inverter gate	A symbol used to draw an electronic logic circuit; for inputs of 1, the output is 0, for inputs of 0, the output is 1.
layer	A method of separating drawing objects so that they can be viewed individually or stacked like transparent acetates, allowing all layers to show. Used to set color and linetype properties for groups of objects.
leader line	A line from a note or radial dimension that ends in an arrowhead pointing at the feature.
limiting element	The outer edge of a curved surface.
limiting tolerances	Tolerances specified by defining an upper and lower allowable measurement.
lock	To prohibit changes to a layer, although the layer is still visible on the screen.
major arc	An arc which comprises more than 180° of a circle.
major axis	The long axis of symmetry across an ellipse.
manufacture	To create a part according to its specifications.
mass properties	Data about the real-world object being drawn, such as its mass, volume, and moments of inertia.
matrix	An array of vertices used to generate a surface.
menu bar	The strip across the top of the screen showing the names of the pull-down menus, such as File, Edit, etc.
minor axis	The short axis of symmetry across an ellipse.
mirror line	A line that defines the angle and distance at which a reflected image of a selected object will be created.
miter line	A line drawn above the side view and to the right of the top view, often drawn from the top right corner of the front view, used to project features from the side view onto the top view of an object.
model space	The AutoCAD drawing database, when an object exists as a three-dimensional object.
Nand gate	A symbol used to draw an electronic logic circuit; when both inputs are 1, output is 0, when any input is 0, output is 1.
nominal dimension	The general identification for the size of a typical feature, for example a 1/2" diameter hole.

Nor gate	A symbol used to draw an electronic logic circuit; when both inputs are 0, output is 1, any input of 1, output is 0.
normal surface	A surface that is perpendicular to two of the three principal orthographic views and appears at the correct size and shape in a basic view.
noun/verb selection	A method for selecting an object first and then the command to be used on it.
nurb	A cubic spline curve.
offset distance	Controls the distance from an existing object at which a new object will be created.
options	The choices associated with a particular command or instruction.
Or gate	A symbol used to draw an electronic logic circuit; any input of 1 results in output of 1, when both inputs are 0, output is 0.
orthographic view	A two-dimensional drawing used in representing a three-dimensional object. A minimum of two orthographic views are necessary to show the shape of a three-dimensional object, because each view shows only two dimensions.
output file	The file to which attribute data is extracted.
overall dimensions	The widest measurements of a part; needed by manufacturers to determine how much material to start with.
override mode	When the desired object snap mode is selected during each command it is to be used for.
palette	A type of toolbar, usually divided into areas, that allows for quick selection of items. AutoCAD Tool Palettes are used to organize blocks, hatches, and more in a location where they can be dragged into a drawing (similar to the way paint is held on an artist's palette for quick access).
paper space	A mode that allows you to arrange, annotate, and plot different views of a model in a single drawing, as you would arrange views on a piece of paper.
parametric	A modeling method that allows you to input sizes for and relationships between the features of parts. Changing a size or relationship will result in the model being updated to the new appearance.
partial auxiliary view	An auxiliary view that shows only the desired surfaces.

parts list	Provides information about the parts in an assembly drawing, including the item number, description, quantity, material, and part number.
perspective icon	A cube drawn in perspective that replaces the UCS icon when perspective viewing, activated by the 3D Dynamic View command, is in effect.
pictorial full section	A section view showing an object cut in half along its vertical center line.
pin registry	A process in which a series of transparent sheets are punched with a special hole pattern along one edge, allowing the sheets to be fitted onto a metal pin bar. The metal pin bar keeps the drawings aligned from one sheet to the next. Each sheet is used to show different map information.
plan view	The top view or view looking straight down the Z axis toward the XY plane.
plus/minus tolerances	Another name for variance tolerances.
point filter	Option that lets you selectively find single coordinates out of a point's three-dimensional coordinate set.
point light	A light source similar to a bare light bulb that casts light in every direction.
pointer	An indicator established from the current drawing to the original drawing, or external reference.
polar array	A pattern created by repeating objects over and over in a circular fashion.
polar coordinates	The location of a point, defined as a distance and an angle from another specified point, using the AutoCAD input format @DISTANCE<ANGLE.
polygon	A closed shape with sides of equal length.
polyline	A series of connected objects (lines or arcs) that are treated as a single object.
precedence	When two lines occupy the same space, precedence determines which one is drawn. Continuous lines take precedence over hidden lines, and hidden lines take precedence over center lines.
primitives	Basic shapes that can be joined together or subtracted from each other to form more complex shapes.

profile	A two-dimensional view of a three-dimensional solid object created using the Solprof (Setup Profile) command.
project	To transfer information from one view of an object to another by aligning them and using projection lines.
projection lines	Horizontal lines that stretch from one view of an object to another to show which line or surface is which.
Properties toolbar	Contains the icons whose commands control the appearance of the objects in your drawing.
prototype drawing	A drawing saved with certain settings that can be used repeatedly as the basis for starting new drawings.
quadrant point	Any of the four points that mark the division of a circle or arc into four segments: 0°, 90°, 180°, and 270°.
ray tracing	The method of calculating shading by tracking reflected light rays hitting the object.
real-world units	Units in which drawings in the database are drawn; objects should always be drawn at the size that the real object would be.
rectangular array	A pattern created by repeating objects over and over in columns and rows.
rectangular view	A view of a cylinder in which it appears as a rectangle (looking from the side).
reference surface	A surface from which measurements are made when creating another view of the object.
reflection	The degree to which a surface bounces back light.
refraction	The degree to which an object changes the angle of light passing through it.
regenerate	To recalculate from the drawing database a drawing display that has just been zoomed or had changes made to it.
region	A two-dimensional area created from a closed shape or a loop.
relative coordinates	The location of a point in terms of the X and Y distance, or distance and angle, from a previously specified point @X,Y.
rendered	Lighting effects, color, and shape applied to an object in a single two-dimensional view.

resolution	Refers to how sharp and clear an image appears to be and how much detail can be seen; the higher the resolution, the better the quality of the image. This is determined by the number of colors and pixels the computer monitor can display.
revolution	Creating a three-dimensional object by sweeping a two-dimensional polyline, circle, or region about a circular path to create a symmetrical solid that is basically circular in cross-section.
roman	A font.
root page	The original standard screen menu column along the right side of the screen, accessed by picking the word AutoCAD at the top of the screen.
roughness	The apparent texture of a surface. The lower the surface roughness, the more reflective the surface will be.
round	A convex arc, or a rounded external corner on a machined part.
running mode	When the current object snap mode is automatically used any time a command calls for the input of a point or selection.
scale factor	The multiple or fraction of the original size of a drawing object or linetype at which it is displayed.
section lines	Show surfaces that were cut in a section view.
section view	A type of orthographic view that shows the internal structure of an object; also called a cutaway view.
selectable group	A named selection set in which picking on one of its members selects all members that are in the current space, and not on locked or frozen layers. An object can belong to more than one group.
selection filters	A list of properties required of an object for it to be selected.
selection set	All of the objects chosen to be affected by a particular command.
session	Each use, from loading to exiting, of the AutoCAD program.
shape-compiled font	Character shapes drawn by the AutoCAD software using vectors.
sign	Positive or negative indicator that precedes a centermark value.
slicing plane	A plane that is defined for use in slicing a solid object. During the Slice command, the object can be removed on either side of the slicing plane or the selected object can be parted along the slicing plane and both sides can be retained.

solid modeling	A type of three-dimensional modeling that represents the volume of an object, not just its lines and surfaces; this allows for analysis of the object's mass properties.
spotlight	A light source used to highlight certain key areas and cast light only toward the selected target.
Standard toolbar	Contains the icons which control file operation commands.
status bar	The rectangular area at bottom of screen that displays time and some command and file operation information.
style	Controls the name, font file, height, width factor, obliquing angle, and generation of the text.
submenu	A list of available options or commands relating to an item chosen from a menu.
surface modeling	A type of three- dimensional modeling that defines only surfaces and edges so that the model can be shaded and have hidden lines removed; resembles an empty shell in the shape of the object.
swatch	An area that shows a sample of the color or pattern currently selected.
sweeping	Extrusion along a non-linear path rather than a straight line.
target area	The square area on an object snap aperture, in which at least part of the object to be selected must fit.
template drawing	A drawing with the extension *.dwt* having certain settings that can be used repeatedly as the basis for starting new drawings. Any drawing can be renamed and used as a template.
template file	Specifies the file format for the Extract Attribute command as *.cdf* or *.sdf.*
tessellation lines	To cover a surface with a grid or lines, like a mosaic. Tessellation lines are displayed on a curved surface to help you visualize it; the number of tessellation lines determines the accuracy of surface area calculations.
threshold value	Determines how close vertices must be in order to be automatically welded during the rendering process.
through point	The point through which the offset object is to be drawn.
tiled viewports	Multiple viewports that cannot overlap. They must line up next to each other, like tiles on a floor.

tilemode	An AutoCAD system variable that controls the use of tiled or floating viewports or paper space.
title bar	The rectangular area at the top of the screen which displays the application and file names.
toggle	A switch that turns certain settings on and off.
tolerance	The amount that a manufactured part can vary from the specifications laid out in the plans and still be acceptable.
tool tip	The name of the icon that appears when you hold the cursor over the icon.
toolbar	A strip containing icons for certain commands.
transparency	A quality that makes objects appear clear, like glass, or somewhat clear, like colored liquids.
transparent command	A command that can be selected while another command is operating.
typing cursor	A special cursor used in dialog boxes for entering text from the keyboard.
UCS icon	Indicates the current coordinate system in use and the direction in which the coordinates are being viewed in 3D drawings.
unidirectional dimensioning	The standard alignment for dimension text, which is to orient the text horizontally.
unilateral tolerance	A tolerance that is applied in one direction from a specified dimension.
union	The area formed by adding two regions or solid models together.
units	The type of metric, decimal, scientific, engineering, or architectural measurement scales used in AutoCAD drawings. These are set with the Units command.
update	To regenerate the active part or drawing using any new dimension values or changed sketches.
User Coordinate System (UCS)	A set of x, y, and z coordinates whose origin, rotation, and tilt are defined by the user. You can create and name any number of User Coordinate Systems.
user-defined hatch pattern	A predefined hatch pattern for which you have specified the angle, spacing, and/or linetype.

variance tolerances	Tolerances specified by defining a nominal dimension and the allowable range of deviation from that dimension; includes bilateral and unilateral tolerances.
vector	A directional line. Also, a way of storing a graphic image as a set of mathematical formulas.
Venn diagram	Pictorial description named after John Venn, an English logician, where circles are used to represent set operations.
viewpoint	The direction from which you are viewing a three-dimensional object.
viewport	A "window" showing a particular view of a three-dimensional object.
virtual screen	A file containing only the information displayed on the AutoCAD screen. Used to allow fast zooming without having to regenerate the original drawing file.
Windows close button	A button in the upper right corner of a window that closes the window.
wireframe modeling	A type of three- dimensional modeling that uses lines, arcs, circles, and other objects to represent the edges and other features of an object; so called because it looks like a sculpture made from wires.
World Coordinate System (WCS)	The AutoCAD system for defining model geometry using x, y, and z coordinate values; the default orientation is a horizontal X axis with positive values to the right, a vertical Y axis with positive values above the X axis, and a Z axis that is perpendicular to the screen and has positive values in front of the screen

AUTOCAD® COMMAND SUMMARY

This grid includes most commands available for use with the AutoCAD 2012 software. You should use the AutoCAD on-line Help feature for complete information about the commands and their options. Most commands can be run at the command line by typing a hyphen (-) in front of the command name. Many commands have keyboard shortcuts that are displayed alongside their names on the menu bar.

Command or Icon Name	Description	Command or Alias
2D Wireframe Shade	Displays objects using lines and curves to represent boundaries.	SHADEMODE
2D Solid	Creates solid-filled polygons.	SOLID, SO
3 Point UCS	Selects a user coordinate system based on any three points in the graphics window.	UCS
3D Array	Creates a three-dimensional array.	3DARRAY, 3A
3D Clip	Interactive 3D view and to adjust clipping planes.	3DCLIP
3D Continuous Orbit	Interactive 3D view showing continuous motion.	3DCORBIT
3D Distance	Make objects appear closer or farther in the interactive 3D view.	3DDISTANCE
3D Dynamic View	Changes the 3D view of a point.	DVIEW, DV
3D Face	Creates a three-dimensional surface.	3DFACE, 3F
3D Fly	Interactively changes your view of 3D drawings so that you appear to be flying through the model.	3DFLY
3D Free Orbit	Interactive 3D view showing free movement.	3DFORBIT
3D Mesh	Creates three-dimensional mesh objects.	3DMESH
3D Mirror	Creates a mirror image of objects about a plane.	MIRROR3D
3D Move	Displays the move grip tool in a 3D view and moves objects a specified distance in a specified direction.	3DMOVE
3D Orbit	Controlled interactive 3D viewing.	3D ORBIT, 3DO
3D Polyface Mesh	Creates a 3D polyface mesh by vertices.	PFACE
3D Polyline	Creates a 3D polyline of straight line segments.	3DPOLY, 3P
3D Rotate	Rotates an object in a 3D coordinate system.	3DROTATE
3D Studio In	Imports a 3D Studio® (*.3ds) file into an AutoCAD drawing.	3DSIN
3D Swivel	Changes the target of the view in the direction that you drag.	3DSWIVEL
3D Walk	Interactively changes the view of a 3D drawing so that you appear to be walking through the model.	3DWALK

Command or Icon Name	Description	Command or Alias
About	Displays information about the AutoCAD software.	'ABOUT, ABOUT
Acadlspasdoc	System variable controlling whether or not the *acad.lsp* file is loaded into every drawing.	ACADLSPASDOC
Acadprefix	System variable that stores the directory path, if any, specified by the ACAD environment variable. (read only)	ACADPREFIX
Acadver	System variable that stores the AutoCAD version number. (read only)	ACADVER
ACIS In	Imports an ACIS (**.sat*) file into an AutoCAD drawing.	ACISIN
ACIS Out	Saves a file formatted in ACIS (**.sat*).	ACISOUT
Active Assistance	Displays Quick Help about the current command in the Info Palette.	ASSIST, 'ASSIST
Adcclose	Closes the DesignCenter™ window.	ADCCLOSE
Adcenter	Manages and inserts blocks, xrefs, hatch patterns, and more.	ADCENTER
Adcnavigate	Lets you specify a path or drawing file name to load in the Folders tree view of the DesignCenter.	ADCNAVIGATE
Administration	Performs administrative functions with external database commands.	DBCONNECT, AAD
Align	Moves and rotates objects to align with other objects.	ALIGN, AL
Align Dimension Text, Edit	Aligns dimension text to Home, Left, Right or Angle position.	DIMTEDIT, DIMTED
Aligned Dimension	Creates an aligned linear dimension.	DIMALIGNED, DAL, DIMALI
AME Convert	Converts AME solid models to AutoCAD solid objects.	AMECONVERT
Angular Dimension	Dimensions an angle.	DIMANGULAR, DAN, DIMANG
Animation Path	Saves an animation along a path in a 3D model.	ANIPATH
Annotation Reset	Resets the location of all scale representations for an annotative object to that of the current scale representation.	ANNORESET
Annotation Update	Updates existing annotative objects to match the current properties of their styles.	ANNOUPDATE
Aperture	Controls the size of the object snap target box.	'APERTURE, APERTURE
Aperture Box	System variable controlling display of the object snap target box.	APBOX
Application Load	Loads AutoLISP® (**.ads*), and (**.arx*) files.	'APPLOAD, AP

Command or Icon Name	Description	Command or Alias
Arc	Draws an arc based on three points.	ARC, A
Arc Center Start Angle	Draws an arc of a specified angle based on the center and start points.	ARC, A
Arc Center Start End	Draws an arc based on the center, start, and endpoints.	ARC, A
Arc Center Start Length	Draws an arc of a specified length based on the center and start points.	ARC, A
Arc Continue	Draws an arc from the last point of the previous line or arc drawn.	ARC, A
Arc Length Dimension	Dimensions the length of an arc, using the symbol set using Dimension Style.	DIMARC
Arc Start Center Angle	Draws an arc of a specified angle based on the start and center points.	ARC, A
Arc Start Center End	Draws an arc based on the start, center, and endpoints.	ARC, A
Arc Start Center Length	Draws an arc of a specified length based on the start and center points.	ARC, A
Arc Start End Angle	Draws an arc of a specified angle based on the start and endpoints.	ARC, A
Arc Start End Direction	Draws an arc in a specified direction based on the start and endpoints.	ARC, A
Arc Start End Radius	Draws an arc of a specified radius based on the start and endpoints.	ARC, A
Area	Finds the area and perimeter of objects or defined areas.	AREA, AA
Array	Creates multiple copies of objects in a regularly spaced circular or rectangular pattern.	ARRAY, AR
Array, Path (Path Array)	Evenly distributes object copies along a path or a portion of a path.	ARRAYPATH
Array, Polar (Polar Array)	Evenly distributes object copies in a circular pattern around a center point or axis of rotation.	ARRAYPOLAR
Array, Rectangular (Rectangular Array)	Distributes object copies into any combination of rows, columns, and levels.	ARRAYRECT
Attdia	System variable that controls whether the Insert command uses a dialog box for attribute value entry.	ATTDIA
Attedit	Allows you to change attribute information.	ATTEDIT
ATTIPEDIT	Changes the textual content of an attribute within a block.	ATTIPEDIT
Attribute Display	Globally controls attribute visibility.	'ATTDISP, ATTDISP
Attribute Editor, Enhanced	Edits attributes of a block reference.	EATTEDIT
Attribute Redefine	Redefines a block and updates its attributes.	ATTREDEF
Audit	Evaluates the integrity of a drawing.	AUDIT

Command or Icon Name	Description	Command or Alias
AutoCAD Runtime Extension	Provides information, loads/ unloads ARX applications.	ARX
Autocomplete	Controls what types of automated keyboard features are available at the Command prompt.	AUTOCOMPLETE
Autopublish	Publishes drawings to DWF files automatically.	AUTOPUBLISH
Back View	Sets the viewing direction for a three-dimensional visualization of the drawing to the back.	VPOINT, -VP, DDVPOINT, VP
Base	Specifies the insertion point for a block or drawing.	'BASE, BASE
Baseline Dimension	Continues a linear, angular, or ordinate dimension from the baseline of the previous or selected dimension.	DIMBASELINE, DBA, DIMBASE
Bitmap Out	Saves AutoCAD objects in a bitmap (*.bmp) format.	BMPOUT
Blend	Creates a spline to fill the gap between two selected lines or curves.	BLEND
Block Attribute Manager	Allows editing of block attribute properties.	BATTMAN
Block Editor	Adds dynamic behavior to blocks.	BEDIT
Block Icon	Generate preview images for blocks created with R14 or earlier.	BLOCKICON
Bottom View	Sets the viewing direction for a three-dimensional visualization of the drawing to the bottom.	VPOINT, -VP, DDVPOINT, VP
Boundary	Creates a region or polyline of a closed boundary.	BOUNDARY, BO, -BOUNDARY, -BO
Boundary Hatch	Automatically fills the area you select with a pattern. Same as HATCH.	BHATCH, BH, H
Box	Creates a three-dimensional rectangular-shaped solid.	BOX
Break	Removes part of an object or splits it in two.	BREAK, BR
Browser	Launches the Web browser defined in the system registry.	BROWSER
Calculator	Calculates mathematical and geometrical expressions.	'CAL, CAL
Calculator, Quick	Performs calculations, converts units, and more.	QUICKCALC
Cancel	Exits current command without performing operation.	[Esc]
Celtype	System variable that sets the linetype of new objects.	celtype
Center Mark	Draws center marks and centerlines of arcs and circles.	DIMCENTER, DCE
Chamfer	Draws a straight line segment (called a chamfer) between two given lines.	CHAMFER, CHA
Chamfer Edge	Bevels the edges of 3D solids and surfaces.	CHAMFEREDGE

Command or Icon Name	Description	Command or Alias
Change	Changes the properties of existing objects.	CHANGE, CH, CHPROP
Check Standards	Checks the current drawing for CAD Standards violations.	CHECKSTANDARDS
Circle	Draws circles based upon center point and radius.	CIRCLE, C
Circle Center Diameter	Draws circles based upon center point and diameter.	CIRCLE, C
Circle Tan Tan Radius	Draws circles based upon two tangent points and a radius.	CIRCLE, C
Circle Tan Tan Tan	Draws circles based upon three tangent points.	CIRCLE, C
Circle 3 Points	Draws circles based upon 3 points.	CIRCLE, C
Circle 2 Points	Draws circles based upon 2 points.	CIRCLE, C
Classic Group	Opens the legacy Object Grouping dialog box.	CLASSICGROUP
Close	Closes the current drawing; prompts to save or discard the changes if it was modified.	CLOSE
Close All	Closes all open drawings.	CLOSEALL
Cmddia	System variable controls whether dialog boxes are enabled some commands.	CMDDIA
Color Control	Sets the color for new objects.	'COLOR, COLOR, 'DDCOLOR, DDCOLOR, COL
Command Line	Displays the command window when it has been hidden.	COMMANDLINE
Compile	Compiles PostScript font files and shape files.	COMPILE
Cone	Creates a three-dimensional solid primitive with a circular base tapering to a point perpendicular to its base.	CONE
Construction Line	Creates an infinite line.	XLINE
Content Explorer	Finds and inserts content such as drawing files, blocks, and styles.	CONTENTEXPLORER, CONTENTEXPLORER-CLOSE
Continue Dimension	Adds the next chained dimension, measured from the last dimension.	DIMCONTINUE, DIMCONT, DCO
Convert	Converts associative hatches and 2D polylines created in Release 13 or earlier.	CONVERT
Convert Color Dependent Plot Style	Converts color-dependent plot style table to a named plot style table.	CONVERTCTB
Convert Old Lights	Converts lights created in previous releases to lights in AutoCAD 2008 format.	CONVERTOLD LIGHTS
Convert Old Materials	Converts materials created in previous releases to materials in AutoCAD 2008 format.	CONVERTOLD MATERIALS
Convert Plot Styles	Converts the current drawing to a named or color dependent plot style.	CONVERTPSTYLES
Convert to Solid	Converts polylines and circles with thickness to 3D solids.	CONVTOSOLID

Command or Icon Name	Description	Command or Alias
Convert to Surface	Converts objects to surfaces.	CONVTOSURFACE
Copy	Copies an existing shape from one area on the drawing to another area.	COPY, CP, CO
Copy Link	Copies the current view to the Windows Clipboard for linking to other OLE applications.	COPYLINK
Copyclip	Copies objects to the Windows Clipboard.	COPYCLIP
Copyhist	Copies all text in the command line history to the Clipboard.	COPYHIST
Customize	Allows customization of toolbars, buttons, and shortcut keys	CUSTOMIZE
Cutclip	Copies objects to the clipboard and erases them from the drawing.	CUTCLIP
Customize	Customizes tool palettes and tool palette groups.	CUSTOMIZE
Customize User Interface	Manages the customized user interface elements	CUI
Cylinder	Creates a three-dimensional solid primitive similar to an extruded circle, but without a taper.	CYLINDER
Data Base Close	Closes the dbConnect Manager and removes dbConnect menu from the menu bar.	DBCLOSE
Data Base Connect	Interfaces with external database tables.	DBCONNECT
	Extracts drawing data and merges data from an external source to a data extraction table or external file.	DATAEXTRACTION, -DATAEXTRACTION
Database List	Lists database information for drawing objects.	DBLIST
Define Attribute	Creates attribute text.	ATTDEF, -AT, DDATTDEF
Delay	Adds a timed pause (33 seconds maximum) within a script.	'DELAY, DELAY
Delobj	Controls whether objects used to create other objects are retained or deleted from the drawing database.	DELOBJ
DesignCenter	Manage drawing content.	ADCENTER
DesignCenter Navigate	Controls path for AutoCAD DesignCenter.	ADCNAVIGAT,
Detach	Removes an externally referenced drawing.	XREF, XR, -XREF, -XR
Detach url	Removes hyperlinks from a drawing.	DETACHURL
DGNADJUST	Changes the display options of selected DGN underlays.	DGNADJUST
DGNATTACH	Attaches a DGN underlay to the current drawing.	DGNATTACH
DGNCLIP	Defines a clipping boundary for a selected DGN underlay.	DGNCLIP
DGNEXPORT	Creates one or more V8 DGN files from the current drawing.	DGNEXPORT

Command or Icon Name	Description	Command or Alias
DGNIMPORT	Imports the data from a V8 DGN file into a new DWG file.	DGNIMPORT
Diameter Dimension	Adds center marks to a circle when providing its diameter dimension.	DIMDIAMETER, DIMDIA, DDI
Diastat	System variable that stores the exit method of the most recently used dialog box. (read only)	DIASTAT
Dimalt	System variable that enables alternate units.	DIMALT
Dimaltd	System variable that sets alternate unit precision.	DIMALTD
Dimaltf	System variable that sets alternate unit scale.	DIMALTF
Dimalttd	System variable that stores the number of decimal places for the tolerance values of an alternate units dimension.	DIMALTTD
Dimalttz	System variable that toggles the suppression of zeros for tolerance values.	DIMALTTZ
Dimaltu	System variable that sets the units format for alternate units of all dimension style family members, except angular.	DIMALTU
Dimaltz	System variable that toggles suppression of zeros for alternate units dimension values.	DIMALTZ
Dimapost	System variable that specifies the text prefix and/or suffix to the alternate dimension measurement for alternate types of dimensions except angular.	DIMAPOST
Dimaso	System variable that controls the creation of associative dimension objects.	DIMASO
Dimassoc	System variable which controls the associativity of dimensions. Set to 0, it creates dimensions with no association between dimension elements— lines, arrows, etc. are all separate objects. Set to 1, it forms elements into non-associative dimension objects, whose values update. Set to 2, it creates fully associative dimension objects.	DIMASSOC
Dimasz	System variable that controls the size of dimension line and leader line arrowheads.	DIMASZ
Dimaunit	System variable that sets the angle format for angular dimensions.	DIMAUNIT
Dimblk	System variable that sets the name of a block to be drawn instead of the normal arrowhead at the end of the dimension line or leader line.	DIMBLK
Dimblk1	System variable that, if Dimsah is on, specifies the user-defined arrowhead block for the first end of the dimension line.	DIMBLK1
Dimblk2	System variable that, if Dimsah is on, specifies the user-defined arrowhead block for the second end of the dimension line.	DIMBLK2
DIMBREAK	Adds or removes a dimension break.	DIMBREAK

Command or Icon Name	Description	Command or Alias
Dimcen	System variable that controls the drawing of circle or arc centermarks or centerlines.	DIMCEN
Dimclrd	System variable that assigns colors to dimension lines, arrowheads, and dimension leader lines.	DIMCLRD
Dimclre	System variable that assigns colors to dimension extension lines.	DIMCLRE
Dimclrt	System variable that assigns color to dimension text.	DIMCLRT
Dimdec	System variable that sets the decimal places for the tolerance values of a primary units dimension.	DIMDEC
Dimdle	System variable that extends the dimension line beyond the extension line when oblique strokes are drawn instead of arrowheads.	DIMDLE
Dimdli	System variable that controls the dimension line spacing for baseline dimensions.	DIMDLI
Dimension, Arc Length	Dimensions the length of an arc, using the symbol set using Dimension Style.	DIMARC
Dimension Edit	Edits dimensions.	DIMEDIT, DIMED, DED
Dimension Status	Shows the dimension variables and their current settings.	DIMSTATUS
Dimension Style	Controls dimension styles.	DDIM, D, DIMSTYLE, DST, DIMSTY
Dimension, Update	Updates the dimensions based on changes to the dimension styles and variables.	DIM (w/update), STYLE
Dimexe	System variable that determines how far to extend the extension line beyond the dimension line.	DIMEXE
Dimexo	System variable that determines how far extension lines are offset from origin points.	DIMEXO
Dimfit	System variable that controls the placement of text and attributes inside or outside extension lines.	DIMFIT
Dimgap	System variable that sets the distance around the dimension text when you break the dimension line to accommodate dimension text.	DIMGAP
Dimension, Inspect	Creates or removes inspection dimensions.	DIMINSPECT
Dimension Jog Line	Adds or removes a jag line to a linear or aligned dimension.	DIMJOGLINE
Dimjust	System variable that controls the horizontal dimension text position.	DIMJUST
Dimlfac	System variable that sets the global scale factor for linear dimensioning measurements.	DIMLFAC
Dimlim	System variable that, when on, generates dimension limits as the default text.	DIMLIM

Command or Icon Name	Description	Command or Alias
Dimoverride	Allows you to override dimensioning system variable settings associated with a dimension object, but will not affect the current dimension style.	DIMOVERRIDE, DIM-OVER, DOV
Dimpost	System variable that specifies a text prefix and/or suffix to the dimension measurement.	DIMPOST
Dimrnd	System variable that rounds all dimensioning distances to the specified value.	DIMRND
Dimsah	System variable that controls the use of user-defined attribute blocks at the ends of the dimension lines.	DIMSAH
Dimscale	System variable that sets overall scale factor applied to dimensioning variables that specify sizes, distances, or offsets.	DIMSCALE
Dimsd1	System variable that, when on, suppresses drawing of the first dimension line.	DIMSD1
Dimsd2	System variable that, when on, suppresses drawing of the second dimension line.	DIMSD2
Dimse1	System variable that, when on, suppresses drawing of the first extension line.	DIMSE1
Dimse2	System variable that, when on, suppresses drawing of the second extension line.	DIMSE2
Dimsho	System variable that, when on, controls redefinition of dimension objects while dragging.	DIMSHO
Dimsoxd	System variable that, when on, suppresses drawing of dimension lines outside the extension lines.	DIMSOXD
DIMSPACE	Adjusts the spacing equally between parallel linear and angular dimensions.	DIMSPACE
Dimtad	System variable that controls the vertical position of text in relation to the dimension line.	DIMTAD
Dimtdec	System variable that sets the number of decimal places to display the tolerance values for a dimension.	DIMTDEC
Dimtfac	System variable that specifies a scale factor for the text height of tolerance values relative to the dimension text height.	DIMTFAC
Dimtih	System variable that controls the position of dimension text inside the extension lines for all dimension types except ordinate dimensions.	DIMTIH
Dimtix	System variable that draws text between extension lines.	DIMTIX
Dimtm	System variable that, when Dimtol or Dimlim is on, sets the minimum (or lower) tolerance limit for dimension text.	DIMTM

Command or Icon Name	Description	Command or Alias
Dimtofl	System variable that, when on, draws a dimension line between the extension lines even when the text is placed outside the extension lines.	DIMTOFL
Dimtoh	System variable that, when turned on, controls the position of dimension text outside the extension lines.	DIMTOH
Dimtol	System variable that generates plus/minus tolerances.	DIMTOL
Dimtolj	System variable that sets the vertical justification for tolerance values relative to the nominal dimension text.	DIMTOLJ
Dimtp	System variable that, when Dimtol or Dimlim is on, sets the maximum (or upper) tolerance limit for dimension text.	DIMTP
Dimtsz	System variable that specifies the size of oblique strokes drawn instead of arrowheads for linear, radius, and diameter dimensioning.	DIMTSZ
Dimtvp	System variable that adjusts text placement relative to text height.	DIMTVP
Dimtxsty	System variable that specifies the text style of a dimension.	DIMTXSTY
Dimtxt	System variable that specifies the height of the dimension text, unless the current text style has a fixedheight.	DIMTXT
Dimtzin	System variable that controls the suppression of zeros for tolerance values.	DIMTZIN
Dimunit	System variable that sets the units format for all dimension family members, except angular.	DIMUNIT
Dimupt	System variable that controls the cursor functionality for User Positioned Text.	DIMUPT
Dimzin	System variable controlling the suppression of the inch portion of a feet-and-inches dimension when distance is an integral number of feet, or the feet portion when distance is less than a foot.	DIMZIN
Disassociate Dimension	Removes associativity from selected dimensions.	DIMDISASSOCIATE
Dispsilh	System variable that controls the display of silhouette curves of body objects in wire-frame mode.	DISPSILH
Distance	Reads out the value for the distance between two selected points.	'DIST, DIST, DI
Divide	Places points or blocks along an object to create segments.	DIVIDE, DIV
Donut	Draws concentric filled circles or filled circles.	DONUT

Command or Icon Name	Description	Command or Alias
Double-click Edit	Turns on and off double-click editing mode used to automatically launch the Properties palette and other editing features.	DBLCLKEDIT
Drafting Settings	Sets Snap mode, grid, polar and object snap tracking.	DSETTINGS
Drafting Settings	Sets the drawing aids for the drawing.	'DSETTINGS
Dragmode	Controls the way dragged objects are displayed.	'DRAGMODE, DRAGMODE
Drawing Adjust	Changes the display options of selected DGN underlays.	DGNADJUST
Drawing Attach	Attaches a DGN underlay to the current drawing.	DGNATTACH
Drawing Bind	Binds DGN underlays to the current drawing.	DGNBIND (-DGNBIND)
Drawing Clip	Defines a clipping boundary for a selected DGN underlay.	DGNCLIP
Drawing Convert	Converts drawing format version for selected drawing files.	DWGCONVERT
Drawing Export	Creates one or more V8 DGN files from the current drawing.	DGNEXPORT
Drawing Import	Imports the data from a V8 DGN file into a new DWG file.	DGNIMPORT
Drawing Properties	Set and display properties of the current drawing.	DWGPROPS
Draworder	Changes the display order of images and objects.	DRAWORDER, DR
DWF Out	Saves drawing objects in Drawing Web format (*.dwf).	DWFOUT, PLOT
DXB In	Imports coded binary files (*.dxb).	DXBIN
DXF In	Imports drawing saved in DXF™ Drawing Interchange (*.dxf) format.	DXFIN
DXF Out	Saves drawing objects in DXF™ Drawing Interchange (*.dxf) Format.	DXFOUT
DWG Props	Sets and displays properties of the current drawing.	DWGPROPS
Edge	Changes the visibility of three-dimensional face edges.	EDGE
Edge Mesh	Creates a three-dimensional polygon mesh.	3DMESH
Edit Attribute	Edits attribute values.	EATTEDIT, ATTEDIT, -ATE
Edit Attribute Globally	Edits attribute values.	DDATTE, ATTEDIT, ATE
Edit Hatch	Modifies an existing associative hatch block.	HATCHEDIT, HE
Edit Links	Updates, changes, and cancels existing links.	OLELINKS
Edit Multiline	Edits multiple parallel lines.	MLEDIT
Edit Polyline	Changes various features of polylines.	PEDIT, PE

Command or Icon Name	Description	Command or Alias
Edit Scale List	Modifies the list of scales displayed in view and plot scale lists.	SCALELIST-EDIT
Edit Spline	Edits a spline object.	SPLINEDIT, SPE
Edit Text	Allows you to edit text inside a dialog box.	DDEDIT, ED
Electronic Transmit	Creates a set of drawings and related files for transmittal.	ETRANSMIT
Elev	Sets elevation and extrusion thickness of new objects.	'ELEV, ELEV, ELEVATION
Ellipse	Used to draw ellipses.	ELLIPSE, EL
Ellipse Axis End	Used to draw ellipses.	ELLIPSE
Ellipse Arc	Used to draw ellipses.	ELLIPSE
End Startup Dialog	Turns off use of the Startup dialog box.	N/A
Erase	Erases objects from drawing.	ERASE, E
Explode	Separates blocks or dimensions into component objects so that they are no longer one group and can be edited.	EXPLODE, X
Export	Exports a drawing to a file of type DXF so that another application can use it.	EXPORT, EXP
Export Links	Exports link information for selected objects.	DBCONNECT
Express Tools	Activate Express Tools if needed.	EXPRESSTOOLS
Extend	Extends the length of an existing object to meet a boundary.	EXTEND, EX
Extract Attributes	Extracts attribute data to an external file.	EATTEXT, ATTEXT, DDATTEXT
External Reference	Attaches, Detaches, Reloads, Unloads, Binds, etc. other drawings as external references, without really adding them to your current drawing.	XREF, XR, -XREF, -XR
External Reference Attach	Uses another drawing as an external reference, without really adding it to your current drawing.	XATTACH, XA
External Reference Bind	Binds symbols of an xref to a drawing.	XBIND, XB, -XBIND, -XB
External Reference Clip	Defines an xref clipping boundary.	XCLIP, XC
External Reference Clip Frame	System Variable that controls visibility of clipping boundaries.	XCLIPFRAME
Extrude	Extrudes a two-dimensional shape into a three-dimensional object.	EXTRUDE, EXT
Facetres	System variable that adjusts the smoothness of shaded and hidden line-removed objects.	FACETRES
Filedia	System variable that suppresses the display of the file dialog boxes.	FILEDIA
Fill	Controls the filling of multilines, traces, solids, and wide polylines.	'FILL, FILL

Command or Icon Name	Description	Command or Alias
Fillet	Connects lines, arcs, or circles with a smoothly fitted arc.	FILLET, F
Fillet 3D Edge	Rounds and fillets the edges of solid objects.	FILLETEDGE
Filter	Creates a list of requirements that an object must meet to be included in a selection set.	FILTER
Find	Finds, replaces, selects, or zooms to specified text.	FIND
Flat Shot	Creates a 2D representation of all 3D objects in the current view.	FLATSHOT
FREESPOT	Creates a free spotlight, which is similar to a spotlight without a specified target.	FREESPOT
FREEWEB	Creates a free weblight, which is similar to a weblight without a specified target.	FREEWEB
Front View	Sets the viewing direction for a three-dimensional visualization of the drawing to the front.	VPOINT, VP, ddvpoint, -VP
Global Linetype	System variable that sets the current global linetype scale factor for objects.	LTSCALE
Graphics Screen	Switches from the text window back to the graphics window.	'GRAPHSCR, GRAPHSCR, [F2]
Grid	Displays a grid of dots at desired spacing on the screen.	'GRID, GRID, or toggle off and on with [F7]
Grips	Enables grips and sets their color.	'grips, grips, 'ddgrips, ddgrips, GR
Group	Creates and manages grouped objects.	GROUP
Group, Classic Legacy	Opens the legacy Object Grouping dialog box.	CLASSICGROUP
Group Edit	Adds and removes objects from the selected group, or renames a selected group.	GROUPEDIT
Handles	System variable that displays the setting for the use of handles in solid models.	HANDLES
Hatch	Automatically fills the area you select with a pattern.	HATCH, -H
Helix	Creates a 2D or 3D spiral.	HELIX
Help	Displays information explaining commands and procedures.	'HELP, '?, HELP, ?, or toggle on with [F1]
Hide	Hides an object.	HIDE, HI
Highlight	System variable that controls object highlighting.	HIGHLIGHT
Hyperlink	Attaches/modifies a hyperlink to an object.	HYPERLINK
Identify Point	Displays the coordinate of a location.	ID
Image	Opens the Image Manager.	IMAGE, IM, -IMAGE, -IM
Image Adjust	Controls the fade, contrast, and brightness of a selected image.	IMAGEADJUST, IAD
Image Attach	Attaches a new image to the drawing.	IMAGEATTACH, IAT
Image Clip	Creates clipping boundaries for image objects.	IMAGECLIP, ICL

Command or Icon Name	Description	Command or Alias
Image Frame	Controls whether an image frame is displayed or not.	IMAGE-FRAME
Image Quality	Controls the quality of images.	IMAGEQUALITY
Image Transparency	Controls whether the background of an image is opaque or clear.	TRANSPARENCY
Import	Imports many different file formats.	IMPORT, IMP
Insert Block	Places blocks or other drawings into a drawing via the command line or via a dialog box.	INSERT, -I, DDINSERT, I
Insert Multiple Blocks	Inserts multiple instances of a block in a rectangular array.	MINSERT
Insert Objects	Inserts a linked or embedded object.	INSERTOBJ, IO
Interfere	Shows where two solid objects overlap.	INTERFERE, INF
Intersect	Forms a new solid from the area common to two or more solids or regions.	INTERSECT, IN
Isolines	System variable that specifies the number of isolines per surface on objects.	ISOLINES
Isometric Plane	Controls which isometric drawing plane is active: left, top, or right.	'ISOPLANE, ISOPLANE, or [Ctrl]-E or [F5]
Join	Joins the endpoints of lines, 2D and 3D polylines, arcs, elliptical arcs, helixes, and splines to create single object.	JOIN
Jpeg out	Saves selected objects to a file in JPEG file format.	JPEGOUT
Justify Text	Changes the justification point of text.	JUSTIFYTEXT
Layer Properties Manager	Creates layers and controls layer color, linetype, and visibility.	'LAYER, LAYER, 'LA, LA, 'ddlmodes, ddlmodes, -Layer, -LA
Layer Translator	Changes a drawing's layers to specified layer standard.	LAYTRANS
Layout	Create, rename, copy, save, or delete layouts for managing plotted views.	LAYOUT
Layout Wizard	Starts the layout wizard which you can use to create and control layouts.	LAYOUTWIZARD
Leader	Creates leader lines for identifying lines and dimensions.	LEADER, Lead, LE, QLEADER
Left View	Sets the viewing direction for a three-dimensional visualization of the drawing to the left side.	VPOINT, -VP, DDVPOINT, VP
Lengthen	Lengthens an object.	LENGTHEN, LEN
Light	Controls the light sources in rendered scenes.	LIGHT
Light List	Opens the Lights in Model window to add and modify lights.	LIGHTLIST
Limits	Sets up the size of the drawing.	'LIMITS, LIMITS
Line	Draws straight lines of any length.	LINE, L

Command or Icon Name	Description	Command or Alias
Lineweight	Sets the line thickness for objects.	LWEIGHT, 'LWEIGHT, Right-click LWT button, pick Settings
Linear Dimension	Creates linear dimensions.	DIMLINEAR, DIMLIN, DLI
Linetype	Changes the pattern used for new lines in the drawing.	'LINETYPE, LINETYPE, -LT 'DDLTYPE, DDLTYPE, LT
Linetype Scale	System variable that changes the scale of the linetypes in the drawing.	'LTSCALE, LTSCALE, LTS
List	Provides information on an object, such as the length of a line.	LIST, LI, LS
List Variables	Lists the values of system variables.	'SETVAR, SETVAR, SET
Load	Makes shapes available for use by the Shape command.	LOAD
Locate Point	Finds the coordinates of any point on the screen.	'ID, ID
Loft	Creates a 3D solid or surface by lofting through a set of two or more curves.	LOFT
Log File Off	Closes the log file.	LOGFILEOFF
Log File On	Writes the text window contents to a file.	LOGFILEON
Make Block	Groups a set of objects together so that they are treated as one object.	BMAKE, B, BLOCK, -B
Make Slide	Creates a bitmapped slide file of the current viewport or layout	MSLIDE
Mapping	Lets you map materials onto selected geometry.	MATERIALSMAPPING
Markup Set Manager	Displays and allows you to add notes to markup drawings.	MARKUP
Match Properties	Copies the properties of one object to other selected objects.	'MATCHPROP, MATCHPROP, MA, PAINTER
Materials	Controls the material a rendered object appears to be made of, and allows creation of new materials.	MATERIALS
Mass Properties	Calculates and displays the mass properties of regions and solids.	MASSPROP
Measure	Marks segments of a chosen length on an object by inserting points or blocks.	MEASURE, ME MEASUREGEOM
Menu	Loads a menu file.	MENU
Menu Load	Loads partial menu files.	MENULOAD
Menu Unload	Unloads partial menu files.	MENUUNLOAD
Mesh, Cap	Creates a mesh face that connects open edges.	MESHCAP
Mirror	Creates mirror images of shapes.	MIRROR, MI

Command or Icon Name	Description	Command or Alias
Mirror3d	Creates mirror images of shapes with options for 3D.	MIRROR 3D
Multileader, Align	Organizes selected multileaders along a specified line.	MLEADERALIGN
	Organizes selected multileaders containing blocks as content into a group attached to a single leader line.	MLEADERCOLLECT
Multileader, Style	Defines a new multileader style.	MLEADERSTY- LE
Model Space	Enters model space.	MSPACE, MS
Modify Properties	Controls properties of existing objects.	PROPERTIES, DDMODIFY, MO
Move	Moves an existing shape from one area on the drawing to another area.	MOVE, M
Mtprop	Changes paragraph text properties.	MTPROP
Multileader	Creates a line that connects annotation to a feature.	MLEADER
Multiline	Creates multiple, parallel lines.	MLIne, ML
Multiline Style	Defines a style for multiple, parallel lines.	MLSTYLE
Multiline Text	Creates a paragraph that fits within a nonprinting text boundary.	MTEXT, MT, T, -MTEXT, -T
Multiple	Repeats the next command until canceled.	MULTIPLE
Multiple Redo	Reverses the effects of previous UNDO commands.	MREDO
MV Setup	Helps set up drawing views using a LISP program.	MVSETUP
Mview	Creates viewports in paperspace (when Tilemode = 0).	MVIEW, MV
Named UCS	Selects a named and saved user coordinate system.	UCSMAN, DDUCS, UC
Named Views	Sets the viewing direction to a named view.	'VIEW, VIEW, -V, 'DDVIEW, DDVIEW, V
NE Isometric View	Sets the viewing direction for a three-dimensional visualization of the drawing.	VPOINT, -VP, DDVPOINT, VP
New Drawing	Sets up the screen to create a new drawing.	NEW
NW Isometric View	Sets the viewing direction for a three-dimensional visualization of the drawing.	VPOINT, -VP, DDVPOINT, VP
Object Group	Creates a named selection set of objects.	GROUP, G, -GROUP, -G
OBJECTSCALE	Adds or deletes supported scales for annotative objects.	OBJECTSCALE
Object Selection Filters	Creates lists to select objects based on properties.	'FILTER, FILTER, FI
Object Selection Settings	Defines Selection Mode.	'DDSELECT, DDSELECT, SE

Command or Icon Name	Description	Command or Alias
Object Snap Settings (Running Object Snap)	Sets running objects snap modes and changes target box size.	'OSNAP, OSNAP, 'DDOSNAP, DDOSNAP, OSNAP, -OS, OS
Object UCS	Selects a user coordinate system based on the object.	UCS
Offset	Draws objects parallel to a given object.	OFFSET, O OFFSETEDGE
OLE Properties	Allows you to control properties of linked objects.	OLESCALE
Oops	Restores erased objects.	OOPS
Open Drawing	Loads a previously saved drawing.	OPEN
Options	Customize the AutoCAD software for your use.	OPTIONS
Ordinate Dimension	Creates ordinate point dimensions.	dimordinate, DIMORD, DOR
Origin UCS	Creates a user-defined coordinate system at the origin of the view.	UCS
Ortho	Restricts movement to only horizontal and vertical.	'ORTHO, ORTHO, or toggle with [F8]
Page Setup	Specifies the layout page, plotting device, paper size, and settings for new layout.	PAGESETUP
Pan Down	Moves the drawing around on the screen without changing the zoom factor.	'PAN, PAN, 'P, P
Pan Left	Moves the drawing around on the screen without changing the zoom factor.	'PAN, PAN, 'P, P
Pan Point	Moves the drawing around on the screen without changing the zoom factor.	'-PAN, -PAN, '-P, -P
Pan Realtime	Moves the drawing around on the screen without changing the zoom factor.	'PAN, PAN, 'P, P
Pan Right	Moves the drawing around on the screen without changing the zoom factor.	'PAN, PAN, 'P, P
Pan Up	Moves the drawing around on the screen without changing the zoom factor.	'PAN, PAN, 'P, P
Paper Space	Enters paper space when TILEMODE is set to 0.	PSPACE, PS
Paper Space Linetype Scale	System variable that causes the paper space LTSCALE factor to be used for every viewport.	PSLTSCALE
Paste From Clipboard	Places objects from the Windows Clipboard into the drawing using the Insert command.	PASTECLIP
Paste Special	Inserts and controls data from the Clipboard.	PASTESPEC, PA
PC In Wizard	Displays a wizard to import PCP and PC2 configuration file plot settings into the Model tab or current layout.	PCINWIZARD

Command or Icon Name	Description	Command or Alias
Perimeter	System variable that stores the last perimeter value computed by the Area or List commands. (read only)	PERIMETER
Plan	Creates a view looking straight down along the Z-axis to see the XY coordinates.	PLAN
Planar Surface	Creates a planar surface.	PLANESURF
Plot Stamp	Places information on a specified corner of each drawing and logs it to a file.	PLOTSTAMP
Plot Style	Sets or assigns current plot style.	PLOTSTYLE
Plotter Manager	Allows you to add or edit plotter configurations	PLOTTERMANAGER
Point	Creates a point object.	POINT, PO
Point Filters (.X, .Y, .Z, .XY, .XZ, .YZ)	Lets you selectively find single coordinates out of a point's three-dimensional coordinate set.	(used within other commands) .X or .Y or .Z or .XY or .XZ or .YZ
Point Light	Creates a point light.	POINTLIGHT
Point Style	Specifies the display mode and size of point objects.	'DDPTYPE, DDPTYPE, PDMODE
Polygon	Draws regular polygons with 3 to 1024 sides.	POLYGON, POL
Polyline	Draws a series of connected objects (lines or arcs) that are treated as a single object called a polyline.	PLINE, PL
Polyline edit (Pedit)	Edits polylines and three-dimensional polygon meshes.	PEDIT
Preferences	Customizes the AutoCAD settings.	PREFERENCES, OPTIONS
Preset UCS	Selects a preset UCS.	DDUCSP, UCSMAN
Press or Pull	Presses or pulls bounded areas.	PRESSPULL
Previous Layer	Undoes the last change or set of changes to the layer settings.	LAYERP
Previous Layer Mode	Enables/disables the tracking of layer changes.	LAYERPMODE
Previous UCS	Returns you to the previously used user coordinate system.	UCS
Print/Plot	Prints or plots a drawing	PLOT, PRINT
Print Preview	Previews the drawing before printing or plotting.	PREVIEW, PRE
Projmode	System variable that sets the current projection mode for trim or extend operations.	PROJMODE
Properties	Used to change the properties of an object.	PROPERTIES, CHPROP, DDCHPROP, CH
PS Drag	Controls the appearance of a PostScript image as it is dragged into place.	PSDRAG
PS Fill	Fills a 2D outline with a PostScript pattern.	PSFILL
PS In	Imports a file in PostScript (*.eps) format.	PSIN

Command or Icon Name	Description	Command or Alias
PS Out	Saves drawing objects in PostScript (*.eps*) format.	PSOUT
Publish	Creates multi-sheet drawing sets for publishing to a single multi-sheet DWF™ (Design Web Format) file, a plotting device, or a plot file.	PUBLISH
Publish to Web	Includes images of selected drawings in HTML page format.	PUBLISHTOWEB
Purge	Removes unused items from the drawing database.	PURGE, PU
Qtext	Controls the display and plotting of text and attribute text.	'QTEXT, QTEXT
Quick Calculator	Performs calculations, converts units, and more.	QUICKCALC
Quick Dimension	Quickly creates dimensions.	QDIM
Quick Leader	Quickly creates leaders and annotations.	QLEADER
Quick Select	Quickly creates selection sets based on filtering criteria.	QSELECT
Quit	Exits with the option not to save your changes, and returns you to the operating system.	QUIT, EXIT
Radius Dimension	Adds centermarks to an arc when providing its radius dimension.	DIMRADIUS, DIMRAD, DRA
Ray	Creates a semi-infinite line.	RAY
Reassociate Dimension	Associates dimension to drawing object.	DIMREASSOCIATE
Recover	Repairs a damaged drawing.	RECOVER
RECOVERALL	Repairs a damaged drawing and xrefs.	RECOVERALL
Rectangle	Creates rectangular shapes.	RECTANG, REC
Redefine	Restores AutoCAD internal commands changed by the Undefine command.	'REDEFINE, REDEFINE
Redefine Attribute	Redefines a block and updates associated attributes.	ATTREDEF
Redo	Reverses the effect of the most recent UNDO command. MRedo has multiple redo capability.	MREDO, redo, [Ctrl]-Y
Redraw All	Redraws all viewports at once.	'REDRAWALL, REDRAWALL, RA
Redraw View	Removes blip marks added to the drawing screen and restores objects partially erased while you were editing other objects.	'REDRAW, REDRAW, 'R, R
Reference, Close	Saves back or discards changes made during in-place xref editing.	REFCLOSE
Reference Edit	Selects a reference for editing.	REFEDIT
Refset	Adds or removes objects from a working set during in-place editing of an xref or block.	REFSET
Regenauto	Controls the automatic regeneration of a drawing.	'REGENAUTO, REGENAUTO

Command or Icon Name	Description	Command or Alias
Regenerate	Recalculates the display file in order to show changes.	REGEN, RE
Regenerate All	Regenerates all viewports at once.	REGENALL, REA
Regenerate Dimensions	Updates the locations of associated dimensions.	DIMREGEN
Region	Creates a two-dimensional area object from a selection set of existing objects.	REGION, REG
Reinit	Reinitializes the digitizer, input/output port and program parameters.	REINIT
Remove Duplicate	Removes duplicate or overlapping lines, arcs, and polylines. Also, combines partially overlapping or contiguous ones.	OVERKILL
Rename	Changes the names of objects.	RENAME, DDRENAME, REN, -REN
Render	Creates a photorealistic or realistically shaded image of a three-dimensional wireframe or solid model.	RENDER, RR
Render Environment	Provides visual cues for the apparent distance of objects.	RENDERENVIRON-MENT
Render Exposure	Provides settings to interactively adjust the lighting global for the most recent rendered output.	RENDEREXPOSURE
Render Presets	Specifies render presets, reusable rendering parameters, for rendering an image.	RENDERPRESETS
Render Window	Displays the Render Window without invoking a render task.	RENDERWIN
Restore UCS	Restores a saved user coordinate system.	UCS, UCSMAN
Resume	Continues an interrupted script.	'RESUME, RESUME
Revision Cloud	Creates a polyline of sequential arcs to form a cloud shape.	REVCLOUD
Revolve	Creates a three-dimensional object by sweeping a two-dimensional polyline, circle or region about a circular path to create a symmetrical solid.	REVOLVE, REV
Revolved Mesh	Creates a rotated surface about a selected axis.	REVSURF
Right View	Sets the viewing direction for a three-dimensional visualization of the drawing to the right side.	VPOINT, DDVPOINT, VP, -VP
Rotate	Rotates all or part of an object.	ROTATE, RO
Rscript	Creates a continually repeating script.	RSCRIPT
Ruled Surface	Creates a polygon mesh between two curves.	RULESURF
Save	Saves a drawing using Quick Save.	QSAVE
Save	Saves a drawing to a new file name, without changing the name of the drawing on your screen.	SAVE

Command or Icon Name	Description	Command or Alias
Save As	Saves a drawing, allowing you to change its name or location, or to a previous version.	SAVEAS
Save Image	Saves a rendered image to a file.	SAVEIMG
Save Slide	Creates a slide file of the current viewport.	MSLIDE
Save Time	System variable that controls how often a file is automatically saved.	SAVETIME
Save UCS	Saves a user coordinate system.	UCS, UCSMAN
Scale	Changes the size of an object in the drawing database.	SCALE, SC
Scale Text	Changes the scale of text objects without changing location.	SCALETEXT
Script	Executes a sequence of commands from a script.	SCRIPT, SCR
SE Isometric View	Sets the viewing direction for a three-dimensional visualization of the drawing.	VPOINT, DDVPOINT, VP, -VP
Section	Uses the intersection of a plane and solids to create a region.	SECTION, SEC
Select	Selects objects with a selection method listed below. Commands must be typed following the Select command.	'SELECT, SELECT
Select Add	Places selected objects in the previous selection set (default method).	ADD (at Select Objects: prompt)
Select All	Places all objects in the selection set.	ALL (at Select Objects: prompt)
Select Auto	Selects objects individually, objects within a left-to-right window, and objects crossing and within a right-to-left window (default selection method).	AUTO (at Select Objects: prompt)
Select Box	Selects objects within a left-to-right window, and/or objects crossing and within a right-to-left window (default selection method).	BOX (at Select Objects: prompt)
Select Crossing	Selects all objects within and crossing the selection box (default selection from right to left).	Crossing (at Select Objects: prompt); C
Select Crossing Polygon	Selects all objects within and crossing a user-defined polygon boundary.	CPolygon (at Select Objects: prompt); CP
Select Fence	Selects objects crossing a user-defined polyline.	Fence (at Select Objects: prompt); F
Select Group	Selects all objects within a specified group.	Group (at Select Objects: prompt); G
Select Last	Re-highlights last selection.	Last (at Select Objects: prompt); L
Select Multiple	Selects objects without highlighting them.	Multiple (at Select Objects: prompt); M

Command or Icon Name	Description	Command or Alias
Select Previous	Places previously selected objects in the selection set.	Previous (at Select Objects: prompt); P
Select Remove	Removes selected objects in the previous selection set.	Remove (at Select Objects: prompt); R
Select Single	Selects a single object.	Single (at Select Objects: prompt); S
Select Undo	Cancels the selection of the most recently selected object.	Undo (at Select Objects: prompt); U
Select Window	Selects all objects within a user-defined window.	Window (at Select Objects: prompt); W
Select Window Polygon	Selects all objects within a user-defined polygon.	WPolygon (at Select Objects: prompt); WP
Set Variables	Changes the values of system variables.	'SETVAR, SETVAR, SET
Setup Drawing	Generates Profiles and sections in viewports created with SOLVIEW.	SOLDRAW
Setup Profile	Creates profile images of 3D solids.	SOLPROF
Setup View	Creates floating viewports for orthographic projection, section views, and multi-views of 3D solids.	SOLVIEW
Shape	Inserts a shape into the current drawing.	SHAPE
Sheet Set Manager	Organizes, displays, and manages named collections of sheets.	SHEETSET
Shell	Accesses operating system commands.	SHELL
Single Line Text	Adds text to a drawing.	DTEXT, DT
Sketch	Creates a series of freehand line segments.	SKETCH
Slice	Slices a set of solids with a plane.	slice, SL
Snap	Limits cursor movement on the screen to set interval so objects can be placed at precise locations easily.	SNAP, SN, or toggle off and on with [F9]
Snap From	Establishes a temporary reference point as a basis for specifying subsequent points.	'osnap, osnap, 'ddosnap, ddosnap, OS, -OS, OSNAP
Snap to Apparent Intersection	Snaps to a real or visual three-dimensional intersection formed by objects you select or by an extension of those objects.	'app, app, Eappint, appint
Snap to Center	Snaps to the center of an arc, circle, or ellipse.	'cen, cen
Snap to Endpoint	Snaps to the closest endpoint of an arc, elliptical arc, ray, multiline, or line, or to the closest corner of a trace, solid, or three-dimensional face.	'endp, endp, end
Snap to Insertion	Snaps to the insertion point of text, a block, a shape, or an attribute.	'ins, ins
Snap to Intersection	Snaps to the intersection of a line, arc, spline, elliptical arc, ellipse, ray, construction line, multiline, or circle.	'int, int

Command or Icon Name	Description	Command or Alias
Snap to Midpoint	Snaps to the midpoint of an arc, elliptical arc spline, ray, solid, construction line, multiline, or line.	'mid, mid
Snap to Nearest	Snaps to the nearest point of an arc, elliptical arc, ellipse, spline, ray, multiline, line, circle, or point.	'nea, nea
Snap to Node	Snaps to a point object.	'nod, nod
Snap to None	Turns object snap mode off.	'none, none
Snap to Parallel	Aligns new drawing vector parallel to an acquired object.	PAR
Snap to Perpendicular	Snaps to a point perpendicular to an arc, elliptical arc, ellipse, spline, ray, construction line, multiline, line, solid, or circle.	'per, per
Snap to Quadrant	Snaps to a quadrant point of an arc, elliptical arc, ellipse, solid, or circle.	'qua, qua
Snap to Tangent	Snaps to the tangent of an arc, elliptical arc, ellipse, or circle.	'tan, tan
Solid Edit	Edits faces and edges of 3D solid objects.	SOLIDEDIT
Space Translation	Converts length values between model space and paper space.	SPACETRANS
Spelling	Checks spelling in a drawing.	'SPELL, spell, SP
Sphere	Creates a three-dimensional solid sphere.	sphere
Spline	Fits a smooth curve to a sequence of points within a specified tolerance.	spline, SPL
Spotlight	Creates a spotlight.	SPOTLIGHT
Standards	Manages CAD standards files associated with AutoCAD drawings.	STANDARDS
Status	Displays drawing statistics, modes, and extents.	'STATUS, status
STL Out	Stores solids in an ASCII or binary file.	STLOUT
Stretch	Stretches the objects selected.	STRETCH, S
Style	Lets you create new text styles and modify existing ones.	'STYLE, STYLE, ST
Styles Manager	Uses dialog box to manage plot styles.	STYLESMANAGER
Subtract	Removes the set of a second solid or region from the first set.	SUBTRACT, SU
Sun Properties	Opens the Sun Properties window and sets the properties of the sun.	SUNPROPERTIES
Surface Blend	Creates a continuous blend surface between two existing surfaces.	SURFBLEND
Surface Patch	Creates a new surface by fitting a cap over a surface edge that forms a closed loop.	SURFPATCH
Surftab1	System variable that sets the number of tabulations to be generated for Rulesurf and Tabsurf.	surftab1

Command or Icon Name	Description	Command or Alias
Surftab2	System variable that sets mesh density in the N direction for Revsur and Edgesurf.	surftab2
Sweep	Creates a 3D solid or surface by sweeping a 2D curve along a path.	SWEEP
SW Isometric View	Sets the viewing direction for a three-dimensional visualization of the drawing.	VPOINT, ddvpoint, VP, -VP
Synchronize Attributes	Updates all instances of specified block to current attributes.	ATTSYNC
System Windows	Arranges windows and icons on screen.	SYSWINDOWS
Tablet	Calibrates the tablet with a paper drawing's coordinate system.	tablet, TA
Tabmode	System variable that controls the use of tablet mode.	tabmode
Tabulated Surface	Creates a tabulated surface from a path curve and direction vector.	TABSURF
Target	System variable that stores location (in UCS coordinates) of the target point for the current viewport (read only).	target
Target Point Light	Creates a target point light.	TARGETPOINT
Text	Creates a single line of user-entered text.	TEXT
Text Screen	Switches from the graphics screen to the text screen.	'TEXTSCR, or toggle back and forth with [F2]
Thicken	Creates a 3D solid by thickening a surface.	THICKEN
Thickness	Sets the current 3D solid thickness.	THICKNESS, TH
Tiled Viewports	Divides the graphics window into multiple tiled viewports and manages them.	vports
Tilemode	When set to 1, allows creation of tiled viewports in model space; when set to 0, enables use of paper space.	tilemode, TI or pick model/layout tabs
Time	Displays the date and time statistics of a drawing.	'TIME, TIME
Tolerance	Creates geometric tolerances and adds them to a drawing in feature control frames.	tolerance, TOL
Tool Palettes	Opens the Tool Palettes window.	TOOLPALETTES
Toolbar	Displays, hides, and positions all toolbars.	toolbar, TO
Tooltips	System variable that controls the display of Tooltips.	tooltips
Top View	Sets the viewing direction for a three-dimensional visualization of the drawing to the top.	vpoint, ddvpoint, VP, -VP
TPNAVIGATE	Displays a specified tool palette or palette group.	TPNAVIGATE
Torus	Creates a donut-shaped solid.	torus, TOR
Trace	Creates solid lines.	trace
Transparency	Controls transparency of background in a bitmap image.	TRANSPARENCY

Command or Icon Name	Description	Command or Alias
Treestat	Displays information on the drawing's current spatial index.	treestat
Trim	Removes part of an object at its intersection with another object.	TRIM, TR
UCS	Manages User Coordinate Systems.	UCSMAN, ucs, dducs, UC
UCS Follow	System variable that allows you to generate a plan view of the current UCS in a viewport whenever you change the UCS.	UCSFOLLOW
UCS Icon	System variable that repositions and turns on and off the display of the UCS icon.	UCSICON
UCS Manager	Manages defined user coordinate systems.	USCMAN
Undefine	Allows an application-defined command to override an AutoCAD command.	UNDEFINE
Undo	Reverses the effect of previous commands.	UNDO, U
Ungroup	Explodes a group.	UNGROUP
Union	Adds two separate sets of solids or regions together to create one solid model.	UNION, UNI
Units	Controls the type and precision of the values used in dimensions.	'UNITS, UNITS, -UN 'ddunits, ddunits, UN
View	Saves views of an object to be plotted, displayed, or printed.	'view, view, 'ddview, ddview, -V
Viewport Clip	Clips viewport objects.	VPCLIP
View Resolution	Sets the resolution for object generation in the current viewport.	VIEWRES
View Slide	Displays a raster-image slide file in the current viewport.	vslide
View UCS	Selects a user coordinate system aligned to a specific view.	ucs
Viewport Layer	Controls the visibility of layers within specific viewports in paper space.	VPLAYER
Visual Basic Editor	Display the Visual Basic Editor.	VBAIDE
Visual LISP	Display Visual LISP® interactive development environment (IDE).	VLISP
Visual Styles	Creates and modifies visual styles and applies a visual style to a viewport.	VISUALSTYLES
Visual Style in Current Viewport	Sets the visual style in the current viewport.	VSCURRENT
Walk and Fly Settings	Specifies walk and fly settings.	WALKFLYSETTINGS
WEBLIGHT	Creates a weblight that is a 3D representation of the light intensity distribution of a light source.	WEBLIGHT
Wedge	Creates a three-dimensional solid with a closed face tapering along the X-axis by specifying the center.	wedge, WE
Who Has	Display ownership info. for open drawing files.	WHOHAS

Command or Icon Name	Description	Command or Alias
WMF In	Imports a file saved in Windows Metafile (*.wmf) format.	WMFIN
WMF Options	Sets options for importing a Windows Metafile.	WMFOPTs
WMF Out	Saves drawing objects in Windows Metafile (*.wmf) format.	WMFOUT
World UCS	Selects the world coordinate system as the user coordinate system.	ucs
Write Block	Saves a block as a separate file so that it may be used in other drawings.	wblock, W
X Axis Rotate UCS	Selects a user coordinate system by rotating the X-axis.	ucs
Xplode	Breaks a component object into its component objects; see also Explode.	xplode
Y Axis Rotate UCS	Selects a user coordinate system by rotating the Y-axis.	ucs
Z Axis Rotate UCS	Selects a user coordinate system by rotating the Z-axis.	ucs
Z Axis Vector UCS	Selects a user coordinate system defined by a vector in the Z direction.	ucs
Zoom All	Resizes to display the entire drawing in the current viewport.	'zoom, zoom, 'Z, Z
Zoom Center	Resizes to display a window by entering a center point, then a magnification value or height.	'zoom, zoom, 'Z, Z
Zoom Dynamic	Resizes to display the generated portion of the drawing with a view box.	'zoom, zoom, 'Z, Z
Zoom Extents	Resizes to display the drawing extents.	'zoom, zoom, 'Z, Z
Zoom In	Resizes areas of the drawing in the screen to make it appear closer or larger.	'zoom, zoom, 'Z, Z
Zoom Object	Resizes display to fit one or more selected objects centered in drawing area.	'zoom, zoom, 'Z, Z
Zoom Out	Resizes areas of the drawing in the screen so that more of the drawing fits in the screen.	'zoom, zoom, 'Z, Z
Zoom Previous	Resizes to the previous view.	'zoom, zoom, 'Z, Z
Zoom Realtime	Resizes the view in a real-time fashion.	'zoom, zoom, 'Z, Z
Zoom Scale	Resizes to display at a specified scale factor.	'zoom, zoom, 'Z, Z
Zoom Vmax	Resizes so that the drawing is viewed from as far out as possible on the current viewports virtual screen without forcing a complete regeneration of the drawing.	'zoom, zoom, 'Z, Z
Zoom Window	Resizes to display an area specified by two opposite corner points of a rectangular window.	'zoom, zoom, 'Z, Z

INDEX

Symbols

@ 19, 20
2D constraint based modeling 182
3D Dynamic View 563
3D Mesh command 479
3D solid models 429–486
3D UCS icon 437, 438, 472
.dwg 11
.dwt 33
.X, specifying x coordinate 491
.Y, specifying y-coordinate 491

A

Absolute Coordinates 18
acad.dwt 10, 33, 133, 144, 165, 195,
    222, 422, 430, 438
Adding Backgrounds 593
adjust mapping 580
adjust viewing area 557
Advanced Render Settings 577, 583
Aerial Viewer 83, 90
Alias 6
Align 515
  text alignment 290
  view alignment 463
align attribute 528
aligned dimensional constraint 183
alignment 523
align section 554
align UCS 379
alternate units 295
And gate 397, 398, 399, 411, 421, 423
angle brackets 14, 54, 527
angular dimensional constraint 183
angular dimension 293, 311
Annotation Scale 283, 319
ANSI-C template 195
ANSI Standards 195, 282, 287
Arc 73, 79
  Arc 3 Points 74
  Arc command 73
  Arc Continue 78
  Arc Start Center End 75
  Arc Start Center Length 76
  Arc Start End Angle 76
  Arc Start End Radius 78
Area 116

Array 171
  dynamic grips and array 522
  path array 171
  polar array 171
  rectangular array 171
  editing 172
arrowheads 282
arrows 288, 289, 315
ASME Standards 195, 282, 287
associative array, editing 172
attribute alignment 528
auxiliary view from 3D model 557
auxiliary views 377

B

Back option, Undo command 32
backspace to erase text 41
ball tags 522, 532
base grip 111, 174, 175, 176, 177, 190,
    269, 558
baseline spacing for dimensions 287
Baseline dimension 303, 304
basic dimension 333
bilateral tolerance 330
Blend 113
Block 200, 314, 395, 397
  create block 398
  defining attributes 525
  dynamic blocks 522
  insert block 200, 399, 532
  insert from DesignCenter 403
  insert drawing 455, 514
  save block 531
  title block 234
  using block with leaders 359
  Write Block 397, 401
Block authoring palette 530
Block Command 396
block editor 523
Boolean operators 429, 431, 448, 450,
    455, 460, 465, 481, 588
Box
  Box command 431, 432
  box filter type 579
  box mapping 592
bump map 601
buttons
  creating new commands 417
  special programming characters 418
Buzzsaw 11

C

Calculator 499, 504, 599
Cancelling commands 6
Cartesian coordinate 18, 54

Cascade drawings 13, 54
commands NOT case-sensitive 6
CELTScale 140
centerlines 87, 136, 138, 139, 226, 256,
    265, 266, 267, 502, 503
  circular view 267
  line precedence for centerlines 256
  using LTScale with centerlines 139
  breaking the centerline 268
  centerlines in 3D drawings 502
  centerlines as extension lines 279
Centermarks 265
chained dimensioning 303
Chamfer
  chamfer 3D solids 488
  Chamfer button 108
  Chamfer command 107
  chamfer on Rectangle 39
Choosing Materials 587
chord length 76, 77, 90
Circle
  Circle command 8
  Circle 2 Point 85, 90
  Circle 3 Point 85, 86, 90
  circle, drawing 40
  circle flyout 86
  Circle Tan Tan Radius 87, 88
  Circle Tan Tan Tan 88
  command options 85
circular view 265, 266, 267, 274
circumscribed 142
  circumscribed hexagon 143
  circumscribed polygon 142
close button 3
  drawing window close button 13
coincident constraint 183
collinear constraint 183
color
  color in layers 69, 225
  colors for generated layers 500
  contrast color 579
  controlling colors 64
  controlling dimension color 287
  ground plane color 599
  index color 65, 69
  layer colors for tutorials 227
  lighting color 599
  material color 590
  night sky color for rendering 599
  object color 223
  select color dialog box 64, 65, 69,
      226, 500, 502, 579
  select similar 163
Color Books 65
Command Aliasing 6